'Alongside sharing their experiences and those of others in terms of changes to employment patterns, the chapters in the book provide a helpful practical resource for both existing independent practitioners and those who are setting up a business with all that this entails.'

Ms Kamini Gadhok MBE, *BSc Hons, Doctor of Civil Law (Honorary), Master of Science (Honorary), MRCSLT, Hon Companionship COP*

BUILDING AN INDEPENDENT SPEECH AND LANGUAGE THERAPY PRACTICE

Set against the context of a changing professional landscape, this book examines the journey of the authors, Jo and Diana, as they transitioned from working in the National Health Service (NHS) to setting up an independent practice following redundancy. Highlighting both the benefits and challenges, the authors outline the steps they took to move from survival mode and crisis management to a position of stability and success.

This book provides readers with a wealth of practical advice, helping them to avoid pitfalls and seize opportunities with confidence when establishing their own independent practice. It also touches on the fall-out from redundancy – pertinent to any job, anywhere.

Chapters explore a variety of topics, including but not limited to:

- The national context, implications for setting up an independent practice and business models
- Practical considerations: financial management, contracts, governance, technology, creating a team and models of clinical service delivery
- Assessing success and identifying areas for improvement; measuring impact, troubleshooting and looking to the future

Written in an entertaining yet informative manner, with the voices of other experienced professionals drawn on throughout in the form of personal stories and specialist contributions, this book is essential reading for speech and language therapists (and others) considering going down the independent route.

Diana McQueen and **Jo Williams** are Co-Directors at Soundswell Speech and Language Therapy Solutions, an independent provider of speech and language therapy services. They both have many years experience both as clinicians and service managers in the NHS.

Diana has written extensively and presented research at speech and language therapy conferences in the UK and Europe. Previously, she has worked as a Specialist Advisor for the Care Quality Commission (CQC).

Jo has a Master's degree in Leadership for Healthcare Improvement. She has worked as a Fitness to Practice Partner at the Health Care Professions Council and is currently a Local Government Early Years Peer Reviewer.

BUILDING AN INDEPENDENT SPEECH AND LANGUAGE THERAPY PRACTICE

A Guide to Support and Inspire Healthcare Practitioners

Diana McQueen and Jo Williams

Routledge
Taylor & Francis Group

LONDON AND NEW YORK

Designed cover image: © Getty Images

First published 2024
by Routledge
4 Park Square, Milton Park, Abingdon, Oxon OX14 4RN

and by Routledge
605 Third Avenue, New York, NY 10158

Routledge is an imprint of the Taylor & Francis Group, an informa business

British Library Cataloguing-in-Publication Data
A catalogue record for this book is available from the British Library

ISBN: 978-1-032-46702-3 (hbk)
ISBN: 978-1-032-46701-6 (pbk)
ISBN: 978-1-003-38292-8 (ebk)

DOI: 10.4324/9781003382928

Typeset in Galliard
by Deanta Global Publishing Services, Chennai, India

CONTENTS

ACKNOWLEDGEMENTS

Specialist contributors:

- Chris Blunt (CISSP, CSTM), Licensed Cybersecurity Assessor, (CE, CE+, IASME)
- Sarah Buckley, Speech and Language Therapist, Practice Manager at Sarah Buckley Therapies Ltd., Chair of ASLTIP
- Dr Claire Ewen, Speech and Language Therapist
- Katie Leedham, Owner/designer, www.bemoreroar.com
- Jenny Marks (FCA CTA), Tax Director, Muras Baker Jones Limited, www.muras.co.uk

We are very grateful for the help of the following people:

- Alan Birch, Facebook page: Alan Birch studios
- Eddie Crouch BDS LDS RCS, GDC, Chair of BDA
- Dr Samantha Cruz Rivera, PhD Research Fellow: Centre for Patient Reported Outcomes Research (CPROR), University of Birmingham
- Dr Samantha Gregory
- Alex Mauser, Business Engagement Officer, School of Chemical Engineering U of Bham
- Officers of the RCSLT: Tom Griffin (Enquiries Coordinator) and Berenice Napier (Strategic Workforce Adviser)

Both respondents to the questionnaire and those who have told their personal stories in more detail have made a huge contribution to this book. The former, in particular, offered unexpectedly detailed information which merits further exploration elsewhere. We have heard some stories which have clearly not been easy to tell and are grateful to everyone who has taken the time to share their experiences with us.

INTRODUCTION AND NAVIGATION

The initial concept of this book focussed on us and our story and that remains the priority. Over time, however, the importance of the contemporary context became increasingly apparent. This was an opportunity to explore the experiences of colleagues not only in speech and language therapy but also in other professions where there has been a move away from the public sector as the majority employer/provider.

We have included a brief foray into previous research as well as using various tools to gather views. Those tools include questionnaires, focus groups, both semi-structured and informal interviews and the sharing of more detailed stories of individuals. We have also included an interview with the (then) Chair of the BDA as there are interesting parallels between SLTs and Dentists.

Personal stories are featured throughout the book, where they powerfully illustrate some of the challenges and successes encountered by many others. Some appear at particular points to support advice and good ideas; others appear in greater detail. For personal reasons, some contributors have chosen to remain anonymous.

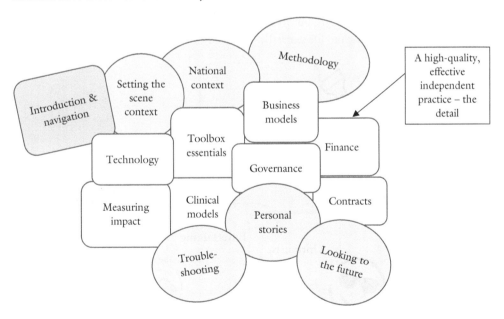

We are firm believers that any event – either good or less so – teaches us something. We are not here to disparage: the more we learn and listen, the more we recognise the problems we (collectively) face in making positive and sustainable change to our public sector health services. In the same way that we have acquired a huge number of skills from our long and often very happy years in the public sector, there are things we would very much like to give back.

Closer co-operation, transparency and mutual respect are surely the foundation stones to a genuine partnership between the public and private sectors. The results of our Freedom of Information (FOI) requests to a sample of Trusts nationally make interesting reading.

Many Trusts operate traded (sometimes called enhanced) services. These work well in some instances but in others they are not sustainable. Are there lessons to learn from the private sector here?

Possibly 15 years ago now, our professional body, the Royal College of Speech and Language Therapists (RCSLT), introduced 'Working in Harmony'. This was a guidance paper aimed at outlining how the public and private sector therapists could work more effectively together. The paper was primarily about respect and keeping each other informed rather than how to engender a deeper level of genuine partnership working. It was a step in the right direction though, and today one of the Royal College's Clinical Excellence Networks (CEN) is entitled 'SLTs on the same team'. This group kindly agreed to a remote focus group; find out more in Chapter 4. There are also strategic links between RCSLT and the Association of Speech and Language Therapists in Independent Practice (ASLTIP).

Some good things are happening on the ground, and where there are 'green shoots', we share some of these stories.

Towards the end of the book, we share thoughts, hopes and ideas as we look to the future.

So yes, the book *will* be serious, but there is a golden thread of optimism which is a big part of our story and our approach to life generally. Hopefully it will inform and entertain you too!

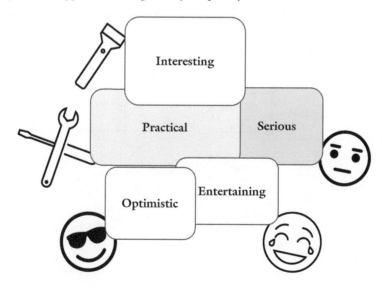

Keeping an eye on the big picture

There are common themes which run throughout the book. Though tackled individually, topics relate to each other: no single subject operates in isolation. To help illustrate both common themes and the interrelationships between each aspect of our independent practice, we have introduced icons/graphics which help to draw things together.

References

All dictionary definitions in this book are taken from *The Concise Oxford Dictionary*.

Pearsall, J. (1999) *The Concise Oxford Dictionary*. Tenth edition. Oxford Walton Street: Oxford University Press.

FOREWORD

I retired as Chief Executive Officer of the Royal College of Speech and Language Therapists (RCSLT) in March 2023 after 22 years. At this time, the RCSLT had over 20,000 members. During my tenure, I have had the privilege of getting to know and working more closely with speech and language therapy service leaders and clinical experts to inform our support and professional guidance to the profession, as well as influencing government policy and legislation.

My connection with Jo and Diana started many years ago, as they had established their reputation as strong leaders of speech and language therapy services in the NHS. When they were made redundant as a result of austerity measures and cuts to NHS services, I was concerned that we had lost them from the profession but luckily, they decided to use their skills to set up an independent practice.

When Jo and Diana asked me to write the foreword for their book, I was more than happy to say yes. After all, I was the one who persuaded them to share their experiences and knowledge at the Association of Speech and Language Therapists in Independent Practice (ASLTIP) conference in 2022.

This book goes one step further in that Jo and Diana have now provided an overview of their journey as well as capturing the experiences of others. One of the areas I always thought was a strength was their approach to collaborative working. Jo and Diana know how strongly I feel about the importance of the profession working together and for us to remove the historic barriers between the NHS and independent practice.

Over time, government policy has resulted in public sector cuts, fragmentation of how services are commissioned and therefore provided. This has been detrimental, particularly for children and young people with speech, language and communication needs (SLCN).

Now more than ever, it is essential that speech and language therapists work together to advocate for, and meet the needs of, people with SLCN. This was brought into sharp focus during the COVID-19 pandemic with data showing how the pandemic had a significant impact on the communication skills of children. Lockdowns also resulted in a sharp rise in referrals and waiting lists in the NHS. It was at this time that I reached out to Jo and Diana to ask them to share their learning. An 'all hands on deck approach' was required.

Alongside sharing their experiences and those of others in terms of changes to employment patterns, the chapters in the book provide a helpful practical resource for both existing independent practitioners and those who are setting up a business with all that this entails. I am aware that there is an ongoing process of change as the external environment continues to throw up new challenges and would encourage readers to reflect on where they are and what more they can do.

**Ms Kamini Gadhok MBE, BSc Hons, Doctor of Civil Law (Honorary),
Master of Science (Honorary), MRCSLT, Hon Companionship COP**

1 Setting the scene

This chapter will establish the context of our story. We will talk about how, after 30 plus years each in the public sector (NHS) with a number of those years in senior management positions, we went through the redundancy process and returned to our roots as speech and language therapists – only this time in independent practice (IP).

Initially it was all about survival; over time, however, we were able to create opportunities to grow and develop what ultimately has become a successful business.

Here we see the emergence of the golden thread of optimism.

We will talk about our individual stories covering the years leading up to redundancy. It's important to understand where we came from and the experiences we had along the way as they help to explain how we were able to draw upon transferable skills to establish and run a business, essentially in sales – but selling speech and language therapy services.

To be successful in sales, you need to know your product.

Product knowledge builds enthusiasm, gives us courage and helps us understand the competition better.
www.salestraininganddevelopment.com/product-knowledge-is-power.html [1]

We look at this in more detail in Chapter 13.

Those skills have given us a wealth of practical experience across a whole range of things to consider when operating in the world of independent practice. They are eminently transferable and as we work through the chapters in this book, we will be sharing everything we hope will be useful to readers, both in terms of managing a business *and* service delivery. We positively welcome readers whose roles may extend beyond speech and language therapy – there will be things that apply to *any* busines*s or* anyone moving away from being employed into running their own business.

The impact of redundancy cannot be avoided as this is one of life's upheavals which has the potential to derail the best of us. The impact of enforced change is strongly related to being made redundant – how can this be turned around into something positive and proactive? Again, adversity can build strength and resilience.

DOI: 10.4324/9781003382928-1

We are grateful to the British Association for Counselling and Psychotherapy (BACP) for their paper entitled 'How to cope with the mental health impact of unemployment' (2020) [2].

Here we share some observations from BACP member Simon Coombs, who runs Working Minds, a Torquay-based service that offers psychological support for unemployed people. Simon says there are some key things to think about when it comes to reducing the impact of unemployment on people's mental health.

> Being made redundant can have a critical effect on someone's mental health. When we're fully invested in our jobs, it becomes more than just something to pay the bills. We put so much of ourselves into the work we do. It's part of our identity. It's linked to our own self-worth and sense of our self.

Simon describes how some people who've lost their jobs initially have a bit of a positive bounce. 'They may have more energy, greater clarity of thought. They sometimes feel exhilarated, especially if it's a job they don't enjoy and they're just doing it to pay the bills'.

However, he observes:

> When it does start to kick in, people can go through different stages. There's a cycle of loss, starting with denial and then moving on to anger.
>
> Some people are much like a ship floating around without an anchor. They have no direction. There's uncertainty. That uncertainty feeds anxiety. They start to over-think; this creates fears. The self-doubt creeps in and the questioning about whether they're good enough.
>
> Family and friends may notice the person has become more emotional, withdrawn, irritable and short-tempered.

Simon stresses that it's 'absolutely critical' to get closure when someone loses their job. 'Without closure, redundancy can be an open wound that festers. It can be very debilitating to people's mental health'.

Part of Simon's role is to educate a person on how important it is to get closure.

> Sometimes people may be too angry, or they don't want anything to do with their former colleagues as it's too painful. But it's crucial to do something for closure.
>
> It may be that when the dust has settled, people meet up for a coffee. They can talk and put some of the pain and anger to bed. If it's left too long, it can really impact someone's self-worth.

As a counsellor, he works with people to help them recover that self-worth. He helps them with positive self-talk – shifting their internal dialogue to be more positive, optimistic and encouraging, rather than negative and filled with self-doubt.

> People feel like they've been selected for redundancy and that they are in deficit, they naturally evaluate their own self-worth against other people who have not lost their jobs.

We conclude the advice from Simon again in his own words: 'Re-framing and trying to see things as an opportunity can help'. These are wise words which resonated strongly with us all those years ago.

Sue (a clinical lead for children's services in her former life) clearly identifies with those feelings Simon talked about. She also came to the realisation of how important it is to take back control and turn things towards the positive.

I was called into my boss's office on Wednesday afternoon and was told I was being made redundant and had one day (Thursday) to clear my office and then would be put on gardening leave from Friday. When I came home Thursday evening I was devastated; it felt that 32 years' service had been for nothing. My whole working world fell apart and I questioned why I had worked 'over and above' so often to be treated this way. The weekend came and I decided I could either be a victim or I would make my life even better. I am pleased to say the latter happened and I have never looked back.

Like Sue, our change of direction wasn't a choice. In Chapter 2, we talk much more about choices and hear the stories of others and the choices they have made.

Starting to think about the context

As the outline for this book began to take shape, it soon became apparent that there is a significant amount of 'movement' within speech and language therapy, there are also misperceptions and a lack of knowledge and understanding about how the world of independent practice works and the networks available to increase awareness and support therapists working independently.

There are different models of professional practice: therapists work in a range of locations, for, with and through others. They move between models of practice, and they deploy their skills and experience in unrelated roles. Without taking a closer look, it's impossible to say whether this is a 'perceived trend' on our part or actual fact.

The first and obvious thing is to turn to the existing evidence base. There is an immediate problem here, however, as there is very little research into both the direction of movement within the profession and, perhaps more importantly, the *reasons why* therapists move.

What do we already know?

We have found four pertinent pieces of research.

The first two studies were by John Loan-Clarke and associate team members. Published in 2009, **study one** looked at why speech and language therapists stay in, leave and (sometimes) return to the NHS [3].

Study two, a year later, was a longitudinal study of allied health professionals (AHPs) in Britain, looking at retention, turnover and return [4].

We came across study one at about the time we were wrestling with what to include in a questionnaire we planned to disseminate to fellow therapists.

We knew what we wanted to find out, and the Loan-Clarke questionnaires contained some strikingly similar parameters – which was reassuring!

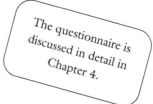

The questionnaire is discussed in detail in Chapter 4.

The third paper available to us looked at well-being, job satisfaction, stress and burnout in speech-language pathologists – a review of the literature published in 2020 [5].

The final paper which contributed to the context of our own information-gathering is a doctoral dissertation study by Claire Ewen, *The occupational and biopsychosocial wellbeing of speech and language therapists practising clinically in the United Kingdom* (2021) [6]. At the time of writing, this study has yet to be published but Claire has kindly made the scope and summary findings available for inclusion in our book.

> Read about these studies (including summaries of the findings) in more detail in Chapter 4.

Other data is available, but it is patchy and lacks detail. What information we were able to secure is in Chapter 4.

Our purpose in writing the book was not to undertake further and rigorous research – although additional large studies would be fascinating to see and could do much to inform migratory patterns and support retention of staff within the public sector. We were interested in exploring the potential for more qualitative information regarding what the current picture looked like. What could we discover and how might we go about it?

We were interested in finding out about:

A. Employment movement within the profession
B. The 'whys and hows' of buying extra support (over and above an NHS service core offer)
C. Students and independent practice
D. Structures and networks which support IPs

> These strands are discussed in detail in Chapters 3 and 4.

A personal story

The book is a personal story: it's not a recipe book – there are no rights or wrongs and nothing is a given. It's more a question of …

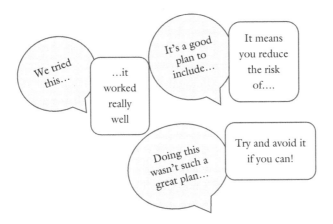

We are immensely proud of being speech and language therapists; we still get a buzz from doing our job but know that for some, the joy of getting up every day and achieving something positive and tangible has gradually been eroded. This is by no means a uni-professional issue, as readers will discover; there are references to a number of other professions at various points throughout the book.

Knowing that one aspect (and that could be *any* aspect – neighbour disputes or relationship problems for example) of life isn't going particularly well can start as a niggle which, naturally, we try to address. Sometimes that works and sometimes it doesn't, for whatever reason. Then the niggle becomes an irritant and is present more than it's absent and despite our best efforts, we can't seem to get it under control. Now it's a worry and beginning to spill over into other parts of life. Maybe we feel irritable or anxious, exhausted or 'wound up'.

Some level of tension and stress is part of everyday life. Stress can build resilience and encourage growth. In fact, some stress is motivating and helps us achieve.

So, when does so-called 'normal' stress tip over into a threat to physical or emotional health and well-being? Counsellor Carolyn Stevens offers some valuable insight.

She says that one way to look at this is by thinking of the difference between stress and anxiety. It can be said that stress is our response to a situation which is perceived as threatening (either physically or psychologically) and anxiety is what happens in response to the stress. However, whilst this is an important survival mechanism, anxiety that doesn't calm when the person is out of the challenging or threatening situation can be a threat to well-being. Anxiety can then become debilitating, impacting life, relationships and the ability to work. It might be triggered by something that reminds the person of a past event, for example, or by an imagined event in the future, i.e. when there is no immediate threat. Carolyn shares this quote with us:

> *Stress is a normal response to a situation or event that feels challenging. It's our body's initial reaction to stressors, such as a demanding job, financial worries or relationship problems. While stress can be uncomfortable, it can also be a positive motivator that helps us to rise to a challenge. However, if stressors persist and become chronic, they can lead to physical and mental health problems, such as headaches, fatigue and depression.*
>
> *On the other hand, anxiety is a set of feelings characterised by excessive fear and worry, even when there is no apparent threat. Unlike stress, anxiety isn't always linked to a specific event or situation. People with anxiety disorders may experience feelings of unease, nervousness or fear that persist and interfere with their daily life.*
>
> www.clinical-partners.co.uk/insights-and-news/anxiety/item/
> what-is-the-difference-between-stress-and-anxiety [7]

We would suggest, both from our own experience of significant life events and from talking to others, that the anxiety may remain for some time after the stressful situation has resolved. That is certainly something worth knowing in terms of 'the road to recovery'.

From our own personal experience (and this is likely to resonate with most people), stress increases when we either can't effect positive and sustainable change where we are, or we can't see a way out of a particular situation. We have both encountered this in previous lives.

At this point we begin to focus on work-related aspects – the principles could apply to *any* role, any job, anywhere. People develop different survival techniques: collusion, avoidance and sickness, for example.

One way of coping is to just ignore the bits that aren't going well, or the fact that we can't change them (ostrich). This might work in the short-term but longer term we might actually make things worse because we aren't being true to ourselves and doing something – anything – to effect change.

> Sandy worked in a team where the leader's style was completely at odds with the vocational nature of the job they were all there to do. Whilst others stood their ground and challenged, resulting in considerable staff turnover, Sandy felt unable to do so and be true to what she really felt. She had recently suffered a family bereavement and was emotionally exhausted. She ended up having a complete breakdown and taking early retirement.

At the other extreme, there is the 'flight' response: we opt to physically distance ourselves from the causes of the stress, either by moving elsewhere …

Hannah worked in the public sector but found her job increasingly unrewarding. She had held out to continue part-time despite the pressure to increase her hours. She felt weighed down with management responsibilities, which included dealing with problems which were just not solvable. Her clinical satisfaction diminished to the point that it was almost non-existent. Hannah wasn't ready to quit the public sector just the job she was doing. She moved to a different role in an unrelated team and, at the time of writing, had begun to combine that role with independent work.

… or by going on sick leave (avoidance) as Jamie did.

I'll be completely honest, the only way I felt I could escape from the pressure and the demands was to just not be there. Initially, it was quite easy to be off for a week and then return – nobody seemed to bother. Now I realise that those absences were probably a cry for help – help which I didn't get until a new manager came along and referred me to occupational health. I wasn't physically ill to begin with, but I think I was in the end. I had trouble sleeping and I let my healthy diet slip. At occupational health, I got to talk to someone but that couldn't change the job I was expected to do. I left and got a post where I could use my skills without the pressure and stress.

In our experience as NHS service managers in our previous lives, frequent sickness absence is a classic cry for help which we ignore at our peril.

Resigning without another job to go to, as Cathy did, is also an event within our own experience. It should most certainly sound alarm bells, loud and clear. Here is her story.

Initially, I think I was in the 'colluding' category. By colluding, I mean that I always seemed to be justifying why I carried on battling.

When I first qualified, I loved work. I was happy and I progressed. Then after several big changes in the Trust, things began to change. It took a while for the changes to impact – it was insidious.

I began to hate work and became more and more stressed. Lots of people were leaving and I felt responsible for the more junior people around me. I had all of the responsibility, but no power to make changes.

I thought I was coping, but my anxiety levels were rising. It opened my eyes to how under-valued I was. I wasn't looked after or ever thanked for what I did. It made me realise that I was killing myself.

With hindsight, I can see that it was almost inevitable that I would go off sick. I was never sick before – it was totally not like me. I was off for some weeks. I hit rock bottom and struggled to do much at all, but it gave me a chance to completely gain perspective. I could see the impact this was having not only on me but my family and friends as well – we were all affected.

I returned to work determined to 'leave work at the door' – there were people in the department who survived by doing that – being able to arrive, do and leave and compartmentalise that part of their life. But I couldn't, it just wasn't in my nature.

I didn't know what I was going to do, but I was lucky that I had support, so I resigned anyway.

We asked Cathy whether she had an exit interview.

I did have but I'm not sure what good it did.

It's a good idea to ask what happens to the content of your exit interview.

Cathy's story is quite extreme but by no means unique. We asked her what she wished she had known before she resigned.

How deskilled I was becoming. Decision-making was all about capacity – not decisions being made based on what a child needs. I wish I'd known that the world is a big place and that there were so many opportunities out there.

The top five most stressful life events include:

1. Death of a loved one
2. Divorce
3. Moving
4. Major illness or injury
5. Job loss

Between us, during the course of our journey, we have experienced all of these events but have lived to not only tell the tale but to share much positivity.

www.uhhospitals.org/Healthy-at-UH/articles/2015/07/the-top-5-most-stressful-life-events [8]

Our story begins with number 5 on the list.

Enforced change is a completely different ball game.

Redundancy may be in relation to a job role being deemed no longer needed as a result of organisational change.

> redundant [adj]: no longer needed or useful; superfluous; unemployed

The individual may feel disempowered and undervalued. There will be readers for whom this will resonate.

Corporate or institutional change is one thing – the skills of management to manage the change are crucial to its success. In the natural course of events, not everyone will be happy with the change and team members may fall by the wayside.

We didn't *choose* to change, so it could hardly be seen as a positive thing – particularly at the outset – but we did have a choice as to whether our *response* was positive or not.

> *The secret of change is to focus all of your energy not on fighting the old, but on building the new.* – Socrates

Oh, how true – if only we had known and believed it at the time. Looking back now on how hard we (and colleagues in the same position) initially fought to *not* be made redundant, brings a rueful smile – but also makes us cringe. Perhaps the fight was more about the impact on our feelings of value and self-worth and far less about what we would do to make a living.

I should just take the money and run ...

Oh, get over yourself!

Well ... if it's just the work that defines you ...

> Excuse the levity – we can laugh about it now!

However, some changes are not so much pre-conceived, planned and implemented (or in our case 'executed'), but rather they are insidious. Over time, things shift and slide and there is a gradual awakening to the fact that the job has somehow changed. Perhaps it becomes more difficult to deploy knowledge and skills to their best effect. Depleted resources and huge demand place heavy burdens on the workforce – and sometimes things become unsustainable.

Regardless of the reasons for change, which as we know can be many and varied, there are really only two key principles which apply.

> Be in charge of the change and plan accordingly.

> Being in control immediately reduces stress.

1. **Where do my skills and talents (and any qualifications) lie?**

   It isn't unheard of for people to make a *complete* (i.e. career) change. We know of a number of people now working out of the speech and language therapy world (counsellors, nurses and at least one ex-therapist now happily employed in sales).

   It may be that a hobby or interest has the potential to be a realistic source of income. However, for the majority of people who are working their way through this opening chapter, staying with what they know, have trained hard to achieve and probably used to very much enjoy, is what they would want to explore first.

   > I want to carry on doing what I know (and love) but just not here .....

2. **If I stay in the profession (whether it be speech and language therapy or any of a number of other professions), what are the employment options?**
   - Continue in the public sector: NHS, local authority (LA) or higher education institute (HEI) for example
   - Become directly employed by a setting. A school or a chain of care homes for example
   - Become directly employed by a private or third-sector company delivering speech and language therapy (or other) services
   - Become self-employed and work as a sole trader (including working as a sub-contractor to a larger company)

Self-employment is the focus of our journey, but we discuss examples of various other configurations.

> Find out much more about the various business models in Chapter 5

3. **What are the pros and cons?**

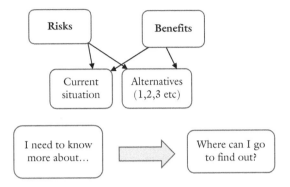

Sounds simple? Well – not exactly simple, but it certainly doesn't need to be complicated!

Beginning our journey

Before we set out on that journey, we want to talk a little bit about our working lives before and leading up to the change. As with everyone, experiences and opportunities have shaped us and equipped us to make significant changes resulting in personal and professional pride and satisfaction.

The point to take from our stories is that we are not extraordinary people; we are essentially no different from anyone else. We took a different path because we *had to* and grew into our new roles over time. We all have skills and talents – we just need to recognise them. We all have the power to effect change for ourselves if we really want to.

Once upon a time in 2011/12, we were senior managers in the NHS … and then we weren't. As a result of one restructure too far, we were both made redundant and were faced with the challenge of what on earth we were going to do.

Jo's story

I was 16 years old, being asked what 'A' levels I wanted to do and really had no clue about what career path I would choose. One day on my return from school, my mum told me about a radio programme she had heard which featured a speech therapist.

It sounded intriguing, and so I investigated a little more and arranged to spend time with a couple of speech and language therapists, one of whom was working with laryngectomee – who turned out to be an old friend of my grandfather.

This gentleman was able to use his dynavox (external/artificial larynx) to tell me what a difference speech and language therapy was making to his life. That was such a powerful moment – I can visualise it as clearly now as all those years ago. I knew from that moment on that I wanted to help people who couldn't communicate to be able to express themselves, and the rest is history as they say.

Graduating in 1987, I began in a mixed post with a few special schools 'thrown in'. One special school I was expected to manage was a residential and day school for pupils aged 2 to 19 with visual impairment. The campus was about two miles from one side to the other and I had to cover all of this on a Friday afternoon!

Clinic sessions were daunting, clients were selected from a 'cardex' (a draw full of handwritten cards) and you literally took whoever's card came next – be it an adult stroke client or a preschool stammerer. Variety is the spice of life but, as a new graduate, it was hard to feel like I had the skills to manage cases as diverse as those I was coming across. As luck would have it, there were some amazing therapists in that team who took me under their wing and made me feel that I could ask questions. Formal supervision was not a 'thing' and as far as I can recall there were no competencies to be evidenced and signed off.

Awareness of Speech and Language Therapy (SLT or SaLT) as a profession was on the increase and as a result so were caseload sizes. A couple of years after I began work, a new trend was emerging where focussed teams were set up to develop approaches and systems which would manage specific client groups more effectively and with better outcomes.

In my department, the first teams were simply paediatric, adult and an ALD (adults with learning disabilities) team. It was time to make a choice, and despite having graduated thinking adults were my happy place, I actually chose paediatrics. This was due in large part to the fact I was better able to access support from team members who also worked with children, and I rarely saw anyone else who worked with adults during my working week. Caseloads were on the rise, and the development of group treatment approaches was being seen as a way to enable easier access to services as well as an effective way to treat children with similar difficulties. There was very little in the way of evidence-based practice, but we could *see* it was working in terms of better outcomes for the children, better engagement with the parents and better throughput of caseload.

A group coordinators post was created, and I jumped at the chance to develop this side of the service even more. I think this is when I began to realise that I enjoy ensuring the systems and structures are right, just as much as I enjoy working with the clients. Naturally, my enthusiasm for organising and managing led me into team leader type roles and eventually to become the manager of a large mixed service in the NHS. With the support and encouragement of an operational manager within the trust, I studied for a Master's in Leadership for Health Service Improvement.

As the NHS was reorganised again and again, the mixed service I managed was split up across different trusts and my role began to morph into something almost exclusively managerial. It was a battle to maintain half a day per week of clinical work, and at one point towards the end of my time in the NHS, I had to keep my clinical work secret from a (non-speech and language therapy) line manager who could not understand the attraction of continuing to hold a clinical caseload as she herself had given up working with clients at the earliest opportunity.

It was an absolute privilege to learn about and manage other professions, but I felt like a fraud – what did I know about the clinical issues facing my colleagues in children's palliative care for example? The mantra of the senior management was that if you could manage one service you could manage any service. The emphasis within the Trust at that time was on everything and anything except the patients, and my enthusiasm for the corporate culture and the constant changes waned. I couldn't really hide my lack of interest in 'dashboards' and 'RAG ratings', re-branding and fancy logos. My face no longer fitted: I didn't really want to be in those endless meetings and, looking back, I can see that it showed.

I was one of a number of redundancies in a reorganisation which I just couldn't get behind. It was a shock – traumatic even – but in the middle of the difficult times, opportunities presented themselves and I was able to adapt, survive and thrive.

Diana's story

 My initial career path wasn't speech therapy (as it was known then) – I began a combined communication studies and English course which was the forerunner of modern-day media studies. I had it in mind to get into broadcasting or newspaper journalism. Ironically, it was my embryonic journalistic attempts which got me ejected from my (24th floor) hall of residence for reporting (unfavourably) on the frequent lift breakdowns. Teaming up with a photography student, we captured some dramatic footage of London Fire Brigade's finest forcing apart the doors of the lift as terrified students fell through the gap gasping for air. By the time homelessness reared its head, though, I had already decided that I wanted to do something more vocational. It took me a while to get a place because I was considered a risk (having already dropped out of one course).

I bided my time waitressing and then working for a number of months as a nursing auxiliary (earlier incarnation of a healthcare assistant), where I learnt to lay out the dead and also managed to mix up 24 sets of false teeth in an attempt to streamline the mouth-care round. This was followed by a year as an 'auntie' in a residential home for 'maladjusted' children (nowadays children with social emotional and mental health (SEMH) difficulties). What I might have been lacking in conventionality I made up for in life experience. It made me all the more determined to succeed.

I loved my job from day one – even if it *did* mean I had sole responsibility for the paediatric caseload in Lichfield and the surrounding villages, plus any and all adult patients in Lichfield and the neighbouring town of Tamworth. This included strokes, degenerative conditions and dementia – about which very little was known then, certainly in terms of what benefit speech therapy could possibly bring. And – like Jo – the obligatory special school was thrown in. It was an era where the length of one's white coat was more of a talking point than support, supervision or evidence-based practice! Yes – times have certainly changed.

I think the fact that I survived (and so did the patients) was down to the rigour of the training I had received and the huge amount of practical work crammed in, week after week. In my final year, my paediatric placement saw me catching the train every Thursday morning to a neighbouring city to run the clinic there. There were always six therapies booked in, so rarely time for a pit stop, whilst the clinician in charge sat in the staff room, squirrelled away in that vast Victorian building, with a coffee, a magazine and her favourite menthol cigarettes. In those days, having a student was the gift that kept on giving!

Three years after I qualified, I began to move towards an adult specialism. I was genuinely fond of those 'old people' and if I had been allowed to return to work on a part-time basis after my first child, my professional life would have taken a very different turn. In those days, part-time wasn't on the cards, so I didn't go back at all! In the interim, I kept my hand in by taking on two private patients.

Of course, I did return, eventually, to a different service with hours to suit in a town where there was no service at all, and they were grateful for whatever they could get. I remember those days very fondly. I was actually part of a team – albeit they were a good ten miles away whichever way you looked – so I could ask for help.

I was proud to work in the NHS for 36 years. The last almost 20 of those for the most part very happy years were in Sandwell, an inner-city metropolitan borough council area in the heart of the Black Country. I had a surprising degree of autonomy whilst also the ability to take advantage of opportunities to learn lots of new skills not traditionally associated with speech and language therapy (investigating malpractice and fraud as well as supporting the practical implementation of clinical governance in non-acute settings) – which have stood me in very good stead during and after the transition into independent practice.

My first foray into management happened by default really. The then-manager had a serious car accident which kept her away for months. It was a steep learning curve, but I realised very quickly how important it was to be able to influence decision-making if we were going to be able to benefit the huge numbers of Sandwell residents who needed help. Equally important was the need to nurture, grow and retain a strong and talented team. The team was the single most important resource without which there could be little or no benefit to the population we served.

Those 20 years were a period of gradually accelerating change, latterly driven almost exclusively by financial constraints. Each reconfiguration included a rather sinister form of musical chairs. As the final reconfiguration approached, there was a bid, primarily led by the Allied Health Professions (AHPs), to try and protect the autonomy and independence which would allow us to focus completely on our community services, by establishing a social enterprise. Sadly that attempt failed to secure enough of the vote to continue and for the musical grand finale, a number of chairs, including mine, were out of the game.

Like all good 'once upon a time' stories, this one has a happy ending (otherwise this book would not have happened). This story is primarily all about the *journey*, the challenges faced – some unforeseen and potentially destabilising – decisions that had to be made and how that happened. A story about how to move from survival to success. Looking back on 12 years of independent practice allows us to see ourselves and others like us within the wider national context.

References

1. https://salestraininganddevelopment.com/product-knowledge-is-power.html (n.d.) Sales training: 10 reasons product knowledge is power. Available at: https://salestraininganddevelopment.com/product-knowledge-is-power.html.
2. https://salestraininganddevelopment.com/product-knowledge-is-power.html (n.d.) Sales training: 10 reasons product knowledge is power. Available at: https://salestraininganddevelopment.com/product-knowledge-is-power.html.
3. Loan-Clarke, J. et al. (2009) Why do speech and language therapists stay in, leave and (sometimes) return to the National Health Service (NHS)? *International Journal of Language & Communication Disorders*, 44(6), pp. 883–900. doi:10.1080/13682820802381334.
4. Loan-Clarke, J. et al. (2010) Retention, turnover and return – A longitudinal study of allied health professionals in Britain. *Human Resource Management Journal*, 20(4), pp. 391–406. doi:10.1111/j.1748-8583.2010.00140.x.

5. Ewen, C. et al. (2020) Well-being, job satisfaction, stress and burnout in speech-language pathologists: A review. *International Journal of Speech-Language Pathology*, 23(2), pp. 180–190. doi:10.1080/1754 9507.2020.1758210.

6. Ewen, C. (2021) The occupational and biopsychosocial well-being of speech and language therapists practising clinically in the United Kingdom. www.ethos.bl.uk. Available at: https://www.open-access .bcu.ac.uk/13347/1/Claire%20Ewen%20PhD%20Thesis%20published_Final%20version_Submitted %20Apr%202021_Final%20Award%20Jul%202021.pdf.

7. Partners, C. (n.d.) Insights and news, clinical partners – Psychiatrists, psychotherapists & psychologists in London and across the UK. Available at: https://www.clinical-partners.co.uk/insights-and-news/ anxiety/item/what-is-the-difference-between-stress-and-anxiety.

8. UHBlog (2015) *The Top 5 Most Stressful Life Events.* University Hospitals. Available at: https://www .uhhospitals.org/Healthy-at-UH/articles/2015/07/the-top-5-most-stressful-life-events.

2 Choices

In this chapter, we will talk in more detail about 'choice', what it means and how to prepare to make a choice. We are looking at change and choice in the context of the personal stories we share, both in this chapter and throughout the book. Also, the information from our question-naire and the findings of Claire Ewen's research (more about both these in Chapters 3 and 4) also contribute to the reasons for making a change.

To effect change we need to consider the options and move ourselves to the point where we can make a decision.

The process of change is a continuum beginning with identifying the pros and cons of every option.

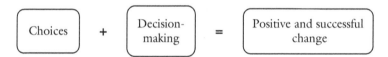

For some, this is hugely difficult for whatever reason. We know that stress and anxiety impact on decision-making.

> Feeling stressed changes how people weigh risk and reward. Stress seems to help people learn from positive feedback and impairs their learning from negative feedback.
>
> This means when people under stress are making a difficult decision, they may pay more attention to the upsides of the alternatives they're considering and less to the downsides.

www.psychologicalscience.org/news/releases/stress-changes-how-people-make-decisions .html#:~:text=%E2%80%9CStress%20seems%20to%20help%20people,and%20less%20to%20the %20downsides [1]

We also know that for some people things reach a critical point before they opt to change. Also, before making any decisions, we need to know what our options are and the pros and cons of each.

So what can be done in such situations?

Before things reach a 'critical point', take back control by looking at what you might do to resolve the difficulties – initially anything goes, no matter how outlandish it might sound. It won't be

DOI: 10.4324/9781003382928-2

long before the options begin to polarise and become more realistic as you begin to look in detail at the pros and cons. This is *absolutely* what we do if we buy a new car or plan a holiday. Making changes to our work life is arguably *much* more important than either of these!

What do we mean by 'critical point'? It could be the point at which inertia sets in or it becomes impossible to

Inertia [n]: a tendency to do nothing or remain unchanged

step off the carousel long enough to reflect and to actively consider alternatives. '*I can't think about that now, I'm far too busy with …* ' (ring any bells?).

Or, further down the line, the decision-making process is affected by the level of stress we feel. It's important to remember that certain levels of anxiety become debilitating.

Taking back control before things reach crisis point helps to maintain a sense of objectivity and avoid the potential for 'out of the frying pan into the fire'.

At this point, it must be said that *choosing* to make a change is a positive thing. The challenges are around weighing up the pros and cons and managing the risks. By sharing our experiences and stories from a range of different people, we hope this book will help with some of that.

People opt for change for lots of different reasons – and by no means are they all negative. The findings from our questionnaire and the personal stories give us a better picture.

Things are going OK here, but if I go there, they could be even better…

There are hundreds of motivational quotes about making choices. This is one of the most pertinent.

One of the hardest decisions made in life is to choose which bridge to cross and which bridge to burn.

The practical aspects of this book are to lay out possible options and to help people prepare for what they choose to do.

However, any change cannot disregard the human element – the emotions, the what-ifs and the fear of the unknown, hence the inclusion of the experiences of others. Something here may resonate: there is always something we can take from others who have been faced with similar issues.

To bring about change, we need to 'do something different'. The crucial questions are 'what', 'how' and 'when' (it's the 'why' which brings us to the realisation that something needs to change).

Our change of direction wasn't a choice. We are well aware that for others who decide to make a change, there *is* a choice but having listened to some of the stories, we would defy anyone who says that making the choice they did was easy. For some, the need to change direction is purely practical: opportunities present themselves and are taken. For others, things have to get quite bad before they begin to get better.

Talking (openly) about our own journey may help others realise that changing direction isn't *just* about having a choice – it's about making an *informed*, *considered* and *positive* choice, where the decision-maker has done their homework, considered the risks as well as the benefits and planned accordingly.

One of the aims of this book is to encourage others (and not just speech and language therapists) who are either considering joining the world of independent practice (IP) or looking to develop what they are already doing to avoid pitfalls and seize opportunities with confidence. As William Cohen said, '*Whenever you see a successful business, someone once made a courageous decision*' (2023) [2].

Let's look at some more personal stories.

> When embarking on this book, we were very conscious that our backgrounds are paediatric; we were keen to understand and include some of the challenges facing therapists working with adult clients. Yes, there would be commonalities, but also specific challenges which would be useful for readers to hear about.

Naomi's story

Naomi is a speech and language therapist working with adults; she is passionate about rehabilitation. Like the majority of people we have spoken to, she began her career in the public sector. 2016 saw something of a pivotal moment for her.

Following the completion of a Master's degree in brain injury rehabilitation and looking for career progression, it became clear that the only way to progress was to move into more of a management role.

> This is a recurrent theme: clinicians (for whom clinical work is their passion and priority) report that in order to climb the career ladder, they need to take on management roles.

I wanted to stay firmly in the clinical world, not management.

This coincided with growing feelings of despondency about the kind of service we were able to provide.

Naomi felt that the importance of communication work was becoming subsumed by the amount of dysphagia (feeding and swallowing) work which was required. '*I couldn't impact on that, despite being the communication lead for the team!*'

Naomi had already dipped her toe in the water, taking on two clients and had also taken the ASLTIP course in setting up in independent practice (see Chapter 4).

When I finally made the move, it was a leap of faith really. I spent the first year or so begin-ning to take on some private clients alongside locuming. I worked in a number of different teams – the environment was often quite highly stressed and it was quite a relief to just be able to get on with the clinical work. That said, I found myself doing a lot of listening and did mentor a band 5 in one of the teams where I spent some time.

At the time of writing, her work was divided between brain injury clients who come via case managers (commissioned by litigation solicitors) and individual, primarily private clients who had suffered a stroke. She worked full time but enjoyed the flexibility, completing reports for example at the weekend or in the evenings as this worked for her.

Her experiences of the ethical and financial considerations are insightful and helpful. Read more about these in Chapters 7 and 8.

Naomi had a pretty clear idea of what she *didn't* want to carry on doing and planned for her change by, as she says, 'dipping her toe' in the water of IP.

Having more than one role is certainly not unusual as we see the development of more and more portfolio careers. The diversity of different roles is an inspiration and will hopefully spur others on to recognise and deploy their transferable skills. It's probably safe to say that very few people will have diversified quite as far as physiotherapist Karris.

Karris's story

She qualified in 2016 and, over time, developed an interest in women's health and perinatal care. However, alongside this, she was working towards a Master's degree in veterinary physiotherapy. In 2019, she established her own veterinary physiotherapy business, Ark Physiotherapy.

'I treat mostly horses but also dogs, cats and any other animals in need of physiotherapy input'.

Today, Karris feels she has the best of both worlds.

The best thing for me about the way I work is that I can work in the NHS in an area which really interests me whilst also giving me the financial security I need to develop and expand Ark. I have the flexibility to in-build time for myself – to do the things that I enjoy – which definitely increases my positivity levels at work.

There is also much more overlap than many people would think. When treating horses, their riders or owners often have pain or injuries which need managing in order to reduce the risk of this negatively impacting the horse.

I always thought that at some point I would give up my 'human' work altogether, but I am so glad that I didn't as my ability to treat people too means that I can take a much more holistic approach to the way I treat horses. I truly feel very lucky to have two jobs that I am so interested in, particularly my veterinary physio which I don't really consider to be work at all!

*My one nugget of advice for anyone thinking of pursuing a somewhat 'outside the box' career, off the back of a job in healthcare, would be to **go for it**. I came up against many negative comments, related to my age, my experience and my commitment to one area of physiotherapy when it became known that I wanted to complete my veterinary physiotherapy Master's degree.*

Some of these comments hit me really hard, making me doubt myself and my abilities. Thankfully, I have an incredibly supportive family and partner who constantly reminded me of my goals and what I was capable of. I can honestly say that I love my jobs and I am extremely proud of what I have been able to achieve.

The theme of collaboration with colleagues in both the public and the private sector comes through from various sources, including the clinical excellence network (CEN) focus group. There are surely things we can all take forward here (more about this in Chapter 16).

The freedom to explore, evaluate and choose – directing our own CPD [continuing professional development] *and integrating knowledge gained into working practice – is what makes independent practice so rewarding.*

Gillian's story

Gillian's story involves leaving, returning to, and then finally parting company with the public sector and the benefits she has gained along the way. By the time she arrived at the point of finally leaving the NHS she came across as 'fully informed' and made her decision for practical and pragmatic reasons. She had given things her 'best shot'.

Qualifying in 1992, I took a full-time post in an NHS SLT service. It was an exciting time to enter the profession. Psycholinguistic and sociolinguistic theories of language acquisition were changing clinical practice. My interests gravitated towards pre- and school-aged children with special needs – putting parents centre stage. Even in those early days, the importance and impact of training others was apparent. I had invaluable support from more experienced colleagues who were generous with their time and knowledge.

After nine years, I stepped out of the NHS to raise my children. An unexpected decision to home educate further fuelled my interest in the role and autonomy of the learner in the learning process. During those next nine years, I maintained and developed my skills by writing and publishing a training course for special school staff, running training days for SLT teams and carrying out a review of SLT provision in two special schools.

I returned to the NHS for a further nine years, my partner and I both working part-time while jointly parenting and educating our children. I couldn't commit to the hours required for a permanent post and took a succession of fixed-term bank contracts. I enjoyed my work, and being part of the team again, but gradually became disillusioned. Caseloads were large, care pathways shifted children frequently between therapists and interventions, which had a good evidence base, were often diluted in 'dosage' and efficacy. My commitment to the NHS made me reluctant to leave but I began to consider independent practice as a serious option.

Two independent SLT friends were generous in their support as I started out. The information and support from ASLTIP were invaluable. Working in IP can feel isolating, but the networks I now belong to are one of the best outcomes.

Independent practice gave me full autonomy to design a SLT service from scratch, focusing on strong relationships with parents and continuity of care. I pursued my interest in placing parents at the heart of therapy by training in VERVE Child Interaction. I then had the freedom, as an independent practitioner, to fully explore this approach with a range of clients and, having witnessed the outcomes, to use my professional judgement in choosing to offer it across my service to all families.

*I have no regrets about **leaving** the NHS because it has given me the flexibility to choose when, where, how I work and who with.*

*Conversely, I have no regrets about my time **in** the NHS. It gave me a strong foundation and nurtured my growth as a therapist and my commitment to our profession. I value my strong link with my local NHS team. Working collaboratively, we can give families the best of both worlds.* http://www.apectraining.co.uk/

The public sector experiences we have, although at the time they appear negative, can be a good preparation for any future changes we might make. The trick is to recognise that any experience, both good *and* bad, teaches us something.

Anna's story

Anna is a Counselling Psychologist. Readers will recognise the (now familiar) themes which cut across different professions. However, there are some valuable additional lessons to learn from her experience. This is Anna's story.

Anna's role has always been with children's mental health. She began working independently about ten years ago, not wanting to return to a full-time post after the birth of her daughter.

Up until that point, her job had included undertaking different roles for local authorities – part of which focussed on building a relationship between health (CAMHS) and education, whilst working towards her post-graduate qualification.

Various aspects of the role began to feel uncomfortable.

> *At that time, there was an awareness of the need for evidence of impact/outcomes but the approaches were quite crude and arbitrary, primarily focussing on quantitative 'measurables' which sit uneasily within a mental health paradigm – especially one working with children and young people.*
>
> *I had ethical dilemmas as the approach was very much 'one size fits all' and there was an over-reliance on cognitive behavioural therapy (CBT) practices as these can be measured. I felt that approaches needed to be far more holistic.*

Anna also talked about 'access issues'. There are parallels here with other services such as dentistry – and SLT too.

> *A child had to reach a critical point before getting seen by the service when it was clearly totally counter-productive to wait for things to get so bad.*

Anna ruefully remembers:

> *To 'go independent' seemed a low risk, as I was married and my husband was able to support us both whilst I got set up. So far so good! I became self-employed and was (and still am) the sole director of a limited company.*

Not many months down the line, Anna found herself in entirely different circumstances and was no longer able to rely on a financial cushion.

> *Suddenly the need to earn money to keep body and soul (and child) together became far more urgent. There was no longer the luxury of being able to spend a protracted period of time getting set up.*

There are definite learning points here for others planning on working for themselves. Know what you need to do and set yourself a deadline to get the basics in place so that you can at least get started. Consider taking out income protection insurance. Also, Anna initially found setting up in independent practice very hard as it conflicted with her belief that a service should be free at the point of delivery.

New business comes 100% from recommendations and ten years down the line, Anna is able to pick and choose what commissions to accept. This is a common theme. At the outset, most people will take on whatever is available as they are getting established and are then able to work towards their areas of particular interest and expertise.

The financial aspects of running a business have been particularly challenging for Anna: keeping a tally on money, managing the cashflow, making the associates aware of appropriate charging for time and making sure everyone is signed up to the same approach.

'I know that cognitively we need to be able to talk about money, but at an emotional level, this can be hard!' Again, another very familiar theme (read more about finances in Chapter 8).

> *My associates are all people I knew and have worked with previously and whilst the relationship between us is important, it can be difficult when things need to be challenged!*
>
> *Looking back, I realise that working in the public sector is a great training ground for later working independently, but at the time I was far more focussed on the clinical aspects of my role. It's only latterly that I have been able to dig deep and realise that I had acquired much broader skills and they were transferable!*

Insightfully, Anna makes the observation:

> *I can see that sometimes it 'takes the mistakes' in order to think about what processes I need to have in place to stop them happening again – and ideally those processes might have stopped some things going awry in the first place!*
>
> *I know there is still a way to go in getting the business to the point that I can be less hands-on, but that way seems clearer.*

The feelings of not being valued, and the frustration of not being able to deliver support to really **make a difference**, come across consistently and continuously from the many conversations we have had. Similar themes can be found across a range of different professions. Charlie is a teacher, specialising in behaviour and special educational needs and disabilities.

Charlie's story

> *In my mid-twenties, I was a mechanical engineer living and working outside the UK. I decided to re-train to work in childcare and education. As a teenager teaching martial arts, I was usually asked to take on the children on the course – none of the other instructors had either the inclination or the patience! This gave me my first taste of supporting behavioural concerns and how some of the children had difficulties following instructions, focussing and impulse control.*
>
> *When I returned to the UK, I built up my experience by taking on a variety of different roles. After 14 years working for various local authorities, I started my own business. I didn't feel valued. I was frustrated and disillusioned by pointless meetings, unpredictable managerial styles, lack of change or change that was unhelpful and the slow movement of systems that were incredibly unhelpful to the children needing help.*
>
> *I should have made the move far earlier but was plagued by the same doubts everyone has – will I have enough work? Will I earn the money I need to make a living? Will I be able to run a business?*

We asked Charlie whether the move he made was the right one.

> *I have absolutely no regrets and striking out as an independent practitioner was definitely the best decision I ever made. I am autonomous. I plan and manage my own time, choosing where I work and who I work with. I can think for myself and am in charge of priorities and developments. I am in control of the direction of travel.*

Have you any advice for someone who is thinking of leaving the public sector?

> *It is important before you choose to become self-employed to do your homework. Make sure there's a customer base to tap into. Build up some financial reserves to tide you over in the early days. Yes, you **are** running a business to earn money, but never lose sight of the importance of the quality of what you offer.*

As we saw in Chapter 1 from Cathy's and Jamie's stories, sadly, many people who shared their experiences with us reached a critical point in their lives before eventually managing to regain their equilibrium and beginning to move forward. Unfortunately, Marianne's story 'has it all' and not in a good way.

Marianne's story

I love being a Speech and Language Therapist (SLT) – it feels a genuine privilege to do what I do. I started my career in the 1990s in the NHS and thought this is where I would always stay. However, a series of events led me to question my career and ultimately to leave the NHS about ten years ago. For a time, I wondered whether I had lost the love for what I did, but after reflecting and talking to those around me, I realised I still had the same desire and drive I had to be an SLT as the day I started my training but the environment within which I found myself working was impacting me greatly.

I had a tough decision to make. When you have worked within the NHS, it can feel like this is the only option. You are often reminded of how fortunate you are. Job security, a good pension and a nice amount of annual leave are often cited as things to appreciate. But my last few years working within the NHS were not positive. The culture I was working within felt toxic and was at odds with my personal values. Reviewing services, downgrading jobs, being undermined and criticised on a daily basis is not conducive to enabling people to perform at their best or to deliver high-quality healthcare services.

It became apparent that what was valued was getting the job done and not questioning anything. I could not work in these conditions. This was the future direction of travel, so I made the decision to resign without another job to go to. I appreciate that this is not something that everyone could do. It wasn't really something I could do, but I had to change something and knew that I was fighting a losing battle trying to do this within the service I was working in. I had worked so hard in all of the roles I had, both as a clinician and leader/manager, and I had always strived to do the best job I could. However, slowly I became a version of me of which I was not proud. I was worn down by what felt like a continual fight. I felt like my role and profession were not respected by many and that I was a payroll number who was easily replaced. I left the NHS feeling like I was not a good therapist, manager or person. What a sad legacy.

So I left the NHS for the good of myself, but also for the good of others. I did not want to be that cynical person who we have all known, that negative voice or the person whose career was decided by those in positions of power above them. Initially, I completed some locum work within the NHS, rebuilding my confidence as a therapist, and it was lovely to feel valued again. I worked in different organisations and had none of the management responsibility of my permanent post. However, having once had that bigger picture thinking, you cannot unsee things. That journey led me to see the same challenges in different places with people continuing to not tackle them. Whether that was because people lacked the skills, the support, the confidence or were just worn down as I was – I am not sure.

Do not get me wrong, I owe a huge debt to the NHS and many of the colleagues I worked with. I learned a great deal and was given opportunities to grow, develop and innovate. I witnessed some amazing people delivering incredible services and going the extra mile for the patients they served all within often restrictive and constraining conditions. However, the work we do takes an emotional toll, and if the right support or environment is not in place, it can take a huge personal toll. My work affected my own health for several years before I was prepared to really accept this. I worked many hours over and above my contract year after year. Whatever I did never felt enough. This was as much about me as it was about the people I worked with and for and the organisational culture. I felt like I constantly had to prove myself. I was once told that I was very expensive for what I did – those statements hit hard and had a long-term impact. Ultimately, I had to accept that I could only change the things within my direct control, and for me, that was to leave for the sake of my health, both physical and mental.

I am now working in private practice and loving it! This provides me with freedom, flexibility and fulfilment which are key values for me. It has been a new challenge as I knew nothing about running a business, so there have been many new skills to learn. I am a sole practitioner within my business so I do miss working as part of a team day to day. However, I have recreated this through building relationships with colleagues in the independent health sector as well as networking locally with a diverse range of businesses. I have found these communities to be hugely supportive and very generous with the skills and time they are willing to share. People are keen to collaborate and see others succeed.

My career has been a real journey so far and I am sure it will continue to be. I have learned so much about myself and life along the way and continue to love what I do. This is a really challenging time for our profession. It makes me sad to know that there is such a high vacancy factor alongside many others questioning their future careers. If people are struggling, I would encourage them to take time to reflect if it is the role itself or the wider environment which is causing the difficulties. The work that we do has such a great impact upon the lives of others that it would be sad to lose more people from our profession. Reach out, talk to others and explore other roles within SLT before deciding that it is no longer the career for you.

When we first spoke to Marianne, her story was almost too painful to listen to. Over time, she has moved forward and is now able to put things into context. Part of that has been about being able to work successfully independently, but also the realisation that 'it's not just me'.

References

1. Association for Psychological Science – APS (2012) Stress changes how people make decisions. Available at: https://www.psychologicalscience.org/news/releases/stress-changes-how-people-make -decisions.html.
2. Cohen, W. (2023) Peter Drucker and the principles of success, process excellence network. Available at: https://www.processexcellencenetwork.com/lessons_from_peter_drucker/articles/drucker-and -principles-of-success.

3 National context

There are two main strands to this chapter:

- We revisit the introductory paragraphs in Chapter 1 where we introduce the current evidence-base and follow this up with the desire to find out more – without the luxury (or constraints!) of undertaking a research project
- We begin, however, by looking in some detail at one particular profession (other than our own) and that is dentistry

Why dentistry, you may ask? It could be argued that there are some interesting parallels – and not just those associated with anatomical location! To find out the true picture, we met with Eddie Crouch, the Chair of the British Dental Association (BDA). The Chair is an elected post – renewed annually. The period of office is for three years. A Chair can serve two terms of three years. The Board is elected directly by the membership. The current Chair has been in the post since 2020, and previously served as deputy from 2014. He is the voice of the profession.

On a serious note, dentists are facing huge challenges and are voting with their feet in alarming numbers. To discuss the problems they face serves to not only highlight the critical issues for dentists, but also illustrates to others that there are commonalities to many other healthcare professions who just may not be quite as far down the road as dentists.

The BDA collects data and is able to regularly report on the challenges facing the provision of services in the public sector (read more here https://www.bda.org/about-the-bda/campaigns /pay/Documents/DDRB-BDA-evidence-2020-21.pdf) [1].

This underlines the importance of comprehensive environmental scanning to illustrate trends which identify the key issues and solution-focussed possibilities.

Eddie told us that dentistry is often seen as something of a barometer for other professions. If this is the case and the issues facing dentists and their response to those issues might potentially be replicated and multiplied, then there is considerable cause for concern.

It's fair to say that almost everyone will have experienced dental services and many of us may have searched, increasingly in vain, for NHS dental services within reasonable travelling distance of where we live. The authors have long suspected that the reasons why dentists move away from NHS contracts may not be dissimilar to why some speech and language therapists make the switch from public to private sector – whether entirely or partially.

At the time of writing NHS Dentistry has featured largely in the press. Headlines have moved from descriptions of a 'shortage' to 'dental deserts' to 'Are UK NHS dentists facing extinction?'
https://www.theguardian.com/society/2022/may/01/dental-deserts-form-in-england-as -dentists-quit-nhs-experts-warn [2]

DOI: 10.4324/9781003382928-3

https://www.healthcarebusinessinternational.com/are-uk-nhs-dentists-facing-extinction/ [3]

To better understand the situation, we need to be aware of how dental services 'work' in terms of commissioning. Dentists either work in the private sector or the public sector and sometimes in both. For the most part, those who 'work in the NHS' are not employed by the NHS. They are independent professionals who agree to deliver a contract within the NHS. The exception to this is a (small) number of 'salaried' dentists. A cohort who are primarily female and a number are approaching retirement age who are directly employed by the NHS and work mainly in community dental services. Historically, this service was for children with special needs and not easily treated in a regular surgery, but now encompasses all the population including domiciliary care for the elderly.

Contracts go out to tender. The shortages are primarily about the dwindling numbers of practitioners who are prepared to undertake NHS contracts. At the time of writing, we are told that tenders will often fail with *no* applicants.

NHS dentistry is *not free*. There are three different levels (or bands) which attract a patient charge. The bands cover what specific treatments can be delivered within each price band. Contrary to what many patients think, this money doesn't go to the dentist – it is a tax in the same way that prescription charges are a tax. Some people qualify for free treatment, in the same way that some qualify for free prescriptions.

The charges were introduced as a deterrent for people seeking treatment – both in terms of numbers and in terms of patients who were under the misapprehension that any and all treatments were free. Charges are no deterrent to those who qualify for free care (and sadly they are the patients most likely to default), but for those who *do* have to pay, the charges have a huge impact, particularly in times of economic difficulty.

Let's return to the possible reasons why so few dentists are choosing to practice within the NHS. Perhaps it is because public sector dentistry is separate from the rest of the NHS. It takes place away from the large main hospitals where attention (and often funding) is usually focussed. This, in tandem with the fact that tooth decay isn't life-threatening and, to some extent, is considered part and parcel of the ageing process, means that dentistry is viewed as 'non-essential'. What dentists are commissioned to offer within the public sector is limited both in terms of available time and range of treatments (does that ring any bells?). Being unable to operate at the level of both professional expertise and client need, the degree of de-motivation is entirely understandable.

In Chapter 13 we talk in detail about being clear about your 'offer' and the importance of being able to agree to the planned activity – and the cost of that activity. A key word here is 'agree'. That level of consensus is not available for a dentist undertaking an NHS commission. One dentist we spoke to said 'I can't understand why anyone would want to work in the NHS'. Having talked at length with Eddie, we can't see why either – apart from, possibly, altruism or a 'need to give back'. That is an emerging theme during the information gathering for this book.

We have learnt a great deal about the pressures and constraints facing NHS dentists. Like us, readers will be understandably curious to find out why anyone continues to undertake public sector work. We were shocked and uplifted in equal part during our interview with Rohan who, in partnership with his wife, has been running his NHS dental practice for 30 years. They are proud to be able to service their local community.

> *Altruism: [n] selfless concern for the*
> *well-being of others*

Rohan's story

This is Rohan's story. It is a story of altruism, but also realism and the ability to work within increasingly unpalatable constraints in order to provide a service to a community (where many are vulnerable and disadvantaged), which would otherwise have limited or no access to a service.

> *I come from the generation that was grant-funded to go to university. At that time, the service was in line with my values and the belief that I should give something back.*
>
> *I found out almost immediately that the world wasn't like that in reality. Already I was having to make compromises – but they were acceptable compromises. I was serving a large urban population and had budgetary control over the work I did, so despite the compromises, I knew I worked hard and felt I could earn a good living.*
>
> *Everything has changed, but the only thing that has adapted is me! I have learnt to cut corners to deliver mass care, which is some way between good and acceptable. Things are allied to the point of the lowest common denominator – it's basic and far from ideal.*

Both Rohan and his wife are now working full-time to cope with demand. Their eight-surgery practice now sees only three of the surgeries in daily use as recruiting and retaining younger dentists to public sector work has become more and more difficult. Two have joined the private sector during the last 18 months and Rohan can't get anyone to fill the vacancies. He describes the experience as 'humiliating' and 'expensive'. He says, *'I am done with taking on new people. This is how things are now'.*

'There are just the two of us and another colleague, and between us we do what five dentists used to do'. They feel they are just about holding that together – unless of course they want to take a holiday or one of them becomes unwell.

> *I accept that colleagues are doing what is right for them and what, physically, they can manage and what's acceptable. I feel that if I don't do it, no one else will.*

Rohan's activity away from the surgery – supporting the profession in a more political role via the various committees – is still as strong as ever, but the NHS commissioners don't attend meetings and use other structures to suggest engagement when in reality no one from the NHS meets local dentists at the coalface.

It's worth remembering too that Rohan is now in his fifties, which is old for a dentist. The work is very physical and as we age things do become more difficult.

> *We are kidding ourselves if we think we can keep going like this. Mentally I am in a better place because I don't give a damn about anyone else anymore (other dentists in the practice) and I can just get on with the work – but luckily I haven't been poorly!*

Rohan advocates that the government needs to change its approach in order to stop the rot.

> *They have let things get so bad that whatever is decided, they can't let it get any worse. They do have a choice. We have a core NHS service and a private service, and they need to explain to the public that's all it is unless they pump more resources into the NHS for dentistry and change that offer. There are things we could do … where money has been recycled elsewhere in the NHS, it never comes back to dentistry.*

At the time of writing, badged as 'flexible commissioning', money has been made available so that '*we can do one-off things*'. Is this enough to attract the younger dentists to join? No, the money is usually not recurrent in real terms, and no one will come for the lack of security that accompanies fixed-term initiatives.

> *It isn't primarily about the money. If I could attract young dentists, I know I could pay them appropriately. People are perfectly willing to work, but they aren't going to work for what they are being asked to do. In the private sector there is less volume, more job satisfaction and better quality.*

Once qualified, a public sector dentist (doing only 'simple, quick fix-it' types of jobs) will only use a limited number of the skills acquired during training. Rohan asks, 'Why don't we make better use of these skills and provide a modern service that is fit for the future?'

> Elsewhere in the book, there are a number of references to therapists becoming de-skilled. This is the same thing described from differing viewpoints – both are equally damaging and demoralising.

> With budgets and volume as the main drivers for decision-makers, and where the plan is to develop the support worker role (dentistry is only one of a number of professions where this is happening), one can see a degree of logic. However, '*it needs to be clear where accountability lies*'.

> Beware the insidious erosion of professional skill base.

Rohan likens his provision of service to '*1980s dentistry*' but with modern materials '*because they make my life easier*'. He is very aware that poor dentition has a knock-on effect on general health. '*I have no time to talk about prevention*'. Surgery is sometimes the first point at which there is developing evidence of underlying health issues – some of which can be very serious.

Let's take a moment to consider the concept of '*prevention*'.

When he wrote *In Place of Fear*, Aneurin Bevan, the founding father of the NHS, argued that 'the victories won by preventative medicine are much the most important for mankind' (1952) [4].

Certainly, pre-millennium, 'prevention' was an important part of the role for SLTs working with children: visiting nurseries, playgroups and antenatal classes to demonstrate ways to help speech and language development.

In her book *Fighting for Life*, journalist Isabel Hardman observes that we don't view preventive healthcare as being interesting or important in the British health service. Why has this basic Bevan principle, which is arguably of equal if not greater importance in modern times than the more emotive 'free at the point of delivery' slogan, been so easily discarded? (Hardman 2023) [5].

Returning to Rohan, his story is made somewhat easier to hear by his wry sense of humour and continued optimism in the face of considerable adversity. It was impossible not to ask him why he continues to do as he does. He smiled and said, '*You are asking, do I have hope?*' Rohan says he has moved past the point of sadness. '*The situation is pathetic*', he says. '*But I am immune. I spend my life delivering small units of patch-up work to large numbers of people and I do it out of compassion*'.

How do Rohan's peers view him? '*Some think we are mad – a bit weird and that we should have done what they did years ago*'.

'*I am an outlier – in a tiny minority. Politically I am not valued*'. But there can be no question of how much his patients value the service they receive.

With SLT in mind, there are some parallels to be drawn here. SLT is not glamorous or 'cutting edge'. Only a tiny proportion of the work is considered essential for life. SLT, like dentistry, is about quality of life and well-being. SLT is life-changing but only a small proportion of what we do is lifesaving. Like dentistry, scarce resources mean a limited menu of options for service users, leading to demotivation and reduced job satisfaction for those skilled professionals providing this limited service.

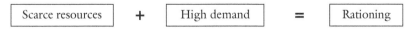

Scarce resources **+** High demand **=** Rationing

When the workforce is depleted and unable to cope with the number of referrals, access to the service must, somehow, be controlled – i.e., rationed. Robust access (or more accurately *exclusion*) criteria, thresholds and prioritisation systems become more and more important.

So what are the issues for dentists and are there parallels with other services?

Dentistry has its own profession-specific problems associated with dental complaints, with the grey areas springing up as a result of skill mix and dilution, with what Eddie describes as 'over-enthusiastic regulation' and increasing amounts of litigation – where solicitors practices are beginning to advertise themselves as specialists in dental negligence.

However, here are the issues which might potentially strike a chord with other professions.

Parallels

Access: there are patients who never arrive at the surgery because they fail to reply to their initial invitation letter for whatever reason. The letters are not (necessarily) designed to facilitate access. Patients are unable to absorb and understand the content, and when there is no reply, the patient is discharged (excluded from the service).

Exclusion criteria: patients are not accepted for secondary care unless dentally fit and with oral hygiene levels matching acceptance into advanced services. So, for example, criteria include only accepting referrals for root canal treatment of certain teeth and certain complexities (to reduce waiting lists).

Providing specialist opinions and returning the patient to 'local services': for example, the specialist service will often design a treatment plan for patients and return them to high street dentists to carry out the work with no additional resources to do so.

Care pathways: these are rigid and prescriptive. They identify what can/cannot be delivered within the value of the commission. Practitioners find this frustrating and professionally compromising.

Professional satisfaction: the rigidity of what can be delivered means that skills and expertise are not stretched. Practitioners are operating within a 'narrow field' knowing that there is more that could be done.

Late referrals: when patients are eventually seen, the problems are very likely to be far worse and even more difficult to satisfactorily resolve within the narrow range of options and time allowable.

Missed appointments: primarily DNAs (Did Not Attends) occur in the group who pay no charges at all (see below). This is misuse of a scarce resource at its worst.

The issues facing our public sector health services are numerous, huge and complex. They are multi-layered and multi-faceted. There is *so much that is good* but there are increasing swathes of services where staff are struggling to hold things together. Somewhere in the middle, practitioners are disillusioned and constrained, essentially by rationing despite funding being at its highest ever level.

Where people can afford to pay something towards their care, should they be expected to do so? If this leads to greater choice and appreciation of scarce resources, then that can only be a good thing. But before this can happen with any degree of success, a seismic shift in public perception is needed. 'NHS services are free at the point of delivery' but *are* they? Some are, some are not and some are 'a bit'. What we *do* need to do, however, is to be far more transparent about options to choose and options to pay where people can and are prepared to do so.

As can be evidenced by visiting the outpatients' waiting area of any local private hospital, business is brisk. Service users who can afford to pay for aspects of healthcare and for whom it is a priority clearly have no qualms about exploring their options.

Interesting thought …

Why do people grumble about paying for a dentist whilst happily using a high street chiropodist – either instead of an NHS practitioner or to top up what they are able to 'get on the NHS'? There is a clear precedent in chiropody: footcare services started life in the private sector before being brought into the NHS.

There are parallels between the patient charge bandings and the core offer in services such as speech and language therapy (except that SLT attracts no charge). There are also parallels with local authority services allied to education such as educational psychology and pupil and school services (such as specialist teachers). Schools receive an agreed number of hours free and then are able to top up what they need by buying additional hours. It isn't too much of a stretch to see how traded (NHS) services have evolved.

Another interesting thought … easier to answer perhaps!

Why does the scarcity of dental services attract more press than the scarcity of speech and language therapy services?

We would venture to suggest that **dental services affect us all** while speech and language therapy services affect only **those in need** – and some won't even *know* they are in need.

Lack of access to dentistry can have serious *health* consequences, and we would advocate that there are also social and emotional components to tooth loss, gum disease and bad breath.

There is a direct causal link between poor dental hygiene and atrial fibrillation (AF).

There are well-documented correlations between poor dental hygiene and various health conditions – including heart problems. The impact on mainstream NHS services has the potential to be significant.

Toothless in Suffolk: campaigners march the streets for better NHS dental care.

https://dentistry.co.uk/2021/10/18/toothless-in-suffolk-campaigners-march-streets-for -better-nhs-dental-care/ [6]

An extreme case – but a case nonetheless.

Seventy-five-year-old Dave (as fit as a flea and a marathon runner) was admitted to hospital with chest pains, which initially pointed to some kind of cardiac problem.

He spent a week in hospital undergoing tests and eventually it was concluded that the root cause of the problem was a large back tooth which needed urgent attention.

Dave lives in Suffolk.

The lack of access to speech and language therapy services can have *serious social, emotional* and *educational* consequences. There are well-documented correlations between poor speech language and communication and literacy difficulties, educational outcomes, SEMH, employment and future life chances. There are numerous statistics emanating from research over years …

Children with a poor vocabulary at five are four times more likely to struggle with reading in adulthood and three times more likely to have mental health issues [7].

Secondary-aged pupils with limited language may have a poor vocabulary, and may find it difficult to put their thoughts into words for explanations or to change their style of talking to suit the situation.

Up to 75% of pupils of secondary schools in certain areas of the UK may have limited language [8].

… however, time and again the same message comes around with depressing frequency.

Disparities in early language and communication development relating to social deprivation are recognisable in the second year of life. They have a negative impact on children's development by the time they start school, in terms of literacy development, as well as social, emotional and behavioural development [9].

Children from socially disadvantaged families are more than twice as likely to be identified with a SLCN.

Due to social clustering, more than 50% of children living in areas of high social deprivation may start school with SLCN [10, 11].

Approximately 10% of children and young people have long-term SLCN which causes them significant difficulties with communication or learning in everyday life [12].

It's useful at this point to reiterate what we first mentioned in our introduction.

'We are not here to disparage: the more we learn and listen, the more we recognise the problems we (collectively) face in making positive and sustainable change to our public sector health services'.

This leads inevitably to considerations about staff retention. Surely, if the powers that be know why, for example, dentists are reluctant to take up public sector contracts, then it is within their gift to take some steps to redressing the balance – or is that too simplistic?

Maybe it is but …

… it's better to start small than not start at all …

The issue of retention crops up at various points in this book.

Training and recruiting more staff is not the answer in itself – but has to be part of a wider retention plan. Nursing is the single largest profession in the health service and is integral to its functioning. The banner headline following recent research by the Nuffield Trust (published in September 2022) identifies that the numbers of leavers and joiners are almost equal: **'Peak leaving? A spotlight on nurse leaver rates in the UK'.**

https://www.nuffieldtrust.org.uk/resource/peak-leaving-a-spotlight-on-nurse-leaver -rates-in-the-uk [13]

At this point, we revisit the following broad areas which both piqued our curiosity and were 'hot topics' at the time we were working on the book.

A. Employment movement within the profession
B. The 'whys and hows' of buying extra support (over and above a service core offer)
C. Students and independent practice
D. Structures and networks which support IPs

What did we have to go on? Gut feeling, discussion with colleagues and anecdotal evidence from a number of SLT departments around the country. The subject of enhanced (or traded) services cropped up on numerous occasions when Diana was part of the Care Quality Commission (CQC) inspections during the first few years post-redundancy (more about CQC in Chapter 10).

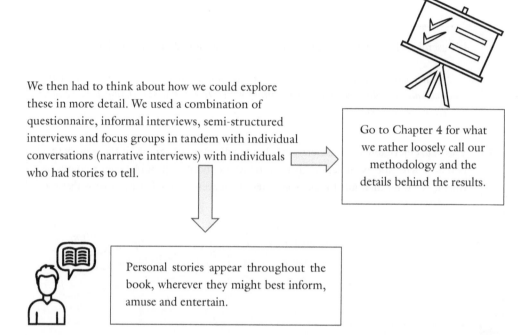

We then had to think about how we could explore these in more detail. We used a combination of questionnaire, informal interviews, semi-structured interviews and focus groups in tandem with individual conversations (narrative interviews) with individuals who had stories to tell.

Go to Chapter 4 for what we rather loosely call our methodology and the details behind the results.

Personal stories appear throughout the book, wherever they might best inform, amuse and entertain.

What was the reasoning behind wanting to delve more deeply into these four areas?

Movement within the profession

This is obviously a key theme as it is one of the reasons behind his book.

However, it's clear from our 'local picture' and conversations with colleagues within ASLTIP that there are *many* therapists working outside of the public sector. Just how many isn't known. Readers may find that surprising – and certainly we did. There are IPs who are not members of ASLTIP – and there are, surprisingly, IPs who have never *heard* of ASLTIP (www.asltip.com).

ASLTIP – the association for speech and language therapists in private practice

What do we already know?

Previous research/mapping is somewhat thin on the ground. Attempts to gain some sense of movement within the profession have had very low returns. Some data *is* available, but it isn't particularly contemporaneous or comprehensive.

We asked the Royal College of Speech and Language Therapists (RCSLT) what information was available, and their response was candid. There is no definitive figure for the number of SLTs working in the independent sector. However, college officers recognise the importance of being able to gather meaningful data about the membership. They were very willing to share what *is* available, both from their own records and from other sources.

Here is a brief summary.

In **2014**, on behalf of the NHS, the Centre for Workforce Intelligence (CWFI) [14] did an in-depth stocktake of speech and language therapy and found that the number of SLTs whose primary role was in the NHS in England was 73% and that 66% of SLTs' contracted time was in the NHS.

Very early trawls with the Horizon Project (see below) and the results of the vacancies survey (see below) would together suggest a continuing trend in this direction.

The **2018** RCSLT member survey did indicate that there is no neat division between the public and private sectors – lots of members work across both. The results of our questionnaire show that there are still there are numbers of therapists who continue to work in both sectors (see Chapter 4).

In **2019**, the RCSLT made a Freedom of Information request to HCPC for more detailed data. The results are available here https://www.hcpc-uk.org/resources/freedom-of-information-requests/2019/speech-and-language-therapists-data---august-2019/ [15].

In **2021**, a sample of 18% of the HCPC register had figures suggesting that 55% of SLTs have more than one work setting (surpassed only by Art Therapists with 65%). Source: The HCPC diversity report 2021 [16].

There is also an SLT-specific factsheet [17] from the same survey which records 7% of the sample worked in an independent or private healthcare provider. This seems a small proportion given what we know historically. The sample size was 3,779 out of a total of 17,240 registrants at that time – 22%.

In **October 2022**, the RCSLT launched their Horizon Project – which they themselves describe as an 'ambitious project to gain a clearer picture of speech and language therapy across the UK'. At the time of writing, there is no deadline for the first results being made available as the RCSLT wishes to wait until a much greater proportion of members have been able to input their profiles.

The HCPC produces regular information about the total number of certified SLTs, which is available here, https://www.hcpc-uk.org/about-us/insights-and-data/the-register/ [18]. In **March 2023**, this shows 18,390 SLTs on the HCPC register. This is a UK-wide 'headcount' figure.

The NHS produces quarterly workforce statistics. This is for England only and counts 'full-time equivalents', so is not directly comparable to the HCPC data. In **January 2023**, there were 7,090 full-time equivalent SLTs counted in this dataset. This number relates to **England only** and only includes NHS employees. So, this dataset does not cover any SLTs employed by schools, independent practices or other non-NHS organisations.

https://digital.nhs.uk/data-and-information/publications/statistical/nhs-workforce-statistics/january-2023 [19]

Also in **January 2023**, the RCSLT conducted a vacancy recruitment survey.

https://www.rcslt.org/news/vacancy-rates-reach-23-in-speech-and-language-therapy/ [20]

There were 21 responses from services in the West Midlands. Paediatric vacancies were running at 35% and adult vacancies at 31% – which does beg the question as to where the new graduates were going. Since 2017, SLT student admissions have risen by 40% and five new courses have come online since 2019. Read more about students and independent practice in Chapters 4, 12 and 16.

Formal research results

1. Loan-Clarke, J. et al. (2009) 'Why do speech and language therapists stay in, leave and (sometimes) return to the National Health Service (NHS)?' [21]
2. Loan-Clarke, J. et al. (2010) 'Retention, turnover and return – A longitudinal study of allied health professionals in Britain' [22]
3. Ewen, C. et al. (2020) 'Well-being, job satisfaction, stress and burnout in speech-language pathologists: A review' [23]
4. Ewen, C. (2021) 'The occupational and biopsychosocial well-being of speech and language therapists practising clinically in the United Kingdom' [24]

Loan-Clark et al. 2009 paper (study 1)

The outcomes and results are summarised below.

Stayers valued:	Leavers not involved in childcare left because of:	Returners returned because of:
• Job and pension security • Professional development and opportunities • The work itself and professional support	• Workload • Pressure • Stress • Poor pay • Not being able to give good patient care	• Flexible hours • Work location • Professional development • Pension provision

Stayers *and* returners primarily wished to see more staff in the NHS, whereas leavers would return if there were more flexibility in work arrangements. Returners were particularly hostile to Agenda for Change (AFC) (which all seems such a long time ago now).

We are now approaching 20 years since the introduction of AFC. In principle, the idea was a good one. It aimed to *harmonise and modernise pay and conditions, terms of employment and human resources policies across the NHS*. However, as with most proposals for change, it met with considerable upheaval and resistance, which the authors remember very well.

The conclusions and implications of study one were that some preferences required increased resources; others such as reducing bureaucracy and valuing professionalism did not.

Loan-Clarke et al. 2010 paper (study 2)

For us, study two is less compelling as it looks at AHPs as a group and does not single out speech and language therapists. However, the researchers did report that there were remarkable similarities between all four groups surveyed (occupational therapists, physiotherapists, speech and language therapists and radiographers). The participants were surveyed at two different points in time which added detail to the study and reflects the changing circumstances within the NHS and economy as a whole.

Capturing the top three broad-brush findings shows that:

NHS stayers did so for:

- Job security
- Pension
- A chance to develop professional skills/good professional development (much reduced in the rankings at time 2 as financial constraints were beginning to bite)

Leavers cited:

- Excessive workload/pressure/stress (strong at both time 1 and time 2)
- Childcare (also strong at both time 1 and time 2)
- Lack of career opportunities, poor pay and not being able to give good patient care

By time 2 leavers were *also* identifying **poor management** and **feeling personally undervalued.** From the results of our questionnaire, these are themes that sadly continue (see Chapter 4).

This study found that there seemed to be more factors pushing people away from the NHS than factors pulling them towards the private sector. This is an interesting distinction.

Reasons for *staying* out of the NHS (time 2 data only)

- Flexible hours
- Enjoy/interesting work/job satisfaction
- Pay – good or better than the NHS

Returners to the NHS

Employment and job-specific issues remained dominant.

NB: researchers noted that the data should be treated with caution as the numbers were very small.

Ewen et al. 2020 paper (study 3)

The third paper available to us was a review of previous studies which had looked at well-being, job satisfaction, stress and burnout in speech-language pathologists. In summary, the authors found that job satisfaction in Canada and the USA was either average or above average, whereas in the UK it was consistently low. Three of the six contributory themes identified were clearly associated with well-being (workload/caseload size, professional support and salary). Evidence for stress and dissatisfaction leading to workforce attrition was found. The review concluded that more work needed to be done to help identify and improve the well-being of the workforce. One of the authors of this paper went on to conduct her own research, the findings of which appear as study 4.

Crucial points we make very early on are about *choices* and *change* – making a planned change rather than being forced into it by pressure and circumstance. We also talk about creating choices and making informed choices when planning a change. We have covered quite a lot of ground about being 'true to yourself' and the feelings engendered when we cannot be true to ourselves for whatever reason. For some, the endpoint is stress and unhappiness, but for others, like Claire, it's about becoming hardened and somehow inured to the lack of control over what we do, the inability to deliver what we know we can and should. This is her story.

Claire has worked as a speech and language therapist for 30 years, in various roles and for various employers over those years. Here she shares a handful of stories that were of particular significance and were a spur along the route to where she is today.

> *One of my most enjoyable, most formative experiences was working with an incredibly driven SLT, who saw that language units in the area where we worked were to be closed as part of an inclusion initiative, and negotiated for the local education authority to fund a service for children with what was then specific language impairment, who were now attending main-stream schools. With manageable caseloads, a degree of autonomy in how we supported the children with whom we worked, and effective support and supervision from two brilliant colleagues, the job was fulfilling and meant I learned and developed as a therapist.*

A degree of autonomy

In early 2003, Claire and her family relocated and she found herself working in mainstream schools for a busy inner-city NHS Trust. She had a caseload of just over 300 children, spread over a number of schools, and direct contact with the children took place during term time only. Each school received support for one term in three – and this was allocated according to the size of the school, so visits were short and with long gaps in between.

A treadmill of loneliness and isolation

> *The itinerant nature of this work meant that I saw my SLT colleagues infrequently. It was all but impossible to feel part of a team in any of the schools, where, essentially, I had the role of a visitor who was expected – at that time – to withdraw children on a one-to-one basis for their support. Everyone was always busy (including me!), so inter-action with school staff was limited. I recall feeling very lonely in my job.*

*I remember very clearly the day that I chose to leave. It was late afternoon and I'd been at a large primary school in the city, carrying out some reviews. I felt exhausted (nothing new). I still needed to score the assessments, generate aims for intervention and write some reports. I was working systematically through my 'to do' list when I suddenly realised that I **didn't care**. Perhaps I should repeat that. **I didn't care**. It was a real 'road to Damascus' moment for me – I was horrified. Here I was, in a job that I had felt passionately about, a job that is described as a 'caring profession', and I didn't care. I was methodically 'getting through' everything that I was required to do, ticking boxes so that the service delivery requirements imposed by the trust could be met, without feeling that I was accomplishing anything worthwhile for the children. It was at that point that I began looking for a non-clinical job, and by September of that year I was working for a university in a teaching role.*

Making a
planned change

Claire stayed in that role for the next seven years, until it became incompatible with raising a young family. She returned to the NHS as a locum, but it quickly became apparent that things were no better. Claire describes the trigger that resulted in her '*not ever wanting to work in the NHS again*'. She describes the seminal moment that '*demonstrated how my lack of control over what I could offer service users had dire consequences for future life chances*'. This is what happened:

I arrived at a nursery, to review a three-year-old girl who was non-verbal. There were A4 sheets pinned up around the walls that displayed some Makaton signs. The staff greeted me with obvious relief, stating that the child didn't engage with them and that they didn't know what to do. One of the staff members brought the little girl over to me, and I realized that she had been watching me from the moment I had arrived. We played a simple game using a form board, and she took turns, copied the signs I used, and then used them independently to label and to request 'more'. The staff were amazed.

No job satisfaction

All I could offer was some advice and the promise to review again in three months. There was no training on offer.

*The child's records showed that the previous SLT had done exactly the same thing. Here was a child who, with support, **could** (and would) learn to communicate, whereupon her world would open up – but the only support that SLT was providing was to 'review and advise'. It was clear that this was completely inadequate to affect any sustainable and positive change. I decided that day not to renew my contract. I went home and told my husband that if I **ever** considered working in the NHS again he was to stop me, and I have worked in the independent sector ever since.*

I'm happy now. I can make a difference, and I can take pride and pleasure in doing what I was trained to do.

Claire's experiences had another consequence for her.

It was only when I began to read the literature on burnout that I came to understand that my tiredness, my feelings of not achieving anything of value, my growing detachment from service users and the fact that I'd stopped caring in 2003 were hallmarks of the elements of burnout – emotional exhaustion, depersonalization and reduced personal accomplishment. And that my despair at repeatedly absorbing the distress of parents, carers and professionals working with the children on my caseload – and not being able to really offer any help – was, in essence, 'compassion fatigue'.

She discovered (somewhat predictably) that she was by no means alone in feeling as she did.

Conversations with other SLTs, whether they work for the NHS or for other employers, whether they are employed or self-employed, raise feelings that I recognise. People say that they love what they do and are passionate about supporting children and adults with SLCN and swallowing difficulties. They are also tired, stressed and anxious about their jobs. Many express doubts about their ability to continue long-term. My personal experiences, together with this anecdotal evidence of a possible problem within the workforce, led me to do a PhD, which evidenced that poor well-being and a lack of job satisfaction are, indeed, problems across the profession.

Here we share Claire's research.

Across the public sector vacancies are a huge cause for concern. Prioritising extending the availability of training places is, at best, only halfway to a solution. We need to understand why people *leave*. Only then can appropriate steps be taken to address attrition rates.

Study 4 has particular significance. It is recent, it has an impressive reach in terms of both numbers and demography and it looks *specifically* at speech and language therapists, wherever they work. However, we know from our own questionnaire that almost 25% of the respondents work in both the public and private sector and a further 18% of those who do any work at all in the public sector were thinking of making a move. A discrepancy between 'well-being' in the public and private sector clearly has relevance. In terms of the current landscape, Claire's research comes at just the right time.

Claire's personal story appears in this chapter. This explains the background to the content and timing of her research project.

In her own words

Some SLTs make the decision to work as independent therapists as a result of needing to leave very stressful jobs with unrelenting demands, little autonomy and a lack of support. Choosing to work as an independent therapist, however, need not be a choice that is *forced* on someone. It can, and arguably should, be an option that any SLT considers as one of the varied opportunities in the ever-evolving landscape of speech and language therapy services. It should be an option that is a first choice, and not only a solution to a problem. Understanding the role that working independently can play in supporting well-being can provide information that contributes to an informed decision, a decision to *choose* to be an independent SLT for the benefits it provides.

Be proactive: search for the information which supports informed decision-making.

In 2018, a study (Ewen 2021), that included therapists from England, Scotland, Wales and Northern Ireland was carried out. A survey consisting of an online questionnaire was completed by 632 practitioners, of which 536 (85%) were employed, 58 (9%) were self-employed and 38 (6%) were partly employed and partly self-employed. These figures were in line with those reported by the RCSLT at the time. Respondents included those working with adults and paediatric therapists. Following the survey, 15 of the 632 respondents were interviewed. Interviews included ten NHS therapists and five working in the independent sector.

Results revealed that …

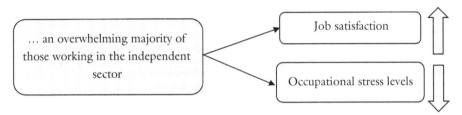

In fact, they tended to have significantly higher job satisfaction and much lower occupational stress levels than those who were employees – either working for the NHS or for other organisations. They were also likely to have lower levels of general anxiety and better overall well-being than those who were employed.

This is encouraging news for anyone contemplating working in the independent sector. So, what are the reasons for these comparatively high levels of well-being?

A good job will promote good well-being. Work *should* be good for us, and good work can indeed benefit us in many ways – it can give us a sense of purpose, contribute to our identities in a positive way, and be meaningful. Being a SLT is no exception to this.

Included in the Health and Care Professionals Council (HCPC) standards of proficiency for SLTs is the ability to 'look after their health and well-being' [25]. This means that currently, the responsibility for a SLT's well-being lies with that SLT personally. One of the things that SLTs *can* have some agency over is what job they choose to do. Because a job itself can contribute to well-being, one strategy to promote positive well-being is to choose a good job.

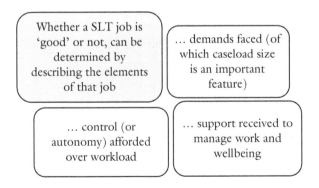

The Job Demand-Control-Support (JDCS) model (Johnson & Hall, 1988; Karasek, 1979) [27] provides useful job 'types' that consider these factors:

Therapists may have busy days seeing many clients, with the planning/report writing/liaison/etc. that accompanies this, but they have the authority to be able to control those demands, for example by not accepting referrals that they might find difficult to accommodate.

… are similar but tend to have fewer demands than active jobs.

It is these types of jobs that are viewed as being 'good' jobs – associated with high levels of job satisfaction, low levels of occupational stress and good overall well-being.

Conversely

Therapists must manage long waiting lists/high caseloads where they have little clinical autonomy (e.g., having to place children on clinical pathways with which they might not agree, having little control over which clients they must see).

Good support (including supervision) can buffer the effects of a high-strain job, but where supervision is repeatedly cancelled due to competing demands such as clinical need, then an SLT might feel isolated, and the effects of a high-strain job can be *exacerbated*.

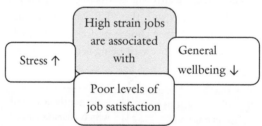

Ewen (2021) found that independent SLTs tend to work in either 'active' or 'low-strain' jobs, so it is unsurprising that their levels of well-being are comparatively good.

Conversations with SLTs

It is not just the demands with which SLTs are faced, the autonomy they hold, and the support they receive that is important for their well-being. **Conversations with SLTs** revealed several areas for consideration when choosing where and how to work, and the next section shares the 'voices' of SLTs to enable some exploration of these areas. Quotes provided are from interviews with five independent SLTs; each interviewee chose their own pseudonym.

> *Identifying what your values are*

A starting point to choosing work that will engender job satisfaction and guard against dangerous levels of stress is to identify what one's values are. If I know what is important to me, I am better placed to match my job with those values. If the values that I hold are aligned to the work that I do, I am likely to enjoy my job more.

One of the main reasons people gave as to why they became SLTs, and an important value that SLTs generally hold, is that they want to help others, to be 'of service'. SLTs frequently described this as '*making a difference*'. Lesley, an independent SLT, was aware that being of service contributed to her positive mental health.

> I think, for me, a *huge* part of my well-being is about making a difference.

Sally, another independent SLT, agreed.

> I think, I love that it's challenging and that it's genuinely a career where you can help people and see the difference

> I feel like I'm making a difference, that I'm positively contributing something to society.

Willow touched on having a sense of utility through contributing to society.

Working in the independent sector, however, is not all plain sailing, when it comes to aligning work to values. In addition to being of service, a value that SLTs discussed was their belief in the ability to access healthcare regardless of financial position. Conflict for self-employed SLTs was typically expressed as concern that their actions were not consistent with this belief.

> The belief that healthcare should be 'free at the point of delivery' was raised a number of times during the course of writing this book.

Willow and Sally's accounts alluded to their belief that healthcare should be freely available to all. In addition, Sally explained the duty that she felt to the NHS, having gained the skills she has while working there. She questioned whether her decision to charge for services was ethical, and her repetition of feeling '*bad*' and '*terrible*' suggested that she really struggled with this aspect of being self-employed.

When *cognitive dissonance* occurs, people tend to take actions to resolve the conflict that they experience due to the disconnect between their actions and their beliefs. An example of how this is achieved is to align actions with a different value. Self-employed participants described a number of different ways in which they were able to achieve this through focusing on the ability to be of service.

Cognitive dissonance [n]: the state of having inconsistent thoughts, beliefs or attitudes

Like Sally, Willow discussed ethical concerns regarding working privately – but seeing that she could affect change allowed her to feel comfortable with her decision.

...*morally, it felt wrong because I feel that the NHS is the service that everybody can have .... I felt bad that only people who are well off enough can afford that now.*

The demands faced by independent SLTs and the authority to manage these

SLTs are busy people. While personal lives in the twenty-first century seem busier than ever, this section focuses on the working lives of independent SLTs. The professional life of an SLT can be very demanding. Student SLTs who attend clinical placements will be made aware of issues around workload, caseload sizes and waiting lists.

Once in the workplace, these issues become the day-to-day reality. Instead of their daily working lives being dictated by management teams that seem a long way from the coalface, independent SLTs have the autonomy to *make these decisions themselves.*

This is not to say that independent SLTs never have too much work to do. However, there appears to be a psychological difference in the way that employed SLTs and independent SLTs view having too much work, as described by Sally:

Certainly liberating – but also challenging.

... maybe the difference is that when I work (overtime) in the independent world, I'm actually able to finish the job, whereas in the NHS, even if I did everything possible, I couldn't ever get it done. It was an impossible target ...

Independent SLTs recognized that the nature of the additional hours spent working was qualitatively different when working independently.

There are other important points to consider when contemplating independent practice.

Struggling to say 'no'.

Being able to balance clinical quality with the need to generate a viable income.

Recognising that running a practice involves elements that go beyond caseload management.

The emotional demands of managing relationships, not only those between the therapist and client, but between other members of a (potentially large) team.

Although many of the potential strains of a practicing SLT are 'part of the role', the impact of these elements of the job *needn't* cause stress.

If well supported, SLTs can manage these responsibilities, as well as the emotional consequences of supporting 'needy' families.

The authors add that all these are extremely valid points which have the potential to be overlooked – particularly at the out-set of what should be an exciting journey.

While being an independent practitioner does not come without practical and emotional demands, or remove all elements of work that could cause stress, those SLTs who are self-employed were generally satisfied with the control that they had – both in terms of operational priorities and clinical decision-making.

In addition, working as an independent practitioner arguably allows an SLT to ensure that they have effective support, in a way that can be difficult as an employee. The next section describes how this is possible.

Support and supervision

Conversations with SLTs revealed that both formal supervision and informal support are important to them, to enable them to manage the practical, emotional and psychological demands with which they are faced.

Professional supervision is known by several terms, with 'peer supervision', and 'clinical supervision' being common. According to the RCSLT (2017) [28], one of the aims of professional supervision is to 'Reflect on professional issues which may be causing concerns, with an aim to promote health and well-being of staff and improving service-user experience'.

Self-employed SLTs, on the whole, receive levels of supervision and support with which they are satisfied. They do not have to adhere to the way an organization manages supervision, and they tend to be flexible about where, and from whom, they receive supervision. Generally, they have good agency over how their support is negotiated, and control over how this support is realised in practice. This control over how their supervision is organized means they can arrange it to meet their needs. Worth noting, however, is that independent SLTs frequently accept that time spent receiving or providing supervision is often not remunerated.

The broad way that independent SLTs define supervision and support, and their flexibility regarding who provides that support, was evident. For example, paediatric SLTs who were not part of teams at a workplace (e.g., through contracting with a larger practice) developed relationships with school staff members to ensure that there was support for them. This can reduce the burden of responsibility that the SLT carries.

> The importance of support networks and access to appropriate supervision is a 'toolbox essential' and a recurrent theme throughout the personal stories in the book.

> A variety of support and supervision models have emerged and paying for supervision is not uncommon. Some SLTs have a supervision income-generation strand to their portfolios.

Being an independent SLT does not, however, guarantee *good* supervision. Isabella provided a contrast to the other self-employed participants. Her account demonstrated that she took responsibility for arranging, and paying for additional supervision when she needed it.

However, although she had access to various avenues of support, she thought that more supervision would be beneficial. This might suggest that support alone is not sufficient in protecting Isabella's well-being, but that there is possibly a need for *other* changes to her job and/or her strategies to cope with the job.

Generally, though, increased autonomy meant that independent SLTs were able to arrange frequent supervision and support; most reported that this was effective and they felt satisfied with their arrangements.

Summary

In summary, therefore, there are numerous strategies that SLTs can employ to support their well-being. This section has focussed on lessons that can be learned from the independent sector. It has concentrated not on personal resources such as resilience, but on the management of demands, the exercising of autonomy and ensuring adequate support.

> The authors return to the subject of employer responsibility in Chapter 16.

While SLTs may have some agency in managing these elements of their work, there are jobs where this is beyond their control. It is, therefore, also the responsibility of *employers* to ensure that the well-being of their staff is supported, through the careful management of demands, the consideration of how SLTs achieve professional autonomy and the provision of effective support.

As readers will appreciate, this short résumé of some key points is only a part of an extensive piece of research. We look forward to reading Claire's research in its entirety in the near future.

We conclude this chapter by introducing the reasoning behind exploring the four areas outlined earlier. The detail is discussed in Chapter 4.

A. **Employment movement within the profession**	B. **The 'whys and hows' of buying extra support (over and above a service core offer)**
To survey as many members of the profession as we could reach seemed a logical way to get a snapshot of movement within the profession	(i) Enhanced or traded SLT services Freedom of Information requests made across the country (ii) How do schools and settings choose providers of SLT?
C. **Students and independent practice**	D. **Structures and processes which support independent practitioners**
What do they know about independent practice?	What do independent/potential independent practitioners need to know and how can they find out?

References

1. (2020) British Dental Association. Available at: https://www.bda.org/about-the-bda/campaigns/pay/Documents/DDRB-BDA-evidence-2020-21.pdf.
2. (2020) British Dental Association. Available at: https://www.bda.org/about-the-bda/campaigns/pay/Documents/DDRB-BDA-evidence-2020-21.pdf.
3. Farbrother, D. (2022) Are UK NHS dentists facing extinction? Healthcare Business International. Available at: https://www.healthcarebusinessinternational.com/are-uk-nhs-dentists-facing-extinction/.
4. Bevan, A. (1952) *In Place of Fear*. Melbourne: Heinemann.
5. Hardman, I. (2023) *Fighting for Life: The Twelve Battles That Made Our NHS, and the Struggle for Its Future*. London: Viking, an imprint of Penguin Books.
6. Bissett, G. (2021) Toothless in Suffolk – Activists March for better NHS dental care – Dentistry. Dentistry.co.uk. Available at: https://dentistry.co.uk/2021/10/18/toothless-in-suffolk-campaigners-march-streets-for-better-nhs-dental-care/.

7. Law, J., Charlton, J. and Asmussen, K. (2017) *Language as a Child Wellbeing Indicator*. Early Intervention Foundation/Newcastle University. Cited in (2018). Why closing the word gap matters – oup.com.cn. Available at: https://www.oup.com.cn/test/word-gap.
8. Hartshorne, M. (2011) Speech, language and communication in secondary aged pupils. www.speechandlanguage.org.uk. Available at: https://speechandlanguage.org.uk/media/1926/ican_talkseries10.pdf.
9. Chiat, S. and Roy, P. (2013) Early predictors of language and social communication impairments at ages 9–11 years: A follow-up study of early-referred children. *Journal of Speech, Language, and Hearing Research*, 56(6), pp. 1824–1836. doi:10.1044/1092-4388(2013/12-0249).
10. Hollo, A., Wehby, J.H. and Oliver, R.M. (2014) Unidentified language deficits in children with emotional and behavioral disorders: A meta-analysis. *Exceptional Children*, 80(2), pp. 169–186. doi:10.1177/001440291408000203.
11. Locke, A., Ginsborg, J. and Peers, I. (2002) Development and disadvantage: Implications for the early years and beyond. *International Journal of Language & Communication Disorders*, 37(1), pp. 3–15. doi:10.1080/13682820110089911.
12. Norbury, C.F. et al. (2016) The impact of nonverbal ability on prevalence and clinical presentation of language disorder: Evidence from a population study. *Journal of Child Psychology and Psychiatry*, 57(11), pp. 1247–1257. doi:10.1111/jcpp.12573.

References 7 to 12 above are cited in:
Public Health England. (2020) *Best Start in Speech, Language and Communication (SLC)*. GOV.UK. Available at: https://www.gov.uk/government/publications/best-start-in-speech-language-and-communication.

13. *Peak Leaving? A Spotlight on Nurse Leaver Rates in the UK.* (2022) Nuffield Trust. Available at: https://www.nuffieldtrust.org.uk/resource/peak-leaving-a-spotlight-on-nurse-leaver-rates-in-the-uk.
14. Library Database. (2014) *Details for: Securing the Future Workforce Supply: Speech and Language Therapy Stocktake.* The King's Fund Library Catalog. Available at: https://koha.kingsfund.org.uk/cgi-bin/koha/opac-detail.pl?biblionumber=116006&shelfbrowse_itemnumber=146143.
15. *Speech and Language Therapists Data – August 2019.* (2019) Health & Care Professions Council. Available at: https://www.hcpc-uk.org/resources/freedom-of-information-requests/2019/speech-and-language-therapists-data---august-2019/.
16. The Health and Care Professions Council (HCPC). (2021) www.hcpc-uk.org. Available at: https://www.hcpc-uk.org/globalassets/resources/reports/hcpc-diversity-data-report-2021.pdf?v=637689354700000000.
17. *HCPC Diversity Data Report 2021: Speech and Language Therapists.* (2021) www.hcpc-uk.org. Available at: https://www.hcpc-uk.org/globalassets/resources/factsheets/hcpc-diversity-data-2021-factsheet--speech-and-language-therapists.pdf.
18. *Registrant Data and Statistics* (2023) Health & Care Professions Council. Available at: https://www.hcpc-uk.org/about-us/insights-and-data/the-register/.
19. (2023) *NHS Choices.* Available at: https://digital.nhs.uk/data-and-information/publications/statistical/nhs-workforce-statistics/january-2023.
20. Mehreen.hussain@rcslt.org. (2023) *Vacancy Rates reach 23% in Speech and Language Therapy.* RCSLT. Available at: https://www.rcslt.org/news/vacancy-rates-reach-23-in-speech-and-language-therapy/.
21. Loan-Clarke, J. et al. (2009) Why do speech and language therapists stay in, leave and (sometimes) return to the National Health Service (NHS)? *International Journal of Language & Communication Disorders*, 44(6), pp. 883–900. doi:10.1080/13682820802381334.
22. Loan-Clarke, J. et al. (2010) Retention, turnover and return – A longitudinal study of allied health professionals in Britain. *Human Resource Management Journal*, 20(4), pp. 391–406. doi:10.1111/j.1748-8583.2010.00140.x.
23. Ewen, C. et al. (2020) Well-being, job satisfaction, stress and burnout in speech-language pathologists: A review. *International Journal of Speech-Language Pathology*, 23(2), pp. 180–190. doi:10.1080/17549507.2020.1758210.
24. Ewen, C. (2021) *The Occupational and Biopsychosocial Well-Being of Speech and Language Therapists Practising Clinically in the United Kingdom.* www.ethos.bl.uk. Available at: https://www.open-access.bcu.ac.uk/13347/1/Claire%20Ewen%20PhD%20Thesis%20published_Final%20version_Submitted%20Apr%202021_Final%20Award%20Jul%202021.pdf.
25. Health and Care Professions Council. (2023) *Standards of Proficiency: Speech and Language Therapists.* Available at: https://www.hcpc-uk.org/globalassets/standards/standards-of-proficiency/reviewing/slts---new-standards.pdf.
26. Johnson, J.V. and Hall, E.M. (1988) Job strain, work place social support, and cardiovascular disease: A cross-sectional study of a random sample of the Swedish working population. *American Journal of Public Health*, 78, pp. 1336–1342. doi:10.2105/ajph.78.10.1336.
27. Karasek, R.A. (1979) Job demands, job decision latitude, and mental strain: Implications for job redesign. *Administrative Science Quarterly*, 24(2), pp. 285–308. doi:10.2307/2392498.
28. Royal College of Speech and Language Therapists. (2017) *Information on Supervision.* Available at: https://www.rcslt.org/members/delivering-quality-services/supervision/supervision-guidance/#:~:text=For%20safe%20and%20effective%20practice,confidence%20in%20the%20long%20term.

4 Methodology, findings and support structures

Here are the broad themes we wanted to explore in greater depth ...

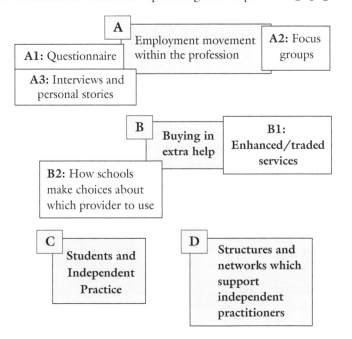

... we turned our attention to how we might do that.

There are various ways to gather views – some lend themselves to specific circumstances better than others. When considering the aim of gathering information from a large number of people who are potentially geographically far-flung, a questionnaire (or survey) seems a sensible option. The challenges here are about:

- Content (there's nothing more frustrating than thinking of something else to ask after the event!)
- Wording (it's essential to avoid any unconscious bias from which inferences might be made by the participant)
- Consideration must be given to how to analyse the data and be able to report on it in a meaningful way

DOI: 10.4324/9781003382928-4

The identification of smaller groups is a good way to pose questions and seek views on more specific topics (qualitative interviewing).

In contrast to questionnaires, qualitative interviewing aims to delve beneath the surface of initial responses, offering the opportunity for those who wish to expand on their feelings and experiences.

Qualitative interviews may take different formats depending on the nature of the research question and the population studied. Here are some we considered:

- Structured interview
- Semi-structured interview
- Narrative interview
- In-depth interview
- Focus group

https://www.healthknowledge.org.uk/public-health-textbook/research-methods/1d-qualitative-methods/section2-theoretical-methodological-issues-research [1]

Below we identify the formats we used and the reasons why.

We settled on:

1. A questionnaire to speech and language therapists
2. A questionnaire under the Freedom of Information (FOI) Act, sent to Trusts who provide paediatric SLT services (as far as we are aware, there are no traded adult services)
3. A questionnaire to local (West Midlands/Birmingham/Shropshire) schools and settings
4. A combination of semi-structured interview and focus groups for our three target groups – the special schools therapists' group, the student group and the Clinical Excellence Network (CEN)
5. Narrative interviews for individuals willing to share their journey in detail (the authors of the personal stories)

A	Employment movement within the profession

A1 Questionnaire for speech and language therapists

Deciding what to ask and how to phrase the questions was very challenging – if the results were to be of any use and reasonably easy to analyse. We were grateful for initial help from Dr Claire Ewen who has recently completed her own piece of research as part of her doctorate (referenced in Chapters 1 and 3). We also had the opportunity to pilot the content with a small number of therapists.

In the later stages, however, we were accepted for support from The Demand Hub [2] at the University of Birmingham. This programme offers bespoke research support from an expert team of biomedical researchers based at the Health Technologies Institute (HTI) at the University of Birmingham.

Soundswell Ltd was identified by the business engagement team as an eligible business entity active in the healthcare sector, where practical support towards a particular project or innovation could be effectively applied. Our research fellow, Sam, was able to advise us about bias and design based on the need to be able to collect and manage the data. As recommended by Sam, we used the online survey and questionnaire tool 'Smart Survey' [3].

Purpose

To find out about 'movement' within the profession: movement between different types of employers and employment, where people move to and from and the reasons why.

Content of questionnaire

The questions were designed to be completed by selecting given options, avoiding as far as possible the use of text boxes, the content of which is difficult to analyse. Participants had the option to select 'other' if their specific niche role did not feature as an option. There was also a 'skip' facility which was designed to both avoid repetition but also ensure that nothing key was inadvertently missed. The questionnaire also included demographics.

Avenues for circulation

We contacted colleagues via professional networks including the clinical excellence network (CEN) Speech and Language Therapists On the Same Team, Royal College of Speech and Language Therapist networks, ASLTIP and our own databases. We included a request for the recipients to forward the link to their own groups too as we wanted to gain as wide and representative a range of views as we possibly could.

Our questionnaire received 305 responses.

Demographics							
Age		A	Exclusively in the public sector				50%
35%	50+	B	Exclusively in the private/third sector				32%
45%	36–49	C	In both A and B				16%
20%	21–35	D	Felt that the above categories didn't fit with their role				2%
Gender			More private sector respondents are self-employed than employed with sole trader being the biggest group				
96%	Female						
Ethnicity							
91%	White British		Sole traders	68%	Limited companies	28%	Partnerships	4%

Geographic location

Where are you based?

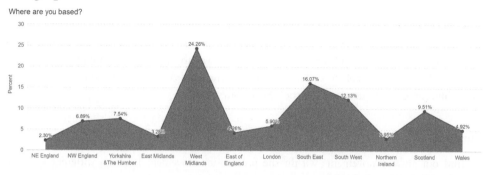

The vast majority of respondents have undertaken public sector work at some point in their careers (for 91%, this was their first role). Almost half of these had worked in the public sector for more than ten years.

In previous and current public sector posts, approximately 60% of respondents worked with children and young people. This figure reflects data reported by RCSLT in their 2021 paper 'Securing the Future Workforce: speech and language therapy stocktake'. SLT contracted time working with children was 61% [4].

We also know that more people work privately with children than with adults.

Moved from ... /had a dual role	All	15+*	%
Private to public *any* point	85	53	63
Public to private at *some* point	180	139	77
Public to private and back (returners)	59	45	76

* 15+ years post qualification

All categories show that the majority of movement occurred in respondents who had been qualified for at least 15 years and had reached middle pay bands (6 and 7).

The role of bank (this is similar to agency) working: for some respondents (and also anecdotally) bank work is regularly used to 'top up' earnings or as a stop-gap when relocating	Job 1	Move 1	Move 2
	3%	33%	22%

'Movement'

We started this exercise with a hunch that there was considerable movement within the profession and that (possibly) this had increased recently (local information, increase in membership of ASLTIP, etc.). The reason for including this section was to try and ascertain the direction of travel, primarily between the private and public sectors.

Whilst providing interesting information, the other options included were to enable respondents to provide as complete a picture of their moves as possible, rather than as a direct contribution to the overall findings.

Moves were defined as changes to either employment or working models – not moves between teams or within one sector, such as career progression within the NHS for example.

Considering the responses received as a snapshot of the profession, the hunch we had was right: 90% of respondents had made a move of some sort, with 40% of the respondents having made at least five moves.

Plotting the direction of travel over the course of four moves, the numbers going from private to public are consistently lower than the ones going from public to private	Move	Public to private	Private to public
	1	98	20
	2	45	35
	3	40	20
	4	27	18

One cannot help but admire the myriad of diverse and interesting roles being carried out, in some instances several roles being undertaken simultaneously – true portfolio careers.

See Chapter 5

The 78 individual free text box comments that accompanied this section were evidence of how resourceful and proactive speech and language therapists are. Here is a typical contribution.

> *I diversified into a mix of charity, HEI and private training work. This allowed me to retain some clinical practice, as HEI and other leadership roles almost always remove clinical opportunities.*

A strong and persistent message here was that respondents recognised when things weren't working for them in one role and were proactive in continuing to strive for what they wanted to do whilst juggling personal, domestic and family responsibilities. For some it took a number of years before they felt they were in 'the right place'.

> *I left the NHS nine years ago and have been directly employed by a multi-academy trust of schools ever since. I was not able to do the job I trained to do in the NHS and things have not improved since I left. I am financially better off, working term-time only and have job satisfaction, making a difference for children. I have also run my own business seeing a few clients privately (school holidays and weekends) for the last 11 years.*

Given the negative reasons which contribute to why a number of people leave the public sector, do they take part in an exit interview? 95 people responded to this question	Yes	43%
	No	50.5%
	Couldn't recall/NA/declined	6.3%
Did people feel they could be honest in their exit interview? 41 responses; 20 comments made	Yes	90%
	No	10%
Some felt hindered by the fact that the interview was conducted by someone within their department – in some instances the person who was a factor in their departure.		
Some felt that yes, they *could* be honest but felt it wouldn't make any difference. 'My views would not have been welcome'. 'No one was interested in my reasons for leaving'.		

Leaving/considering leaving the public sector

Of the 45% of respondents working *exclusively* in the public sector, 90% were employed by the NHS. 18% said they were *considering* a move away.

Respondents were offered ten choices which were rated between extremely important through to not important at all (not applicable was also an option). Combining the extremely and very important percentages, here are the top four.

Why respondents left *the public sector*			*Why some respondents were* considering *leaving the public sector*		
The top four 'pushes' are as follows			The top four 'pushes' are as follows		
1	Job satisfaction	83%	1	Job satisfaction	91%
2	Work-life balance	67%	2	Work-life balance	86%
3	Management styles	54%	3	Management styles	50%
4	Flexibility	53%	4	Flexibility	46%

Contrary to the received wisdom in some quarters, 58% of respondents indicated that income and earning potential *didn't* influence their decision to leave the public sector. However, for those *considering* leaving, 45% (the fifth highest 'push') said that this *was* a motivating factor. One might speculate that those 'considering' are doing so during a time when public sector pay is one of the critical issues facing the NHS at the time of writing.

Why do people stay?

Not everyone is dissatisfied with their public sector role. There were comments from a number of respondents who wished to make it clear that they were happy where they were.

It's important to make this point, not only to further emphasise that this exercise is about finding out information in a balanced way, but also to understand why people stay (what are the 'pulls'?) – so that lessons can be learnt in places where *almost exactly the same* reasons appear as 'pushes'. Why do some teams seem to get things right and others don't? We return to this question in Chapter 16.

For reasons of completeness, all options are listed here and ranked in terms of importance.

1	Job security	80%
2	Job satisfaction	73%
2	Belief in a service free at the point of delivery	73%
4	Terms and conditions	70%
5	Work-life balance	66%
6	Career opportunities	52%
7	Income and earning potential	49%

> Job satisfaction is clearly both a strong push and a strong pull for all three categories (leavers, those considering leaving and those who stay).

No matter what the move was, for 75% of respondents it was the 'right decision' – although in many cases it had taken several moves for respondents to eventually get to where they feel comfortable and fulfilled. For 3%, the move was a mistake and the remaining answers were a mixture of pros and cons.

Returners

We know from the Loan-Clarke research [5, 6] that returners do so because of

- Flexible hours
- Work location
- Professional development
- Pension provision

In the second paper [6], employment and job-specific issues remained dominant.

In our experience, and from comments made by some of those who returned, returners do so for a variety of reasons which did include trying the independent world and deciding it wasn't for them. In general, reasons for returning were pragmatic.

For some, geographical relocation meant there were fewer choices *other* than the public sector (this also worked conversely in that people left the public sector when relocation reduced their public sector options). Changes in personal circumstances (the need for greater financial security) also contributed to reasons for returning.

Returns also happened when individuals felt they should give the public sector a 'second chance' – i.e. perhaps their unsatisfactory experience the first time was an exception. We also heard from a therapist who had returned twice before finally settling on a portfolio career in the private sector and higher education.

Our findings

Of the respondents who left the public sector, 59 (33%) returned. Unfortunately, we were unable to gather enough reliable quantitative data from all the returner respondents. The picture is too small to be representative. However, from the useable data we *did* gather, the ranking of importance for the reasons for returning are below (and show *some* correlation with the reasons given by stayers).

	Returners			Stayers
1	Job satisfaction	90%	1	Job security
2	Terms and conditions	70%	2	Job satisfaction
3	Belief in service free at point of delivery	60%	2	Belief in service free at point of delivery
4	Career opportunities	54.5%	4	Terms and conditions
5	Work-life balance	50%	5	Work-life balance
5	Income/earning potential	50%	6	Career opportunities
5	Job security	50%	7	Income and earning potential

 **Findings**

A2 Focus groups

Similar questions were used for both these groups, although the amount of information gathered around each of the points below varied considerably according to the makeup of the group. Broad questions covered the following:

- For SLTs who had moved into independent practice: what prompted the move and what did they know about IP *before* they moved? Were people influenced either positively or negatively for example by their training establishment, friends or colleagues? What did people wish they had known in advance/what advice would they give to anyone considering a move?
- For those in the public sector: what were the things which kept them there?
- For those who work in both the public and private sectors, what's the attraction of this combination?
- Positives and negatives of both independent practice and the public sector

Group 1: therapists working in specialist settings across Birmingham

Held at one of the special schools in the city, this was a group of SLTs all of whom are either employed or self-employed and working in specialist settings in the city. The membership comprises both public and private sector therapists (the majority are private sector, plus teaching assistants and, on the day of the focus group, a student).

This is a fairly recently established group, dynamic and mutually supportive. Their agenda items vary from the routine and domestic – sharing of resources etc. through to the more strategic (discussions around new legislation for example) and supporting each other in preparation for Ofsted visits etc.

Summary of responses

Group 2

The Clinical Excellence Network (CEN) SLTs on the same team

A group of nine attended and all but one were working independently. However, there were some very well-expressed views which interestingly covered key points already emerging from interviews and discussions with others (including people outside the speech and language therapy profession). It was possible to identify common themes well before the questionnaire results were available.

25% of CEN members work in the NHS and 31% are self-employed independent practitioners. The remaining 44% work in a variety of different models and settings including local authority, third sector and HEIs [7].

Summary of CEN

There were continuing common themes for moving away from the public sector:

- Family needs
- Wanting more flexibility (including term time only working)
- Stress in the NHS
- Juggling commitments
- Humungous caseloads
- Being able to deliver what best suits the client

I tried my best but I never seemed to be I the right place at the right time

There was a perceived perception for some that those who made the move had, somehow, 'sold out'. Sadly, the view that financial gain is the priority for IPs was still in evidence.

What did the group wish they had known before they made the move?

SLTs having 'portfolio careers' is becoming increasingly common – wish I'd known that.

There's a lot to be gained from working/having worked in different environments (NHS, local authority, independent practice, specialist school settings). '*I'd encourage people to try new things*'.

Placements in independent practice would also help people to understand more about what it's like.

'More about the business side of things' has been a recurrent theme. Hopefully, by sign-posting people to what they need to know and do, there will be fewer surprises in the future.

The organisations you have to join, the mandatory stuff, data protection, clinical wills, what you can claim through your business.

Pricing: '*people need to afford your services, but you also need to cover your costs – it would be nice if other IPs were willing to share that a bit more*'.

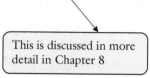

This is discussed in more detail in Chapter 8

The group gave some good, practical examples of where there might be opportunities to build more sustainable relationships with the public sector and to maintain closer collaboration. These have been included in Chapter 16.

A3 Informal interviews and personal stories

A number of informal interviews were conducted – with speech and language therapists but also with other professionals.

Purpose

To learn about individual journeys from a range of others and to find out more detail about particular circumstances and the reasons behind the decisions made.

NARRATIVE INTERVIEW

A narrative interview is unstructured. The only proviso is that the interviewer has a list of topics s/he wants the participant to talk about. Participants have the freedom to tell their own stories in their own words (with some prompting if needed).

The narrative interview objective is to *find out* what kind of things are happening, rather than to try and prove the frequency of *predetermined* kinds of things (i.e. what the researcher already believes is happening).

This second point is important. In just the same way as a questionnaire must work hard to avoid what might be perceived as bias, a narrative interview warrants *no* steer, other than to identify the subject matter. The experiences, feelings, views and emotions are those of the person whose story is being shared.

Key themes

Individual **personal stories** have added considerable value to this book. Common themes have been abstracted and used anonymously to illustrate important points to bear in mind when setting up in independent practice – no matter what your professional background. In general, stories are in the authors' own words. Some journeys have clearly been tough, but the overriding conclusion is about triumph over adversity.

B	Buying in extra help

B1 Questionnaire under the Freedom of Information Act (2000) [8]

Purpose

To get some idea about traded services within speech and language therapy, we made a number of Freedom of Information (FOI) requests to NHS Trusts across the UK.

GEOGRAPHICAL LOCATION OF TRUSTS THAT RESPONDED TO FOI REQUEST

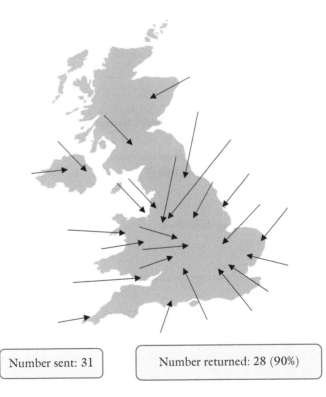

Number sent: 31	Number returned: 28 (90%)

Summary of responses

The full-time equivalent (FTE) establishments of the Trusts we surveyed ranged from tiny (8.5) through to very large (152.83). Neither of these extremes offers a traded service. The range of FTE for Trusts offering a traded service ranged from between 25.71 and 80. It is sensible, perhaps, to assume that the core service needs a 'critical mass' before looking to establish an enhanced offer.

Trusts were asked whether they had *ever* offered a traded service (yes: 48% and no: 52%)

Of the 13 services that have *ever* offered a traded service:

- Three (23%) have ceased entirely
- Two (16%) offer a reduced service
- Eight (61%) continue to offer a service

Services were **established** between 2005 and 2020, with one service saying 'pre-2000'. 77% were still offering a traded service of some description.

When asked to give reasons why the service had either reduced or been discontinued themes included:

- Reduction in demand
- Where training is offered the range of topics has been reduced
- Not possible to staff the bespoke support packages being requested
- Unsustainable as therapists were recruited as school contracts were secured – with no permanent contracts there was a high staff turnover

One Trust refused to give reasons.

Services were asked *why* they had established a traded service ...

The most frequent theme was to be able to provide a service for those who don't meet the core service criteria, followed by 'demand' from schools for more and the delivery of training.

... and ... what were they hoping to achieve?

Common themes here include:

- To meet the needs of school-aged children
- Increase capacity in schools
- Reduce non-attendance
- To enable NHS specialist support services to enhance the schools offer

One Trust said '*ensuring a service that has the assurances of being backed by the NHS safeguards (such as mandatory training, supervision, CPD etc.)*'.

Terms and conditions: the majority of staff involved in traded service delivery also work in the core service (69%). The 31% working exclusively in the traded service are all on permanent contracts.

92% of responses confirmed that staff in the traded service enjoyed the same terms and conditions as those in the core services.

One Trust refused to answer this question.

Banding: staff working in the enhanced services range from band 3 through to band 8. The highest proportion are band 5s, closely followed by bands 6 and 7.

Balancing demand and capacity: the overwhelming majority (67%) said that they absorbed staff back into the regular service by moving staff between different teams. One service refused to answer this question.

The length of contracts ranged from between 12 months (67%) and three years (22%) with just one service accepting contracts as short as three months and another saying that length was variable.

Payment arrangements were usually in arrears (80%) with 20% asking for payment in advance. There must be a degree of risk here if there are capacity issues.

Managing staff absence: 67% of the solutions were reactive (pausing the contract, ceasing/terminating the service, reducing the price). 33% would try to recruit on a fixed-term contract (which is easier to do with a planned absence such as maternity leave but realistically would still leave a significant gap, given the length of time recruitment can take), or look for spare capacity elsewhere in their service. In the same way that normal sickness absence is very unlikely to be covered in the regular service, it isn't covered in the traded service.

Reflection

Interestingly, nowhere in the information we received was money mentioned as a reason for establishing a traded service or 'income generation' given as an anticipated outcome. This is a potential missed opportunity. Could this be because there is a pressure for the NHS to continue to be seen as 'free at the point of delivery', when in fact it isn't?

In the current climate, it must be very difficult to justify a traded service when the core offer is under enormous pressure. *However*, as we know, the demand for SLT is so great that it must surely be worth exploring whether a well-thought-out traded service could actually help to support the core offer by generating income. We consider this in a bit more detail in Chapter 16.

Offering additional services which are '*assured*' (which implies 'good quality' and is verified) is entirely laudable – however, one could be forgiven for thinking there is an inference here that, somehow, a service which is *not* under the auspices of the public sector is not '*assured*' and somehow less safe. This is an interesting point which deserves to be revisited in a little more detail.

In Chapters 10 and 16, we talk more about whether private sector SLT services should be subject to regulation of some sort.

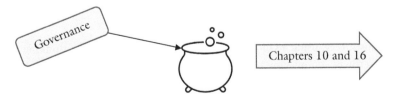

A traded service is almost (but not quite) a 'bridge' between the public and private sectors. The FOI results show that traded services contract with schools and settings in a way which is not dissimilar to our own.

What *is* different, however, is that therapists working in the traded service enjoy the same terms and conditions as those delivering core services (i.e. NHS terms and conditions). They also have the safety net of redeployment into core services if contracts are terminated: 'we would absorb staff into the regular service'.

Despite the inequities in terms and conditions and job security between therapists working in a public sector traded service and a therapist in the private sector (whether employed or self-employed), traded services are an important part of the provider landscape and, done well, can extend the choice available to schools and settings.

Are they done well? Are they robust? Do they have longevity? Are managers of SLT services suitably skilled and supported to set up traded services? The FOI results indicate that perhaps the answer to 1 and 2 is 'not especially': not being able to provide what the customer wants, terminating the contract if staffing becomes an issue and (especially) asking for the money in advance of delivering the service. In terms of question 3, anecdotal evidence from the CQC inspections of which Diana was a part (at the time when traded services were springing up across the country) is that managers felt unprepared and, in some cases, as described by one service manager, 'desperately unprepared' to design, cost, market and deliver a commercial entity. To do this successfully (and avoid the stress and additional burden involved), a new skill set plus appropriate support is required.

So... what's the verdict on traded services?

Don't **not** do it - but do it **better**, more **transparently** and ensure the people at the helm have the skills and confidence to deliver.

Go to Chapter 16 for a deeper discussion about how the independent sector has the potential to support public sector colleagues delivering a traded service

B2 How do schools and settings choose providers of speech and language therapy services?

Purpose

The aim of this survey, using a Google Forms survey, was to explore the thinking behind why schools and settings commission additional support for children with speech, language and communication needs (SLCN). What is available and what are the benefits and restrictions? How do they find that additional support and do they commission other support?

Findings

As to be expected, the information gathered has, indirectly furnished us with a 'wish list' of what schools are looking for (and, in some instances, what they are not looking for), which is a clear signpost for public and private providers alike to look at ways they can improve their offer.

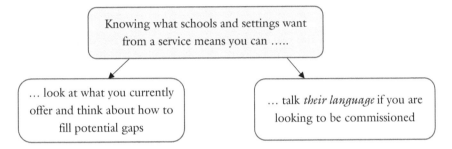

73 questionnaires were distributed and 24 were returned (33%). This was a relatively low return, so the consistency of responses is important.

Here we summarise the key themes.

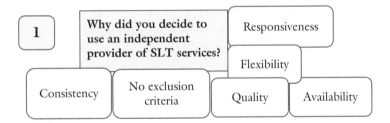

Summary

We have a large proportion of pupils who require support with their speech and language needs and the NHS was not able to provide the service these children required. They were often discharged within six weeks if not less.

We are unable to meet need without independent providers' expertise and specialism in this area.

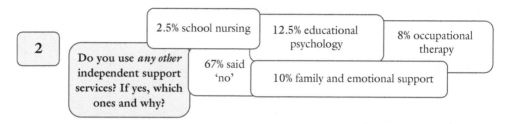

2 Do you use *any other* independent support services? If yes, which ones and why?

2.5% school nursing

12.5% educational psychology

8% occupational therapy

67% said 'no'

10% family and emotional support

Summary

Speech and language therapy is by far the highest priority for schools and settings.

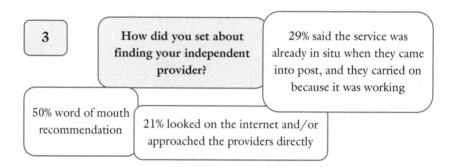

3 How did you set about finding your independent provider?

29% said the service was already in situ when they came into post, and they carried on because it was working

50% word of mouth recommendation

21% looked on the internet and/or approached the providers directly

Summary

Clearly an internet presence is necessary, but more importantly, the quality and impact of what you provide means that people will recommend you to others and, once you are successful in being commissioned, that same quality and impact will mean the setting will want to keep you.

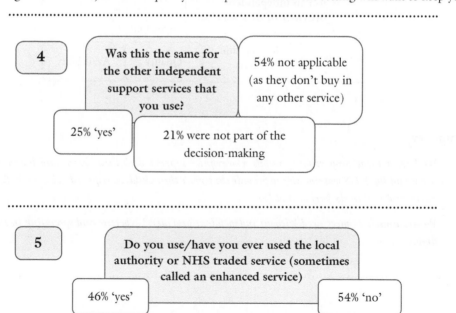

4 Was this the same for the other independent support services that you use?

54% not applicable (as they don't buy in any other service)

25% 'yes'

21% were not part of the decision-making

5 Do you use/have you ever used the local authority or NHS traded service (sometimes called an enhanced service)

46% 'yes'

54% 'no'

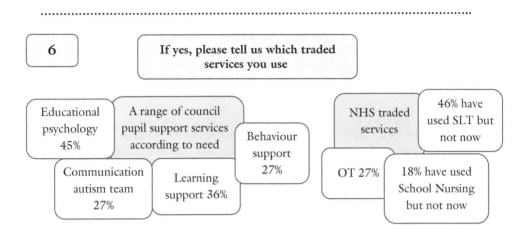

6

If yes, please tell us which traded services you use

Educational psychology 45%

A range of council pupil support services according to need

Behaviour support 27%

NHS traded services

46% have used SLT but not now

Communication autism team 27%

Learning support 36%

OT 27%

18% have used School Nursing but not now

Summary

Schools have bought and continue to buy additional educational and behavioural support from council traded services.

7

How did you find out about the traded services?

Summary

There are lots of different routes and sources – word of mouth was particularly important.

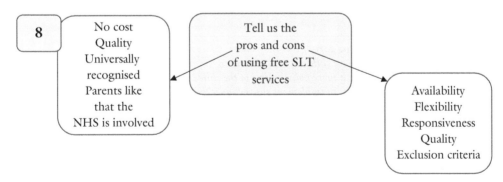

8

No cost
Quality
Universally recognised
Parents like that the NHS is involved

Tell us the pros and cons of using free SLT services

Availability
Flexibility
Responsiveness
Quality
Exclusion criteria

Summary

*It **is** free but you can't get it!*

<table>
<tr><td>9</td><td>**Tell us the pros and cons of using traded speech and language therapy services**</td></tr>
</table>

Summary

There are still issues with flexibility, responsiveness and consistency. Some of the traded service offerings seemed very similar to the NHS core offer and ways of working. This ties in well with the reasons why some traded services either ceased or cut back their activity because they couldn't meet what they saw as the 'bespoke' requirements of some settings.

<table>
<tr><td>10</td><td>**Tell us the pros and cons are of using independent speech and language therapy services**</td></tr>
</table>

Summary

Predictably, cost was the biggest disadvantage, although it's difficult to understand quite why schools should be surprised that the cost is similar to the cost of a teacher for a day.

The benefits list revisits and builds upon the original reasons given for seeking an independent provider.

This is why we did it   *This is what we got*

> *The therapist becomes part of the school team. Children, staff and parents get to know them. They see children in different environments over the school day therefore providing a more holistic view of the child. Therapists can train and work with school staff to implement support quickly.*

<table>
<tr><td>C</td><td>**Students and independent practice**</td></tr>
</table>

Students are the future of the profession. We all have a duty to not only ensure that they are clinically fit for purpose but also that they fully understand the provider landscape – and they learn about it without fear or favour.

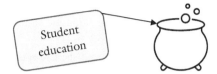

Student education

The clinical element is not the main focus here, but suffice it to say that the private sector is potentially under-exploited in terms of what it has to offer to student therapists. The reasons why private sector businesses do or don't take on students are important to capture so that as a profession we are able to maximise opportunities for learning and development. We revisit this in more detail in Chapters 12 and 16.

Purpose

The primary thrust here was to find out how, post-qualification, the opportunities to work in the private sector were presented and discussed – or indeed if they were at all. The group was dynamic, interesting and informative.

What do students know about the provider landscape?

We have not looked in great detail at the information given to students about IP in *all* the various training establishments across the UK, but what we *do* know, however, is what happens in one particular establishment, where a third-year student focus group revealed some interesting findings.

We were well aware that as research tools, both focus groups and semi-structured interviews have their limitations. The advantages of combining these two approaches far outweighed the disadvantages. Formal research was never our objective. We were interested in knowledge, experiences, opinions, impressions and hard facts (where they existed).

 Summary

Around 10% of the final-year students joined the focus group. They were invited by one of their fellow students who was already known to the authors. This was a mix of younger people and mature students looking for adult and paediatric posts.

A theme which strongly emerged was that 'the message from the university seems to be you have to be in the NHS for at least a year before considering independent practice'. The necessity of being supported by a multi-disciplinary team was also highlighted. Two students reported that they had been told to wait until they had a bit of experience.

The group all mentioned that available NHS jobs were few and far between. This sits oddly with the vacancy rate survey carried out by the RCSLT in January 2023. Several students were able to identify exactly one (or maybe two) jobs they felt they could apply for – travelling/location was a constraint for some, but also what the job offered (the right client group etc.).

We asked about the 'observation days' the students had done. One student came away from having spent a day in a mainstream primary school alongside an independent practitioner, with the feeling that there was a lot less admin/paperwork in IP.

Another spent her day with an NHS SLT who said she had spent the whole of her first year doing assessment – this student had made her decision to work with adults based on the fact that she wanted to 'do therapy'.

The student group left us with a 'wish list' of what they felt would be beneficial:

- A presentation at the university would be good, with the opportunity to ask questions
- To know about the different models in independent practice
- Information about job security
- Where to go to find what jobs are available in independent practice (we spoke to the director of an independent practice who had made a number of unsuccessful attempts to recruit a new graduate – there has to be a better way of sharing information and opportunities with students)
- Knowing how independent practice works and what clinical pathways are followed so that myths are dispelled
- Everyone wanted to know if there was the opportunity to do 'a lot more therapy' in independent practice

It is important to reiterate that we only managed to speak to a group from one university, and we have heard via other sources that other universities have different ways of reflecting the IP route. It may be that when these issues were raised, the students were early on their learning journey and perhaps the information seemed less relevant at that point.

As one of our questionnaire respondents wrote:

> *I think it's important to educate SLT students about employment options so they are able to make informed decisions, particularly to be curious around private companies and how profits are spent.*

We talk more about students in Chapters 12 and 16.

| D | **Structures and networks which support IPs** |

As we discovered when putting together the submission for the book, there is very little in-depth information available to therapists looking to establish themselves in independent practice. We were able to find various blog articles and some information on independent practitioners' websites. Quite a lot of the information comes from the USA. The Association of Speech and Language Therapists in Independent Practice (ASLTIP) has good information for members.

ASLTIP is the obvious 'go-to' resource for independent practitioners. During the course of researching this book, we were surprised to learn that ASLTIP is by no means as widely known as we had thought. We spoke to several independent practitioners who had little or no knowledge of it. Similarly, the student focus group showed that, weeks from graduating, fledgling therapists had never heard of the organisation.

We began by looking at the information available on the website and then followed this up by an interview with Sarah Buckley, who, at the time of writing had just begun her four-year tenure as Chair. Sarah had begun to identify the priorities for the organisation. She described her vision going forward as encapsulating an entity which is *dynamic, responsive and agile*.

Raising the profile: she is firmly committed to developing productive relationships with **all** stakeholders and we will return to some of the ideas discussed in Chapter 15 as we look to the future. Sarah poses the question: (how) **does** ASLTIP interact with stakeholders? In the first instance, the board will be looking at relationships with the charitable sector. '*The external profile of the organisation needs to be way higher – we need to get on the map!*'

Sarah is aware that there are 'lots of' independent practitioners out there who are not members of ASLTIP, and given that in some cases IPs hadn't even heard of ASLTIP, let alone joined, there is work to be done to raise the profile on all fronts.

Data is another priority area. As there is currently no comprehensive record of the workforce across the profession in all sectors, we can only surmise what percentage of the total independent workforce this might be. What we do know, however, is that at the time of writing there were approximately 1,600 members (up from 1,300 in 2020). There are fewer members in Scotland and Wales – whether this is because there are fewer independent practitioners, differences in local NHS provision, or just fewer practitioners who join ASLTIP, as it isn't a mandatory membership organisation, isn't known.

Sarah describes the membership as 'very fluid', people can join at any point in the year. New members join, others lapse or retire and then some re-join. An action plan is to record the number of new joiners each month and then to make personal contact from the ASLTIP Board to find out more information and to learn about their journey.

There is a feeling that once members are at capacity in terms of clients, they no longer see the need to feature in the ASLTIP register of independent practitioners, which is accessed by the public looking for a therapist. Sarah is keen to raise the profile of the fleet of member benefits (which is much more than the independent practitioner register), to encourage members to maintain their membership.

There is certainly a role for both ASLTIP and the RCSLT to work jointly to try and resolve topical issues which impact widely within the profession. One such topical issue, the resolution of which would make a huge difference to children, their families and the schools who are striving to secure the additional support to meet needs, involves the speech and language therapy contribution to Education and Health Care Plans (EHCPs).

Whilst this has been resolved as a result of local dialogue in some parts of England, there are still authorities where a report by an independent practitioner will not be accepted –despite the fact that **all** members of the

> An EHCP is a legal document which sets out the education, healthcare and social care needs of a child or young person for whom extra support is needed in school, beyond what the school can provide.

profession are qualified, registered and accountable no matter **where** they work. Interestingly, this is not the same for educational psychologists.

Authorities are quite happy to accept a private EP report.

This refusal is questionable in terms of legality and something of a paradox when, in the absence of capacity in the public sector, authorities are faced with little alternative other than to turn to private practitioners to **deliver** what is specified on an EHCP.

IP and students: Offering student placements makes sound business sense to private companies who can future-proof their workforce – particularly in times of high demand and low capacity. So why is it that some IPs offer student placements, but many do not – despite the fact that they are committed to investing in the next generation? There are barriers both in terms of finance and risk assessments. The tariff for student placements is insufficient and doesn't cover costs. A larger practice might see this as akin to a loss leader and be prepared to cover the shortfall, but this is unlikely to be the case for a sole trader.

Single-handed practitioners, delivering a service from their own premises, may not be comfortable inviting a student into their home. A much more significant difficulty would be that the sole trader would not have the necessary insurance that the HEI would require. There is always the option to take out additional insurance, but this has cost implications. Proactive sole traders could band together to support a student placement but the tariff from NHS England cannot be shared – just one more obstacle to overcome!

ASLTIP also offers an online course for therapists considering going down the independent route.

As the focus of this book is our journey into independent practice, we have taken a little time to talk about the remote training course offered by ASLTIP to support therapists setting up in independent practice.

The course is around three hours of content: 100 slides (with video links) for (at the time of writing) £100. We are advised that the ASLTIP board regularly reviews and updates the information in the training package. Purchasers can view the materials as often as they need to. This is followed up by an invitation to 'meet the Board' online or face-to-face for people wanting to 'set up' as independent practitioners. Sarah Buckley, ASLTIP Chair, says:

> *This offers an opportunity not only to speak to those running the organisation, but also to come together with other like-minded therapists who are in the process of setting up in independent practice. There's a whole range of different people to speak to.*

ASLTIP courses used to run in centres across the country and a local independent practitioner would be invited to come and speak. This element has been lost with courses being an online package – but, as the Chair observes, the lack of the personal story removes the potential perception that what attendees may hear is a 'one size fits all' approach. It is important to emphasise that everyone will come from a slightly different starting point.

We purchased the training course, worked our way through the content, and this is what we found. The material is good with well-presented and easy-to-follow slides. We particularly liked the two slides very early on which look at the pros and cons of setting up independently. You can almost hear the questions everyone thinking of 'going independent' will be asking.

The presentation covers all the 'key areas' with reminders and signposts to find out more about points raised – rather than provide so much detail that there is the potential to overwhelm – or even put people off!

Different business models are discussed and attention is also paid to the details behind finances. From our own experience and talking to numerous others, talking about money can be difficult for all sorts of reasons (go to Chapter 8 for much more about finance) – especially the non-pay element, including the detail of fixed versus variable costs, which can so easily get overlooked. Independent practitioners are advised not to under-sell themselves – very sound advice and something we also strongly advocate. Lone working is also covered.

The importance of supervision is highlighted – what practitioners need to source and the fact that there may be a cost implication (see Chapter 12).

Later slides offer a series of Dos and Don'ts in bullet point form as a useful summary.

The presentation concludes with lots of information about ASLTIP and benefits for members.

 Some of the terminology we use to describe structures, processes and procedures (the SPPs we refer to throughout our book) differs but essentially, we are all talking about the same things.

The course is a good place to start for anyone exploring the idea of becoming an independent practitioner. Sarah said that this is exactly what it was intended to be – raising awareness of all the things people need to know so that they can go away and find out more as and when required.

ASLTIP is, and should continue to be, a valuable source of advice and support for members.

To summarise

We have gathered together lots of information from a variety of sources. We know what the latest research says, and, at a number of levels, we have the views of a sample of SLTs from across the country – from questionnaire data, from focus groups and from personal stories (extracts from which will continue to feature in subsequent chapters). We also have a snapshot of the student view. There are snapshots, too, from other professionals who have shared their experiences of leaving the public sector and the reasons for that.

We have also gathered information about ASLTIP and what it can offer independent practitioners.

 No amount of information has any particular value unless it contributes to the building of a 'bigger picture'. Moving forward, as our story unfolds, we continue to draw upon the views and information gathered.

A word to the wise!

Towards the end of the book, we take a little time to think about the future and the lessons we can learn from what has gone before.

So … all to play for as we get down to sharing the practicalities of running an independent speech and language therapy practice.

References

1. Semi-structured, narrative, and in-depth interviewing, focus groups, action research, participant observation | Health Knowledge. Available at: https://www.healthknowledge.org.uk/public-health-textbook/research-methods/1d-qualitative-methods/section2-theoretical-methodological-issues-research.
2. Demand hub (data-enabled medical technologies and devices hub) is an ERDF-supported programme for the Black country, Greater Birmingham and Solihull, Coventry & Warwickshire, and Stoke-On-Trent & Staffordshire LEP regions.
3. www.smartsurvey.co.uk.
4. Library Database. (2014) *Details for: Securing the future workforce supply: Speech and language therapy stocktake*. The King's Fund Library Catalog. Available at: https://koha.kingsfund.org.uk/cgi-bin/koha/opac-detail.pl?biblionumber=116006&shelfbrowse_itemnumber=146143.
5. Loan-Clarke, J. et al. (2009) Why do speech and language therapists stay in, leave and (sometimes) return to the National Health Service (NHS)? *International Journal of Language & Communication Disorders*, 44(6), pp. 883–900. doi:10.1080/13682820802381334.
6. Loan-Clarke, J. et al. (2010) Retention, turnover and return - A longitudinal study of allied health professionals in Britain. *Human Resource Management Journal*, 20(4), pp. 391–406. doi:10.1111/j.1748-8583.2010.00140.x.
7. Audit of membership carried out by CEN in 2023 (audit ongoing at time of writing therefore data is not yet complete).
8. *Freedom of Information Act 2000*. Legislation.gov.uk. Available at: https://www.legislation.gov.uk/ukpga/2000/36/contents

5   Business models

In this chapter, we will consider the various 'structural' options for individuals (or groups) considering working independently. It's important to know what the options are and to be able to make an informed choice as to what best suits you, including the options for employment versus self-employment.

We also share three personal stories, illustrating very different business models. Also, this chapter is a sensible place to talk a little bit more about 'portfolio careers' which are certainly becoming more popular and numerous amongst speech and language therapists.

Understanding the difference between the public and private sectors

The **public sector**: here, services are owned and operated by the government. Obvious examples include education, law enforcement and healthcare.

The **'private sector'**: this is the part of our economy run by individuals and companies, rather than a government entity. This sector includes large corporations, small businesses, self-employed people, and independent contractors. Most private sector organizations are run with the intention of making profit.

For the purposes of consistency and clarity, when we refer to the 'public sector' in terms of healthcare, we are referring to NHS services.

This book is about healthcare professionals but much of the content has relevance for *almost anyone*. From accountancy to website design via counselling, floristry, carpentry, plumbing, dentistry, law, physiotherapy and many more besides, individuals with skills and qualifications across the board may choose to set up their own business.

A number of the examples given are of trades and professions which *traditionally* belong in the private sector. Routinely, newly qualified accountants and lawyers seek employment within an established practice. That practice is a business first and foremost: a business selling financial services or a business selling legal services.

Staying with healthcare: counselling services are routinely available in the private sector, as is physiotherapy, particularly for sports injuries. Podiatrists too have a long history of working outside of the NHS – in fact, chiropodists (as they were originally called) were independent licensed practitioners *before* they became part of mainstream medical services in the early 20th century. More and more dentists operate almost entirely in the private sector, with fewer and fewer seeking to undertake contracts with the NHS. The scarcity of NHS dentistry is well-known and, at the time of writing, quite critical, leading to 'dental deserts' in some parts of the country. Dentistry has been discussed in some detail in Chapter 3.

DOI: 10.4324/9781003382928-5

Where do GPs fit in?

GPs are independent contractors. Most GP practices are operated by a partnership of two or more GPs. The GP or GP partners are contracted to the NHS to provide primary care services (the general medical services [GMS] contract) [1]. The GP partners are responsible for employing other staff to provide services.

To all intents and purposes, GPs work exclusively within the NHS and many people see them as being NHS employees.

The Alternative Provider of Medical Services (APMS) contract (2004) [2] allowed the contract to be held by a private entity or not-for-profit organisation; the contract no longer had to be between a named GP or GP partner and the NHS. The structure of these contracts means that the NHS does not gain if efficiencies and savings are made, they only increase the profits taken by the entity.

Beginning to think about setting out as an independent practitioner

Can we consider the terms 'private' and 'independent' as interchangeable?

In terms of SLT, in many instances, they *are* used to refer to the same thing: an individual might be receiving 'private therapy', or a chosen therapist is described as an 'independent practitioner', or perhaps merely as a 'private therapist'.

At the risk of pedantry, however, there **is** a distinction to be made and worth making here as it has some bearing on terminology used in this book.

What is an independent practitioner?

According to The Joint Commission (2023) [3], a licensed independent practitioner is 'any individual permitted by law and by the organization to provide care and services, without direction or supervision, within the scope of the individual's license and consistent with individually granted clinical privileges'.

What structural options are available to an independent practitioner?

There are a *number* of different options and, at first look, the terminology can seem bewildering. What do these words mean and do they mean what we *think* they mean … in the context of working outside the 'public sector'?

The different options bring with them rules and regulations, advantages and disadvantages, depending on individual circumstances: it's sensible, therefore, to begin by looking at the terminology in more detail.

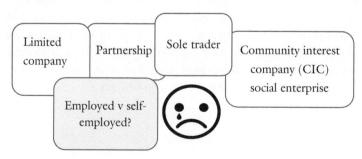

We have already established the difference between the public and private sectors.

Independent operators are individuals, trading via *limited company, partnership* or as a *sole trader* or through an *umbrella company*. They provide services for an organisation under a *contract for services*. Independent contractors are not employees and are typically highly skilled, providing their clients with specialist skills or additional capacity on an 'as needed' basis.

A limited company and a partnership are not the same.

Limited company: there are two types of limited company (private and public). The difference is in how shares might change hands. For the purposes of this chapter, we are referring to a private limited company. Here, the shareholders own the company, but the directors are responsible for operating it. In a small private company, shareholders and directors may be one and the same. The directors are deemed to *be employed by the company*. Limited companies do not put the shareholders' personal assets at risk like a sole trader or partnership would do.

The company is obliged to submit annual accounts and pay corporation tax.

Partnership: this consists of two (or more) people working together towards a common goal. All partners share responsibility for the business, including risks, profits and losses. The partnership itself isn't taxed: money passes directly to each partner who (as a self-employed person) completes a self-assessment form.

Sole trader: is an individual business owner who has 100% responsibility for his/her business operations. Registering as a sole trader doesn't mean that you have to be a single-person business. You can hire staff as a sole trader – but only you own and control your business.

Under current law, as a sole trader, you and your business are considered the same. This means that should your business incur any losses or debts, you are personally liable. This is an important factor to consider when deciding whether to register as a sole trader or a limited company.

Q: What do we mean by '*self-employed*'?

A: 'Self-employed' means neither being on the payroll nor being employed. If, therefore, you operate via a limited company you are not strictly self-employed as you are either an officer (director) or employee of the company. You can only be 'self-employed' as a sole trader or partnership. To help clarify this point, a better way to describe 'self-employed' might be to say 'being in business on your own account'. A sole trader is classed as being self-employed (i.e. one person in business on his or her own account).

An **umbrella company** is an intermediary between a contractor and an end client or agency. The agency/end-user pays the umbrella company which in turn pays the contractor under PAYE as if they were an employee. (Some) locum agencies operate in this way.

Of the respondents to our questionnaire who were 'in business on their own account', 88% were sole traders and 28% limited companies.

Kezia's story

Kezia is a sole trader. We share her story here because, throughout the book, we have heard about the things people wish they had known before setting out on the independent path. We have also heard about what causes anxiety. The positive steps taken to get to grips with the challenges of running a business and to deal with the worries that feature in this story will be an enormous encouragement to others. Kezia is open and transparent about the choices she has made and the steps she has taken (and continues to take) to build a strong and supportive network – not only for herself but also to build resilience in others. She also has two distinct roles (a portfolio career which we talk more about later in this chapter).

Kezia works with adults and, like most people, started her career in the NHS. She rose up the ranks to a management (team leader) position and had settled into a kind of acceptance that '*this would be me for the rest of my working life!*'

> *I was a single parent and the increasingly stressful demands of the job were hindering my ability to parent my child as I wanted to. While I desperately didn't want to let down my team and our caseload, I knew that my priorities needed to change. At around the same time my son needed speech and language therapy and the excellent care he received from an independent practitioner opened my eyes to opportunities beyond the public sector.*

At the time of writing, Kezia is two years down the independent road. She talks eloquently about the initial feelings of 'crippling guilt': guilt at leaving her team, guilt at leaving the patients and guilt about charging clients a realistic rate to cover all the tasks associated with delivering the service. Good for Kezia that she recognised that running your own business isn't just about the clinical delivery.

> *I also faced moments of panic looking ahead to a quieter diary in the month ahead and fearing the financial implications. I found the visibility and exposure that comes with marketing a business intimidating; I spent months creating a website then didn't want to share it with anyone out of embarrassment and fear of judgement!*

This may be a familiar feeling to others, although not something most of us would freely admit!

The message here is that it's **okay** to feel less than thrilled once the cloak of anonymity we had in the public sector has gone and it feels as though our every move is out there for all to see (and potentially disparage) It's a bit like writing a book perhaps – once your head is above the parapet, there *will* potentially be detractors. Yes, our every move is down to us, but turning this on its head means that we are in charge of our own destiny.

> *Around the same time as setting up my private practice, I also trained as a life coach, and the skills I learned have been invaluable in navigating the ups and downs of running a business. It's these same skills I also now use as an independent Speech and Language Therapy supervisor, supporting therapists in independent practice as they too navigate the challenges of establishing and running a business, prioritising their well-being alongside business development and clinical supervision.*

The skills of reflection are key to recognising what is challenging and looking at ways to rise to those challenges. Kezia shares the things which have helped her on her journey.

- *Knowing my worth and recognising when I'm spending too long on unpaid tasks in an attempt to 'prove my value'*

- *Establishing clear terms and conditions to establish boundaries within the work I do, which also serve as an important reminder to not over-extend myself*
- *Identifying what's important to me and keeping this in mind when making work-related decisions. For example, my primary motivation for transitioning to independent practice was to prioritise time with my son and fit my work into school hours*
- *Identifying the aspects of my work that energise me and those I find draining. For example, focusing my professional development and marketing efforts on the client caseloads I love working with, whilst automating and outsourcing tasks I don't enjoy*
- *Accessing support through supervision, coaching and peer support groups. Self-employment can feel isolating and having a community that can offer support and understand the challenges involved has been crucial.*

> *Despite the challenges private practice brings, I have no regrets. I absolutely love the flexibility self-employment offers. My clinical skills have developed significantly, as I've been able to invest a lot more time in my own development. Running a business has been the ultimate lesson in personal growth and I know this self-awareness and experience also makes me a better therapist, coach and supervisor.*

Steph's story

Steph is a single-handed limited company. Her story is one of optimism and is interesting because she had wanted to work for herself very early on. It wasn't a decision forced upon her by circumstances as it was with others. The reasons for wanting to work independently resonate through many of the stories and are borne out by the findings of our questionnaire. Similarly, things that worried her at the outset crop up in many stories but **are** manageable. It's all about weighing up the risks versus the benefits.

The themes running through her story are about making *active choices* and *seizing opportunities* as they present themselves. Steph moves seamlessly between various options as her capacity waxes and wanes. Maybe that degree of agility isn't for everyone, but it illustrates how 'saleable' our skills can be.

> *I always wanted to work independently from the day I qualified as a speech and language therapist in 2002. I didn't know how I'd do it or when, but I knew I would.*
>
> *I remember attending an ASLTIP 'working in independent practice' course way back in 2003. It took a decade to actually take the leap!*
>
> *I worked for the NHS for 12 years and then once my youngest child was born, I began to become very unhappy with my current set-up. Long waiting lists and regular therapy with clients getting less and less. I just lost interest.*
>
> *It just so happened that the universe was listening and I bumped into a therapist who was locuming in my NHS clinic. She told me that she was leaving to work for an independent company. Straightaway I was interested, and she agreed to pass on my details.*

We made contact but I decided to not leave the NHS immediately as my son was still only a year old and that took priority, but I had already started to get the itch. It was maybe six months later that I decided it was now or never. I was scared of the self-assessment tax; I was scared of the loss of NHS pension and I was scared of the unknown.

Little did I realise that none of the above would ever be a problem once I took the leap.

I decided to work in the best way for me and my young family and to work three days for the NHS and two days independently for the private company. I was working full time with a one-year-old and a three-year-old but I loved it so much it didn't matter. Within six months I had left the NHS altogether. I just loved working independently in mainstream schools delivering therapy every week.

Eventually, it was a logical step to go it alone completely and I started to get enquiries through my own website. This was scary but very exciting. I eventually built up my own group of schools over the next 12 months and left the private company. I had a few years of drowning in work and taking on far more than I could cope with – a common issue other independent therapists share with me. I am not complaining though, I was earning very well in a few short years.

When COVID-19 hit, I lost several of my school contracts. I was happy to return to private companies to tide me over. For two years I also locumed for the NHS over the summer holidays which was great for my CPD.

I now happily move between my own school contracts, locuming for the NHS and working for other independent companies. It is great for CPD and great for never getting complacent or bored. My only advice where this is concerned is to never burn your bridges. Respect other people's independent practices and appreciate the autonomy that being independent gives you. It can be a lot of fun.

I have never regretted the decision I made to venture into independent working. I have never learnt so much in all my working life or met so many lovely people.

Q: Does working outside the public sector automatically mean working in the private sector?

A: No. The third alternative (sometimes called the third sector) is the 'voluntary sector'.

The **'voluntary sector'** refers to organisations whose primary purpose is to create social impact rather than profit. It is often called the third sector, civil society or the not-for-profit sector.

The voluntary sector is independent of local and national government and distinct from the private sector. Charities are the largest single category within the voluntary sector. Others include community benefit societies and co-operatives, not-for-profit community businesses or **community interest companies (CICs)** (which is one example of a social enterprise), credit unions and small informal community groups.

https://reachvolunteering.org.uk/guide/what-voluntary-sector [4]

Social enterprises are businesses which trade for a social or environmental purpose.

A community interest company is a type of company designed for social enterprises that want to use their profits and assets for the public good.

We make specific reference to CICs as this is the business model of choice for a number of companies selling speech and language therapy services.

Natalie's story

After 14 years in the NHS, and during a time of considerable change, Natalie made the decision to move into independent practice. Service delivery within the NHS was moving to a predominately consultative approach and Natalie no longer felt like she was able to deliver the service she felt the children she worked with needed.

In 2013, Natalie set up an independent therapy business, Integrated Therapy Solutions Ltd. Having always worked within a multi-disciplinary framework, Natalie knew that effective management of children with significant communication and feeding difficulties required a team effort. She established a small team that included experienced professionals from SLT, occupational therapy and nutrition and dietetics. Alongside the communication work, Natalie's specialism was children's feeding and swallowing difficulties. She wanted to be able to offer a service to children with feeding difficulties who were only able to access limited or fragmented support within the NHS.

> *We launched the feeding clinic in response to parents' frustration that their children with chronic and sometimes very complex feeding needs were visiting lots of different professionals but not receiving any help that addressed the underlying problems with learning to eat. Our therapists wanted to offer families interdisciplinary, evidence-based treatment, to support the child and their family on their journey of learning to eat.*

The feeding clinic and team at ITS grew in response to increased demand for its services. In 2020, Natalie relaunched the feeding clinic as a **not-for-profit community interest company**, a social enterprise model of delivery that enabled families who were unable to self-fund to access services via Individual Funding Requests (IFR) to the NHS. This model grew rapidly, with a large increase in referrals and requests for education and training from around the UK. However, not all families were successful when applying for IFR and the financial burden remained a barrier to accessing treatment and support.

> *To meet the increased demand and requests for support with fund-raising, we knew we would need to expand. In 2023, I applied to the Charity Commission to convert the company to a charity: The Feeding Trust. We are the only charity in the UK for paediatric feeding disorders (PFD).*

Natalie now works alongside partners in the USA to raise awareness of PFD within the medical and wider population. As a charity, Natalie is hoping to extend links with the public sector through education and training for professionals within the NHS and collaboration with local universities to conduct research into PFD. Through fundraising activities, the charity also hopes to provide grants of financial assistance to enable economically disadvantaged families and children with PFD, to access treatment not available on the NHS.

https://www.feedingtrust.org/ [5]

Employed versus self-employed

Before we move on to our second personal story, let's take a whistle-stop tour through the pros and cons of employment versus self-employment. We know from informal conversations with others from a range of professions (and it also cropped up at our student focus group) that financial instability is a worry and is one of the 'pulls' which keeps people in the public sector (see Chapter 4).

Our specialist contributor Jenny Marks (Tax Director at Muras Baker Jones Chartered Accountants) [6] says:

> *Being in business on one's own account (either through self-employment or via your own limited company) and traditional employment for a third party have their benefits and drawbacks. Choosing between them requires careful consideration.*
>
> *The decision to 'work for yourself' or seek traditional employment depends on individual preferences, circumstances and financial goals. While having your own business or working for yourself offers more flexibility, unlimited earning potential and tax benefits, it also carries financial instability, responsibility and potentially higher tax obligations.*
>
> *Traditional employment, on the other hand, offers financial stability, employee benefits and possibly reduced tax obligations, but comes with limited earning potential, less flexibility and limited control over job responsibilities and career growth.*

We made a conscious decision to not become employers. Whilst fully accepting that for some, the journey into independent working would be more attractive as an employee rather than a sub-contractor, we had both managed teams in the NHS for many years and were ready to relinquish that responsibility. We were also aware that there were independent practitioners who actively *didn't want* to return to employee status. It's all about finding the model which suits you – whether you are a business owner or a team member.

Why *do* some business owners opt to become employers?

We now turn to the company run by Sarah Buckley, the second of the two very different business models mentioned in the introduction to this chapter. Sarah is one of our specialist contributors. She runs her own independent company (Sarah Buckley Therapies Limited), providing speech and language therapy to mainstream nursery, primary and secondary schools in the Southeast. Unlike us, Sarah opted to *employ* rather than subcontract. Let's begin by sharing some of Sarah's story.

Sarah's story

Sarah is a Speech and Language Therapist who, in her own words, '*has been sitting proudly in the independent sector for nearly 20 years*'. She decided to set up in 2004 to '*do things differently and on reflection, to take control of my career and working life*'. Sarah continues, '*I managed a portfolio career for a while, combining a part time NHS role, working as a Visiting Clinical Tutor at City, University of London, and working as a sole trader in Southeast London*'.

> *In 2010 I decided to incorporate my own Limited Company. I had too much work coming in and there was an opportunity to grow a small business. There were also external familial drivers, which I understand are always a factor for individuals who set up in business. I was really fortunate to have been working with students at City, University for London for a fair amount of time, and in 2009-2010 I was working with a postgraduate final year student who lived really close by and was looking for their first opportunity. I decided to take them on a full-time employee. I incorporated my company in May 2010 and lined up work for my new starter for September.*

Why did Sarah choose to employ?

> *Reputation has been key in the growth of my business. I was well-known locally as a go-to provider of SLT services. When I incorporated I decided to put my own name as the company name to capitalise on reputation, build a brand and hold myself accountable for the quality of services, no matter who in my company was providing them. I also wanted a level of control and scrutiny over systems and processes and presenting these to an employee as business as usual meant that we were working in a similar way.*

Things went from strength to strength.

> *In January 2011, I recruited another new graduate from the same graduating cohort and then again in March 2011. This was a fairly rapid expansion! My new team and I continued to offer student placements and my model evolved to recruiting new graduates, supporting them through their NQP year, skill and experience building and supporting them to move on. The average retention of my team is 2–4 years, which feels fair in terms of my investment and support and the work that they do – although my first employee did stay with me for nine years in total. I now employ a team of 17 SLTs, not all of whom are full-time, alongside a SLTA and three part-time administrative staff.*

> In Chapter 12, we talk more about Sarah's experience of working with her local HEIs to offer student placements in an independent setting.

It is at this point that we have asked Sarah to talk us through the things to be considered when opting to become an employer.

There are two critical elements when thinking about employment. The first, the top down and my favourite is the *vision and values* of the organisation. What kind of work environment are you trying to craft and what underpins your beliefs about employing a team?

Vision and values is your opportunity to build an organisation that matches your own beliefs. In my team, I hero learning, development and professional growth. The majority of my team join as new graduates and stay with me for 2–4 years, so I aim to provide a secure and solid foundation to start their career as a speech and language therapist. Your experiences and learning in the first year can drive your journey. I also encourage diversity in my team and am a certified 'disability confident' employer which appeals to some potential new team members.

I don't use traditional performance appraisal. Instead, I use an approach to HR called Agile www.agilepeople.com [7]. This strategy uses incremental goal setting to reach larger overarching goals. Meetings are very regular, minimum monthly and can be very short. Short frequent meetings keep goals on track, allow adjustment, and give an opportunity for the employer and employee to share ideas and suggestions in both directions. As well as individual goals, we have company goals and all employees have the opportunity to contribute to company strategy and development during their time with SBT (Sarah Buckley Therapies).

As an employer, I think carefully about what is the SBT offer and why would a new graduate choose my company over another opportunity. I review this offer regularly and make sure that the benefits I offer stand out in the marketplace.

The second element is more *bottom-up* and takes a lot of research. This element is the *administration* involved in employment.

You can access a wide range of legal advice online from either the gov.uk website or from corporate service providers who provide a level of advice and guidance for free. If you are confident and have the time to do the research, the information is there. There are a lot of HR specialists and HR companies around that offer free introductory meetings, which can end up as a bit of a sales pitch, but this can give you a starting point for employment.

There is a minimum level of statutory documentation to get in place. For example, job description and person specification, employment contracts, staff handbook, health and safety policy etc. This list is not exhaustive and changes all the time as legislation changes.

I outsource my HR and health and safety to a company with some experience in health and social care. There are lots of them about. They provide a platform for administering contracts, allocating policies and procedures and statutory training for my team. There is a cost associated to this, but having costed up the amount of time it would take me personally to do the research and stay up-to-date with changes to legislation, I consider this a valuable spend. They also give me back-up as an employer should there ever be any dispute, which I'm very happy to say hasn't happened yet.

The important thing to remember with employment, as your organisation grows, is to cost up your time and work out the relative costs of outsourcing. It may seem cheaper in the short run to do your own research, but as your team grows, there will reach a tipping point where you are better off doing income-generating work rather than HR admin. For example, if I think about how long it would take me to administer monthly payroll, do the relevant calculations, submit to HMRC and generate transactions for all my employees, the cost of my time in hours is far greater than paying a payroll manager.

Having said all of this, employment is not necessarily an easy option. It requires a high level of thinking and investment of both time and money to get it right and over the years I have made some mistakes as well as had some great ideas. If employment is the route you are looking to take, do the research, speak to someone who has gone down this route (it doesn't need to be another SLT) and cost up the implications for your ongoing time commitment to the role.

Read more about Sarah's recruitment strategy in Chapter 12.
We leave the conclusion to this section to Sarah herself.

Alongside my clinical work, I'm also in the final stages of completing my Master's in Business Administration (MBA). This has provided structure, frameworks and theory to evolve my business and tipped me over from the SLT world to the business world. It has also helped me reflect on mistakes made and poor decisions and helped me to understand how and why things went wrong over time. I have ambitious plans ahead, particularly around expanding my SLTA workforce and the new apprenticeship degree. Onwards and upwards.

Portfolio careers

We first refer to this concept in Chapter 2.

... a way to define a career that has encompassed several related or unrelated jobs ... and a variety of job types.

https://www.flexjobs.com/blog/post/how-to-have-a-portfolio-career/ [8]

Done well, portfolio careers can be rewarding and extremely empowering. There are significant opportunities for deploying skills in different ways and in different roles. Our questionnaire respondents indicated that some had four or more successful strings to their bow. Here is a typical view from amongst the questionnaire respondents.

I'm very glad I worked in a variety of employment settings/types within my career. I gained a lot of experiences useful to my career. It has made me more philosophical and balanced in my responses when things aren't just-so in my role today.

Others have started modestly – usually continuing to work in the public sector and taking on some independent work. Kezia, Karis and Gillian are all good examples of this.

Kate's story

There were numerous examples of people using their skills in a more diverse range of roles, people like Kate.

This is Kate's story.

Becoming a Speech and Language Therapist happened almost by chance, but once I started to look into it, I was fascinated. Throughout the years, the more I have been involved in understanding and supporting children's speech language and communication development, the more fascinated I have become!

In the early days, post-qualification and outside of speech and language therapy, I had set up and was running a charity providing short breaks and holidays for disadvantaged children and those excluded from school.

My frustration with the NHS capacity and waiting times, and my enjoyment of the children's holiday work, soon meant that I changed direction. I took a fixed-term contract leading an out-of-school-childcare development initiative. I returned to the NHS when my fixed-term contract ended and I started work in a specialist primary speech and language resource, which I loved.

Whilst on maternity leave and sharing childcare with my teacher sister-in-law, an unexpected opportunity presented itself.

I answered an advert for a job-share role for a teacher and speech and language therapist, with children's communication charity I CAN (now Speech and Language UK). The Chief Executive's description of the organisation's 'can do' approach chimed with me and I started work as a part-time development advisor, supporting the development of specialist early years settings for children with significant SLCN, working from home (before it was a 'thing') and also travelling across a wide geographical area.

I stayed for nearly 20 years, working on exciting projects. Latterly, I became the Director of Development. Meanwhile, I also brought up three children and worked independently in schools, early years settings and family homes.

Lack of charity-sector funding finally led to redundancy and an opportunity to set up fully on my own. I wanted to increase my impact by focusing on the systems of support available in local areas and I used my skills and knowledge with organisations like Speech and Language Link, the Early Intervention Foundation and the Local Government Association.

Lockdown provided the opportunity to realise my long-held ambition to develop books for children at the very early stages of language development. I also trained as a Registered Intermediary, supporting the police and court to communicate with vulnerable witnesses.

I absolutely love what I am doing now, especially the chance to impact at a local authority level, plus working with a variety of different professionals. I aim to make a difference to children and families through what I do. My professional and personal experience is that many children don't fit the system that is meant to support them, with families fighting to ensure that individual needs are met. This is what gets me up in the morning.

https://www.routledge.com/Words-Together/book-series/WTOG

Not all portfolio careers are a happy balance undertaken through choice, however. With many years' experience in the profession, this is what one of the questionnaire respondents had to say.

> *I no longer have job satisfaction within the NHS. There is so much I could do to help children which the service priorities do not allow me to offer. Instead, I spend almost all my time doing things in a way I know, and research says, to be ineffective; and not in a way that services users, education partners and parents want either. Not only is everyone unhappy with the service they get, but I cannot disagree with them. It simply spreads the service too thinly, with the wrong person in the wrong place and at the wrong time.*
>
> *So I maintain a bank role for security of income and my work-life balance/mental health, and I now work as an associate of a private practice in order to do the work I was trained to do and offer an effective service to a small number of children, again for the sake of my work-life balance and mental health.*

This respondent has taken a pragmatic approach to keeping sane whilst, as she says, safeguarding her financial requirements.

> *I am simply looking forward to my retirement at 60, when I can top up my partial pension with more of the effective work, either within private practice or even outside of SLT altogether.*

We ignore, at our peril, stories like these.

One can only admire the resilience of this questionnaire respondent.

> *I think it's fine to hop around and try different areas, places to work and develop a range of skills. The NHS ground me down. Working in different sectors, where they're so much better at things like flexible working and looking after and developing and supporting their staff, has made such a difference to my career and work-life balance. I think SLTs should be encouraged to think outside of the traditional model of working and to not be afraid of dipping their toes into other waters. Be curious!*

In Chapter 12, we mention the 'Off-Payroll Working' rules, which require independent practitioners to evidence more than one source of income, otherwise they are deemed to be employed rather than self-employed, which has implications both for the contractor and the entity providing the work to the contractee.

Here are some real-life examples of individuals with portfolio careers, generating income from a variety of sources, which are becoming increasingly popular.

> I work in schools as a contractor for an independent limited company and also hold a small individual caseload. In addition, I am a fitness to practice partner for HCPC.

> I work with adults with acquired brain injuries. I am directly employed for a day a week by a chain of care homes, and also undertake medico-legal work for various solicitors' practices.

> I work part-time for the NHS, whilst also undertaking advocacy work for the Ministry of Justice and delivering a college contract for an independent company.

> I am directly employed by a private KS1 and 2 school for two days each week. I also provide supervision to other IPs and hold a small individual caseload. I do occasional work at the local HEI, teaching alongside permanent staff.

> I work with children and subcontract my services to several mainstream schools.
>
> I am Makaton tutor and also deliver training on other commercially available tools.

A 2021 national survey conducted by HCPC reported that speech and language therapists were the second largest group (with 55%, surpassed only by Art Therapists) reported as operating within *at least* two different work settings.

hcpc-diversity-data-report-2021.pdf (hcpc-uk.org) [9]

References

1. (2023a) *NHS Choices*. Available at: https://www.england.nhs.uk/gp/investment/gp-contract/.
2. (2022) *Standard Alternative Provider Medical Services Contract*. NHS England. Available at: https://www.england.nhs.uk/wp-content/uploads/2022/01/B1210_v_Alternative-Provider-Medical-Services-Contract_06012022.pdf.
3. *Lip Ome Prepub July2023 – The Joint Commission* (2023) www.jointcommission.org. Available at: https://www.jointcommission.org/-/media/tjc/documents/standards/prepublications/effective-2023/lip_ome_standard_prepub_july2023.pdf.
4. *What Is the Voluntary Sector?* (2021) Reach Volunteering. Available at: https://reachvolunteering.org.uk/guide/what-voluntary-sector.
5. *The Feeding Trust*. Available at: https://www.feedingtrust.org/.
6. *Muras Baker Jones Accountants Wolverhampton*. Available at: https://muras.co.uk/.
7. *Agile People*. Available at: https://agilepeople.com/.
8. Flexjobs. (2022) *Portfolio Career: Definition, Pros & Cons, and Getting Started*. FlexJobs, Flexjobs Job Search Tips and Blog. Available at: https://www.flexjobs.com/blog/post/how-to-have-a-portfolio-career/.
9. *Diversity Data Report 2021 Health & Care Professions Council*. Available at: https://www.hcpc-uk.org/resources/reports/2021/diversity-data-report-2021/.

6 The toolbox essentials

In this chapter, we will introduce the **systems, procedures** and **processes** (SPPs) we consider essential to run our business effectively.

These are the essential items in our business toolbox. We will also talk about essentials for a clinical toolbox, and both will be revisited in greater detail in later chapters.

We start with the business aspects.

A strange new feeling

The initial (and obvious) question to ask is why are systems, procedures and processes (SPPs) necessary at all? At the simplest level of any market, an individual sells goods or services to another individual in exchange for money which s/he then uses to acquire goods and services. This is the model used very successfully by many single-handed independent practitioners.

When we began working for ourselves, the feeling of liberation was immediate and powerful. There *were* no 'must-dos' – in fact, the focus was entirely on making a living: as long as we met professional standards, any arrangements and agreements were informal – we didn't quite hold a finger to the wind to inform our decision-making, but it was pretty close!

Don't throw the baby out with the bathwater

From the outset, we were definitely inclined towards a minimalist approach – largely as a result of the heavy bureaucratic load we had experienced in the NHS. The seemingly endless gathering of information, compiling of dashboards, the monthly/quarterly/annual reporting across a range of activity and behaviour – much of the reporting was related to governance,

> KPIs: a set of quantifiable measurements used to gauge a company's overall long-term performance.

DOI: 10.4324/9781003382928-6

key performance indicators (KPIs) and budgets etc. Human Resources data was also required, including information about mandatory training, supervision and appraisals.

Instinctively we felt we wanted to dispense with much of this – but not so fast! It was important to hold onto the useful and essential elements whilst dispensing with the rest.

The whole point of having systems in place is to *minimise risk*.

Understanding risk

Let's take a moment to think about what we mean by risk

> *Risk [n]: a situation involving exposure to danger; the possibility that something unpleasant will happen*

> *Risk [v]: expose to danger or loss*

Some risks are clear and obvious, such as leaving a naked flame unattended or not wearing a seatbelt. Others are less obvious and the impact not so immediate. It's important to understand the different types of risks your business may face so you can recognise and plan ahead for them.

This holds good for each and every structural model described in Chapter 5.

Once again, we were able to draw upon the skills and experiences from our NHS days.

Here is a simple cyclical model which has four stages. It's a good idea to use some kind of template to record what you are doing. This provides an audit trail, i.e. helps you keep an eye on things and make changes as required (go to Chapter 10 for an example). It is part of your governance system.

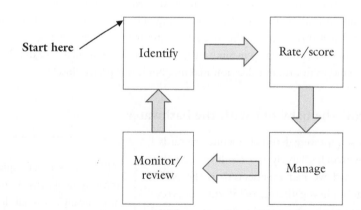

What risks are pertinent to your business? Examples would include:

- Financial risks such as losing market share
- Reputational risks such as sub-contracting work to others who don't share your ethos or work ethic

There will also be risks around security and data protection. The Data Protection Act (2018) [1] has necessitated a much more rigorous approach – and the importance of being able to evidence that rigour.

If you are sub-contracting to (or employing) therapists, not having enough people to deliver the work you have agreed to take on is a significant risk.

As a sole trader, becoming ill and unable to work also poses a risk. In Chapter 8, we talk about insurance (one of the ways you might choose to manage the risk as a sole trader).

Some risks will carry a greater impact than others. How will you know that? It's a good plan to use some kind of risk rating system. This helps you to keep an eye on whether your management strategies are actually doing what you need them to do. Here is a couple of examples.

More about risk rating in Chapter 10

Having identified, scored and managed the risks, revisit your risk register at least once a year – and as often as you need to if new risks crop up or some kind of adverse incident actually takes place or almost takes place (a near miss).

It's impossible to eliminate risk entirely. The trick is to put in place systems and processes to *reduce the impact* of the risk. Here is an obvious example which relates to data security.

Paper records are used by the therapist working in a particular setting. Transporting records carries a risk, as does sharing a cabinet with school staff. The solution is to provide a lockable filing cabinet and identify and limit the key-holders.

Risk versus incident

Incident [n]: an event or occurrence; an instance of something happening i.e. the identified risk actually coming to fruition

Near miss [n]: an incident where, under slightly different circumstances harm would have been caused

It's important to learn from near misses. In Chapter 15, we talk about 'trouble-shooting' and include several real-life examples of where an incident or a near miss (perhaps an occurrence which we might have not even considered), *becomes* a risk which we need to put on the risk register and manage, to make sure the likelihood of it ever happening again is reduced as far as realistically possible.

How do risk and toolbox essentials fit together?

The toolbox essentials are all about managing the risks your business faces. They provide structure, a sense of direction and valuable information – not only for you and your team but also for your customers.

It's worth mentioning here that the majority of our client base is in the public sector (education). Schools and settings are governed by similar processes and procedures as other public sector bodies (such as the NHS). In the same way as therapists try, wherever possible, to adopt the language and terminology used in schools, understanding their structures, processes and procedures (SPPs) helps us in a number of ways. Examples include being asked to provide accessible data security information and evidence of safeguarding compliance and verifying our banking details in advance of being added to schools' finance systems or generating purchase order numbers (PONs).

   Our business toolbox essentials fall into six broad groups

1.   The day-to-day running of the company
2.   Finance
3.   Contracting
4.   Governance
5.   Technology
6.   The team

Help to establish your brand by using your logo on any outward-facing paperwork (contracts, invoices, quotes, information about your offer etc.).

The groups are interrelated and interdependent. It doesn't matter if you make a decision to site an SPP under one heading rather than another – what *does* matter is that everything gets covered somewhere.

This is a good moment to revisit earlier advice: *it's important to understand the different types of risks your business may face so you can recognise and plan ahead for them.*

Only include what you need for *your* business structure: a single-handed independent practitioner, for example, is likely to have fewer requirements than a company employing a team of therapists.

- What is your business model?
- What will you actually be *doing*?
- What are the risks associated with your activity?
- How will you manage those risks (i.e. what SPPs do you need to have in place)?

We will now look at each of those six broad groups in turn.

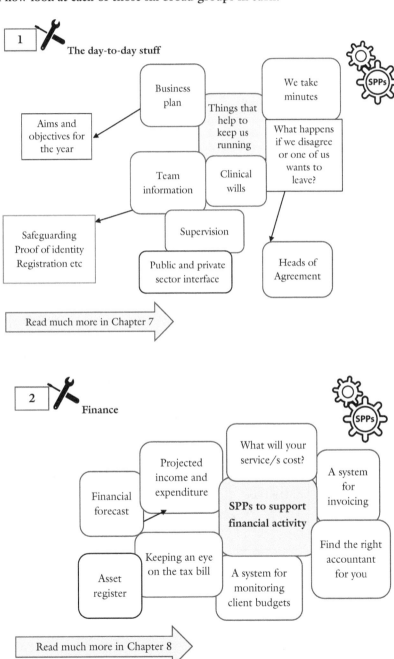

1 The day-to-day stuff

Business plan

We take minutes

SPPs

Aims and objectives for the year

Things that help to keep us running

What happens if we disagree or one of us wants to leave?

Team information

Clinical wills

Safeguarding Proof of identity Registration etc

Supervision

Public and private sector interface

Heads of Agreement

Read much more in Chapter 7

2 Finance

SPPs

Projected income and expenditure

What will your service/s cost?

A system for invoicing

Financial forecast

SPPs to support financial activity

Find the right accountant for you

Asset register

Keeping an eye on the tax bill

A system for monitoring client budgets

Read much more in Chapter 8

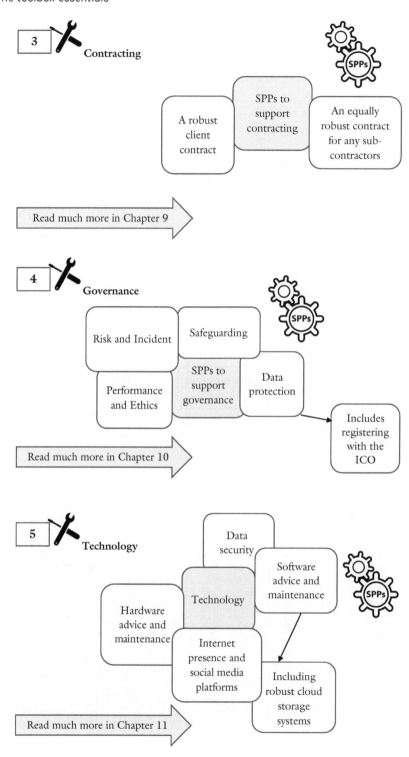

3   Contracting

A robust client contract

SPPs to support contracting

An equally robust contract for any sub-contractors

SPPs

Read much more in Chapter 9

4   Governance

Risk and Incident

Safeguarding

Performance and Ethics

SPPs to support governance

Data protection

SPPs

Includes registering with the ICO

Read much more in Chapter 10

5   Technology

Data security

Software advice and maintenance

Hardware advice and maintenance

Technology

Internet presence and social media platforms

Including robust cloud storage systems

SPPs

Read much more in Chapter 11

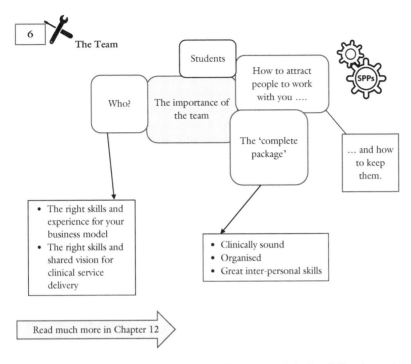

We conclude this chapter by identifying the toolbox essentials for delivering a high-quality, effective clinical service.

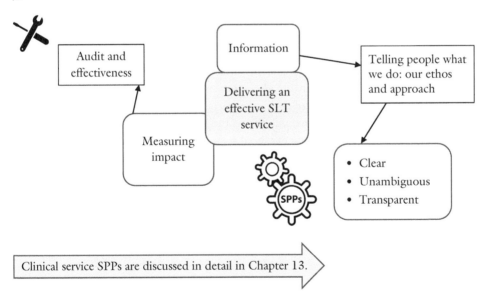

References

1. GD Service. (2015) *Data Protection*. GOV.UK. Available at: https://www.gov.uk/data-protection.

7 The everyday stuff

In this chapter, we pull together the structures, processes and procedures (SPPs) which don't fit naturally together in any of the other toolboxes. Some are seemingly mundane systems which help to keep the show on the road. Others are important points to keep in mind. It's surprising how easily things can get forgotten or memories of a meeting and what has been agreed become hazy – particularly as clients become more numerous.

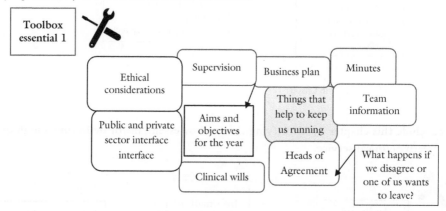

In Chapter 6, we talked about the toolbox essentials being all about managing risk. Any and all of the processes we will discuss here are also about managing and minimising risk. Use SPPs which support what you *do* and *need to do* in terms of **your** business model. Here, we will go through the systems we have in place and discuss the reasons why we find they are invaluable. You may not need all of these – or you may need some different ones.

Business plan

A 'business plan' sounds very grand and some readers might be thinking …

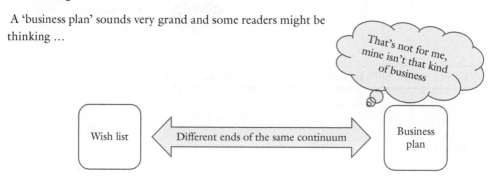

DOI: 10.4324/9781003382928-7

Never lose sight of your dreams – whether you are a sole trader or running a company, aspirations are one pretty good reason for putting together a business plan. 'This year I/we am/are focussing on … so that next year I/we will be able to …'. A business plan reminds you where you want to be and keeps you on track … and helps avoid the dangers of *Mission Creep*.

> *the gradual addition of new tasks or activities to a project so that the original purpose or idea begins to be lost*

This is particularly important in business, where a piece of work is agreed upon and a quote provided. Any and all activity outside of that which has been costed will mean *a reduction in profit*.

So what does a business plan look like and what should it include?

- **Overall aims:**
  - Over-arching statements
  - Don't have too many
  - Some may be new
  - Some may be rolled over from the previous year
- Targets (the specifics under the aims)
  Group your targets under headings relevant to you. Remember, if it doesn't protect (or increase) your profit margin or manage risk (either now or further down the line), don't do it.
- **Half-year review date**
  Summarise activity towards your targets to check you are making progress.
- **RAG rating (red, amber, green)**
- **End of year review date**

Record the evidence towards your targets (wholly, partially or not at all). Circumstances might be out of your control in which case you either need to take radical action – or abandon the target which it's *okay to* do.

Changing tack is, in itself, a learning experience. Next time round it helps you to be even more objective. And when you think you might be having the same idea again, you can look back to see what you have already tried …

Was that activity really necessary?

If yes, how are you going to make it work?

If no, why are you doing it?

Year X business plan (beginning of financial year → end of financial year)

Overall Aim/s	*Review date (halfway through financial year)*	*RAG*	*Review date (end of financial year)*	*RAG*
1.		red		
2.		amber		
3.		green		
Targets				
1. **Market share**				
2. **Financial**				
3. **Workforce**				
4. **Assets**				
5. **Governance**				
6. **Marketing**				

As demand increases, marketing targets will fall away. Don't do what you don't need to do!

Clinical wills

A clinical (sometimes called a therapeutic) will is a document which details what would happen to your business in the event of an 'unplanned' (unforeseen) circumstance such as accident, illness or death. The implications will differ according to your business model, but it is good practice to write a clinical will whatever your circumstances.

The document should include a named person (or people) who would be able to access your premises (if you have them) or your business files, client base and clinical caseload. The reason for this is so that your business can be either suspended or closed; clients informed and all records can be secured and managed appropriately, and retained in archive as per the prescribed period of time.

The named person is the executor of your clinical will and your intentions should be discussed with this person in advance and they should be made aware of your processes and procedures and where to look for key information.

Consider what that person would need in order to be able to access. For example, keys, usernames and passwords. Think about how and where passwords will be stored and who will know where to access them. Read more about password security in Chapter 11.

Keep your information (including and especially client lists and contact details) as up-to-date as possible.

Your personal will should contain reference to your business and to the executor of your clinical will.

The clinical will includes:

- An introduction (purpose of the document)
- Full details of the executor/s
- Full details of your next of kin
- Full details of the executor/s of your personal will

- The circumstances in which this will should be activated
- Directions as to what needs to be done in the event that you are (either temporarily or permanently) not able to continue
- Directions as to where to locate the necessary access requirements

Templates and examples are available online.

Heads of agreement (HoA)

Sharing the workload and decision-making with a trusted partner or co-director is an absolute blessing. However (depending on your business model), it's wise to build in what steps you (and your partner/s or co-directors) will take should your business relationship come to an end for whatever reason. This is essentially practical. Will one or more of the parties leave and other/s remain? How will residual profits be divided? Will the business be dissolved? Will it be sold? If there is a sale, who is eligible to purchase the shares of those who are exiting? To agree to these things at the outset can offset difficulties further down the line when events may have overtaken the reliability of the relationship or the people in it.

Heads of agreement (sometimes called heads of terms) are a document setting out the main terms of a commercial agreement reached between parties in a transaction. Heads of terms can also be known as a letter of intent or memoranda of understanding.

Following the parties' initial negotiations, heads of terms are prepared to set out the agreed basic terms of a contract or commercial lease before the finer details are negotiated.

It's a good idea to revisit the HoA every couple of years or so – just to make sure they are still current.

Although heads of terms are usually not legally binding, the document records the future intentions of parties wishing to take part in a transaction but does not enforce obligations on them.

Minutes

Making and taking notes may be something we feel we could do without – particularly at the beginning when everything is new and fresh and very much at the forefront of our minds.

A word to the wise!

Much of this will depend on your business model and the type of work you do. However, over time, especially if you expand and/or other people join you, you *just won't* be able to keep all the information in your head! We keep two kinds of notes.

i) Business-based

ii) Client-based (client = customer here)

> Taking minutes in support of running your business

> For example
> • On initial contact
> • Contract review

Record enough information to act as an aide-memoire and to ensure you complete actions

• Date your minutes and store the back numbers (there is a legal requirement to keep them for 10 years) [1]
• Delete things as they are actioned/over/become part of the routine

What does the client want?

Are you sending any information – if so what?

Over time, you may record:

• Progress against objectives agreed with the client (e.g. school contracts, where case notes are not used)
• Training delivered
• Feedback from associates if you have them

Team information

Whether you employ or sub-contract, you will need to collect and retain certain information about the therapists who deliver contracts on your behalf.

Seek advice as to what you need to collect as an employer. In terms of sub-contractors, we collect the following information, which we store in line with GDPR legislation.

• Full name (as registered with HCPC)
• Address
• Mobile phone number
• e-mail address
• Next of kin details
• CV
• References
• HCPC registration
• RCSLT registration
• DBS details
• ICO registration number
• Date of safeguarding training
• Nature of business model (associate or self-employed)

What's the difference between an associate and a self-employed therapist and is it important?

An associate is a self-employed speech and language therapist (SLT) operating as a limited company. He/she operates as a fully qualified, autonomous practitioner without supervision, direction or control.

A self-employed speech and language therapist (SLT) is a fully qualified, autonomous independent practitioner operating without supervision, direction or control.

See Chapters 5 and 12.

For the purposes of safeguarding, we provide the following assurances for our schools and settings:

Therapist				
DBS number		Date of issue	HCPC registration	

Check	Here are examples of evidence we collect	Date
Identity check	Passport	
Proof of address	Utility bill/bank statement	
Enhanced DBS check	Number and issue date recorded	
Professional qualifications check	Checked via HCPC registrations website	
GDPR compliance	1. Data processing agreement signed 2. Security arrangements checked 3. Soundswell data protection and privacy policy read	

Check carried out by:	*(name)*
Date	*(Signature)*
Role: (Director Soundswell Ltd)	*(Signature)*

It's also good practice to keep a record of safeguarding training undertaken, including dates of refreshers, so that we're reminded when this is due.

Supervision

Supervision is a formal arrangement whereby a speech and language therapist (SLT) discusses their work regularly with someone who is experienced and qualified.

It is not only an essential component of a good quality service and able to identify and manage risk, but also part of the professional registration requirements for HCPC. Each profession will have its own requirements, and whilst for some, it is not mandatory, it is associated with the development of professional skills and competence, management of stress, effectiveness of care and patient safety.

RCSLT identifies two types of supervision and recommends that both are in place for SLTs. These are managerial and professional supervision.

https://www.rcslt.org/speech-and-language-therapy/guidance-for-delivering-slt-services/what-is-supervision/ [2]

The first is an opportunity to discuss service-related and wider professional issues. It can be provided by someone from a different professional background.

Professional supervision is provided by someone from the same profession and allows the supervisee to raise clinical and professional issues in a non-judgemental environment.

Both of the above should be part and parcel of working life, and it is entirely legitimate to ask for evidence of this when working with colleagues in either the public or private sectors.

Some IPs engage the services of a business adviser or business coach. This is a useful approach when looking to establish or expand a business and arguably could contribute to managerial supervision, it is not a substitute for following professional guidelines in terms of supervision requirements.

Public and private sector interface and why it's important

It's important because we all need to be aware of and understand what is meant by 'conflict of interest'.

> The personal interests (family, friendships, financial or social factors) of an individual could compromise his or her judgment, decisions or actions in the workplace.

a) *Individuals* who choose to access private healthcare

When we started our independent practice some 12 years ago now, we did come across occasional misperceptions where some settings (and NHS staff too) were unclear as to how receiving additional help from non-public sector therapists would affect access to NHS involvement.

The Department of Health and Social Care has published guidance for NHS patients who pay for additional private care on GOV.UK [3]. This document was last reviewed in 2022. At the time of writing, things are much more transparent. Whilst examples given are very much in the medical model, it is explicitly stated that 'You're still entitled to free NHS care if you choose to pay for additional private care'.

In our experience, 'on the ground', there are emerging examples of good practice. During the course of writing this book, a number of therapists have shared their experiences of how the NHS and independent therapists not only keep each other informed, but actively work to provide seamless support.

Our advice to schools and settings is **not** to stop making referrals to the NHS service. Should circumstances change and the independent provider is no longer in the picture for whatever reason, there needs to be access to some support. At the very least, commissioners need to be aware of the unmet need.

b) *Staff* who opt to work in both the public and private sectors

Considering speech and language therapists here, there are lots of people who work across both public and private sectors. Some do this on a regular and permanent basis, others dip their toe in the water with a view to possibly making the move into independent practice. Whatever the pattern, in order to not compromise your professionalism, it's important to be aware of what is a potential conflict of interest.

If you plan to work for the NHS and also independently, this should be declared. Although we were unable to find any specific reference, some NHS trusts will not allow you to work independently in the same geographical area that is covered by the trust. The sensible thing to do is to check your public sector contract carefully as this is what has been agreed to and signed.

We revisit this again in Chapter 16.

It is not appropriate to 'tout for business', i.e. discuss the fact that you do private work, with any client you are treating via your NHS role. Also, you must not directly recommend an independent provider but can signpost an NHS client to where and how they can find out about private services for themselves.

Ethical considerations

Gaining consent in paediatrics is relatively straightforward. With some adult clients referred by their families, it can be less clear. Here are some real-life examples of potentially tricky situations.

Beware the enthusiastic relative and the less enthusiastic (or able) client. Naomi, whose story appears in Chapter 2, shares her experience.

> *I am very mindful when it isn't the right time – I am mindful of the outcomes.*

The first case is of a client whose family were concerned that her language functions were, somehow, different, but there was no clear neurological diagnosis. The client was on a long NHS waiting list. It had been very hard for this lady to admit that anything was wrong, but she consented to being seen. The conclusion in the therapist's report was that the client needed to be referred for a neurology assessment and also to a memory clinic. The client read her report and although initially seemed accepting, after having had time to process the contents properly, she became upset and refused any onward referral, despite the concerns of the family.

> *It was a really uncomfortable situation. This lady was at a relatively early stage of her developing illness and, in the same way that it had taken her a while to accept assessment, having seen the result of that assessment, she wasn't ready to take things any further. It makes one wonder whether if fast/er tracking to a memory clinic were the norm, acceptance and the access to earlier help and other specialists that would bring, would have resulted in a different outcome.*

The specialist intervention that the therapist provides is only part of the picture. The ongoing intervening practice and exercise delivered by a supportive family are crucial.

In the second case, a youngish male stroke victim was so severely disabled that he needed nursing home care after his stroke. Following referral from his daughter, Naomi had completed a course of treatment and then passed the client on to his local NHS team. When this NHS intervention had been completed his daughter contacted Naomi again requesting further help.

The daughter's understanding of the severity of his needs and prognosis was unrealistic and the request had to be declined.

References

1. Participation, E. Companies Act 2006. Legislation.gov.uk. Available at: https://www.legislation.gov .uk/ukpga/2006/46/part/10/chapter/9/crossheading/records-of-meetings-of-directors.
2. *What Is Supervision?* (2021) RCSLT. Available at: https://www.rcslt.org/speech-and-language-therapy /guidance-for-delivering-slt-services/what-is-supervision/.
3. Department of Health and Social Care. (2009) *NHS Patients Who Wish to Pay for Additional Private Care*. GOV.UK. Available at: https://www.gov.uk/government/publications/nhs-patients-who-wish -to-pay-for-additional-private-care.

8 Let's talk about money

The focus of this chapter is finance and all that involves. We have done our best to include the things which apply to *every* business model. However, the examples and tables we use are our own and relate to *our* business model. There will be software packages which can manage certain aspects of your business. We make no reference to them in this chapter as things can quickly become out of date and superseded by new developments. The key point is that no matter what systems you might decide to use, they need to cover the toolbox essentials below.

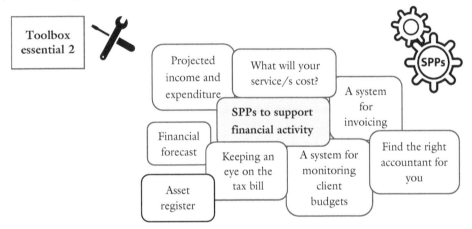

For many people, the financial aspects of being an independent practitioner are the most off-putting. For some, it's the challenge of knowing what to charge, for others it's the feelings of embarrassment that raising the subject of money engender.

There is often anxiety around understanding national insurance contributions and preparing one's own tax return – both personal and for the business.

A common theme emerging from conversations and personal stories.

In this brave new world, business skills are as equally important as professional skills and talent. To build a successful and sustainable business, we need to understand why that is.

DOI: 10.4324/9781003382928-8

> Interestingly, one director of a private company employing a number of therapists told us that now, when asked 'what she does', she no longer refers to herself as a speech and language therapist. She says: '*I run a small business*'.

Taking a post-graduate qualification in business is becoming popular, as is employing the services of a 'business coach'.

Becoming a business owner can change the way you view yourself. This is quite important if you are going to make the business side of things work well. Increasingly, we have spoken to individuals who felt overwhelmed by 'all the things you have to know and do'. One independent practitioner described it as 'death by subscriptions: accountant fees, ICO, all the other things, admin stuff and business stuff. I am 18 months in and I wish people had told me!' Another said, 'it took me about five years to get on top of the finances'. Even allowing for a degree of poetic licence, this is less than ideal.

There seems to be a real sense from some of the people we talked to that they were operating entirely in the 'here and now'.

Some struggled to answer basic questions about:

- What do I earn versus what it costs me to run my business?
- What's the % difference and is it enough to live on?
- Am I busier than I was this time last year?
- Am I earning the same (or less? or more?)?

> As long as I can put food on the table I'm doing OK.

> This employer, a psychologist, (let's call her Sally) realised that, on a regular basis, she was having to redo reports from one of her team as they weren't up to scratch. The quote for services given to the client obviously didn't include costing for the reports to be written twice!

> I seem to work all the hours God sends, I should be earning a fortune

> Sally had normalised this cycle of events and found herself making excuses for the employee (a friend who she had taken into the business) as she was 'really good at' other aspects of the work.

In Chapter 12, we talk in detail about the three skills and attributes that make the best employee or associate and how all three are of equal importance in the world of independent practice.

Being in control will reduce anxiety and stress

Any aspect of life where we don't feel that things are working as well as they should will create stress. Finding out what you need to know and do as an independent practitioner will put you back in control.

Financial toolbox essentials range from accountancy to tax, via budgeting, financial projections, invoicing, pricing and profit margins and preparing for the end of the year.

Finding it difficult to talk about money

There are (probably unsurprisingly) a number of blogs and articles associated with our inherent inability to feel comfortable talking about money. For many people, the financial aspects are a 'real issue' but they are crucial. Sarah Buckley (Practice Manager and ASLTIP Chair, with her business head on) is very familiar with the issue and her advice is succinct.

> *We need to understand that we are providing a paid healthcare service. Understand what you're selling and look professionally competent. If we take the speech and language therapy (i.e. the emotional component) out of the equation, we can be much more logical and objective'. When setting your fees, you need to bear in mind your overheads and factor in a margin for holiday, sickness and any benefits you may need. You need to set your fees to reflect your own level of skill and experience.*

The information below comes from an unlikely source for us in terms of business, but has sound common sense which applies in the widest sense.

In May 2022, writers Caroline Bloor and Joanne Finley said: '*finances are a sensitive subject for many of us. But if you can learn to be open, it will have a positive impact on your life*'.

https://www.goodhousekeeping.com/uk/consumer-advice/money/a28897308/how-to-talk-about-money-taboo/ [1]

Oh, how true!

These authors talk about the subject from the point of view of household and personal spending, but the big points they make are eminently transferable to us as (almost complete) novices in largely unchartered territory.

Based on some of the points they make, we have added examples from our own experience to illustrate how moving forward to be comfortable talking about money doesn't have to be difficult.

Here are some things to think about.

1. **Be open and transparent.** Know what to expect in terms of income and outgoings.

> Make a financial projection: look at income versus expenditure (including pay and non-pay)

2. Make it part of the routine to talk about money

Look at your finances on a regular basis so you can keep tabs on cash flow and check the actual picture against your budget projections.

3. Plan ahead to avoid a financial ambush

Alert your business partner/s to plans you might have to make a substantial spend. If you're a sole trader/single-handed, at least run your ideas past someone else. Anything significant should be in your business plan – but we all get seized by moments of madness from time to time...

More about business planning in Chapter 7.

4. Choose your confidantes carefully

For all sorts of reasons, it makes good business sense to keep financial information close to your chest, but there are times when it is good to share. Some of the practitioners we spoke to said they wished their 'competitors' would agree to share their fee structure – indeed some do have this on the company website. Would this work for you? What would be the pitfalls and benefits? The service you provide is not *just* about cost and a little later in this chapter we look at this in a little bit more detail.

5. Ask for help if you need it!

If you don't understand something, don't wait! Ask someone who does. This applies to any aspect but as we know it's hard enough to talk about money – let alone tax matters, off-payroll working (IR35) and what you can/cannot draw from your business.

There are lots of things you can get some idea of from using the internet, but it is no substitute for a conversation with a professional.

A good accountant is worth their weight in gold. Later in this chapter our specialist contributor Jenny Marks will outline what you can expect from an accountant.

It's crucial that practitioners get themselves to a place where they are comfortable and confident to talk about money.

'*We need to be realistic when costing the services we provide*', says Jo who runs a successful independent practice in Birmingham. She works clinically with adult patients who have been subject to medical negligence. It is a rarified and highly specialist role. Her clinical work has brought her into contact with different teams of people and she has learnt from the way they view the value of the work they undertake.

> *I am vetted by the case management team and almost all my work now is in the arena of case-managed litigation. Part of my role is to design and cost an individual client plan with a lifespan of six months. My working environment involves as many different teams as there are clients – each with different personalities and idiosyncrasies. It can be challenging but at the same time it's dynamic. These teams understand what it's like to work at this level and accordingly they know what it costs.*

Now we are comfortable talking about money

As we work through our financial toolbox essentials, bear in mind that business models differ and some of the things *we* deem to be essential to keep us on the right track may not be necessary for every business.

Financial forecast

This is sometimes called a financial projection – although there are discrete differences between a projection and a forecast. A projection is usually longer term and makes assumptions based on the status quo. A forecast includes more immediate predictions, based on known values.

For our purposes here, what we mean is a document which identifies the expected income and expenditure for any given year (i.e. a forecast). We work in academic years because the nature of our business is in schools and settings that run on a termly basis. Other people may work to their financial year or to the tax year.

The document doesn't need to be complicated.

We list the contracts and their value which have been agreed upon with the schools. Each setting has their budget broken down in terms of the number of regular days it will purchase over the agreed period (almost always a year). Where a contract is for a term only, for example, this is noted. Sometimes we add the words '+ *ad hoc days*', when a school indicates, if finances allow, they may want to buy in a few extra days as the year progresses.

Chapter 9 will tell you more about notice periods.

There are good reasons for agreeing to a shorter contract with a setting (or an associate). For example, where the client is new and 'untried' and you are not entirely sure that you will fit well together, we commit to a school term initially so that either side has an escape route. This is infinitely better than entering into a relationship which founders and having to give notice.

Go to Chapter 14 to see more detail about establishing objectives for a small commission.

Where there are, for example, 'performance issues' or niggles with how a school is engaging with the service, set some objectives and measure them termly. If things are not improving, it's much easier to just not renew the contract than to have to give – and work through – a notice period.

Pricing and profit margins: how to work out what to charge and what to pay any associates

Before working on this aspect, the **daily rate** the client will pay for your services needs to be identified.

Daily = session/hour/block/any configuration or time scale appropriate to your delivery model.

How to decide the daily rate

This is entirely up to the individual service provider but will obviously be influenced by current market forces. If services are scarce there is the potential to charge more and vice versa. If client resources are scarce, as they were in early 2018 and then a year or so later, when two swingeing budget cuts were made by Birmingham City Council (where the majority of our work was at the time), raising prices will mean clients are highly likely to commission less.

A sensible starting point might be to think about how much you *need* to earn (perhaps think about the salary you could earn if you were employed) and work back from that to what you charge the client and pay the associates.

Whilst it's always useful to have some idea what other providers charge for their services, in our experience, however, this information isn't easy to come by. Many independent providers we know have taken careful note of point 4 mentioned earlier (choose your confidantes carefully)!

During the course of researching this book, we found that views tended to polarise into two distinct camps:

1. Those who *wanted* to know what other people charge for their services (so they could charge similarly)
2. Those who were clearly comfortable about their own fees and never raised the subject at all

Clearly no consensus there then!

However, by aiming to find out what competitors charge and adopting a similar charge yourself, you aren't necessarily taking into account the rounded view of what you offer. Although cost is an important aspect, a service is much more than price. Other factors include for example the time you spend, the quality of what you provide and the outcomes of your intervention.

> Chapter 13 talks about what your offer will be and how to explain this to clients.

A more robust (and transparent) way of working towards your daily rate is to be clear about what you are offering for the fee you intend to charge, what is included and what is not included (for example, what constitutes a session, how long is a day?), in tandem with what *you* need to earn from your business (so knowing your personal financial situation is important).

> This is covered in Chapter 9 (contracts)

Where services are delivered by others, whether directly employed or sub-contracted, what will therapists be paid? Bear in mind that if more income is available elsewhere and requirements are broadly commensurate, team loyalty can never be guaranteed. It's worth considering what other factors influence team stability. For example, flexibility, support, access to training and resources and a strong team ethos help people to feel valued and committed. Loyalty is certainly not all about money.

Planning cautiously (but realistically) can leave some room for manoeuvre.

> Go to Chapter 12 to find out more about valuing your team

Making the financial forecast

> When to start?

As you are negotiating contract renewals and as new business is confirmed.

Here is a simple table to sketch out a financial forecast.

Table 8.1 Financial forecast: the big picture

Financial Forecast (from … to …) for us this is the academic year

A	B	C	D	E	F	G
Name of setting/ client	**Value** *(Total budget the client has allocated for your service)*	**Number of regular days** *(Column B divided by the daily rate charged to the client)*	**Associate/s** *(If SLTs are paid at different rates it will affect column E)*	**Cost of sales** (This is what you will pay someone to deliver the contract. Column C X by your daily associate rate)	**Total profit on contract** (B minus E value of contract minus cost of sales)	**Notes** *(e.g training: our forecast doesn't show any additional sales such as training as this is unknown at the forecast stage)*
Example: (daily/sessional rate = £100)						
Daisy Daycare	£1,000	10days/sessions	£80	£800	£200	

Other useful information you might include

Add more rows as commissions are confirmed

Now it's time to establish your budget in greater detail. There will be other costs which do not appear on your financial forecast.

Table 8.2 Financial forecast: the detail

Income			Running total
1	Total	*(from Table 8.1 column B)*	**£**
Expenditure			
2	Cost of sales	*(from Table 8.1 column E)*	*(total income minus cost of sales)*
3	Director's/owner's income	*(what you will pay yourself)*	*(as above minus director/owner pay)*
N.B	A limited company gets tax relief for Directors' pay. A business which is not a limited company does not (the tax is calculated before the owner/s' pay is deducted).		
4	Other costs	*(all expenditure not directly related to Table 8.1 column E)*	*(as above minus total of other costs)*
5	Tax @ X	*(the percentage varies according to the profit the business makes)**	*(as above multiplied by tax % requirement)*
6	Profit	*(from Table 8.1 column F minus the tax figure)*	**Ask your accountant**

*When identifying the tax you might pay, it's better to over rather than underestimate. If this isn't your first year of trading, last year's accounts will give you a guide.

> The contracts we have with our settings and SLTs always identify the date when renewal discussions will start. We need to know if we will be recommissioned. Therapists need to confirm their own income requirements. We start to renew at the latest at the start of the term known as Summer 1 (after the Easter holiday) in the academic year. Go to Chapter 9 to find out more about contracts.

Working out non-pay requirements: List all the items you will need to pay for. Here are some examples – don't forget to include everything. There may be dividends and 'trivial' benefits depending on your business model. To find out if this applies to you, ask your accountant and/or consult the various fact sheets available from HMRC. You may have rent and service charges for premises.

Administrative expenses (i.e. non-pay)		
Item	*£* (budgeted sum)	*Notes* (or to compare year on year)
Bank charges		Always check whether there is any room for negotiation. Many banks have offers for new businesses.
Stationery		Think about what you really need as more and more notes and records are now held electronically.
Resources		For us this is primarily the expensive assessment materials, some therapy materials and textbooks/ journals.
IT		Check what your contract includes. Ours is a monthly fee, plus a charge for any remote assistance which can't be fixed quickly. Find out much more about what to expect from an IT provider in Chapter 11.
Subsistence		Drinks and snacks out on the road.

Hospitality		We take colleagues out to lunch or meet in a local pub or café for a drink as necessary.
CPD		A bi-annual event for our team (read more on valuing the staff team in Chapter 12).
Storage unit		We rent a storage unit for equipment and marketing materials.
ICO		Mandatory annual registration fee for the business.
Shredding and archiving		You will potentially need this service. We store our archives electronically (including clinical records). However, we pay for collection and shredding of the redundant paper files. We also pay an archivist.
Postage		
Accountancy fees		This may include charges such as registered office fees (if you wish to use your accountant's address as the registered address for your business) and Companies House registration fees – ask your accountant what is included and whether there is anything *not* included that you will need to pay for separately.
Marketing		Our budgeted sum for this has all but disappeared as (at the time of writing) there is more business out there than we can take up. Don't spend money on advertising (including shows and exhibitions) unless there is an obvious financial advantage in doing so.
Other professional fees		Depending on your business model and circumstances, there may be other professional fees (legal fees for example).
Phones		Search for deals which might be available.
Video communications platform		We started using this during COVID-19 and now use it daily. Again, check what your IT package includes (see Chapter 11).
Travel		Mileage, parking, tolls or public transport costs.
Petty cash		
Total		

Will the books balance?

Line 6 in Table 8.1 *must* show a profit and preferably a healthy profit. A 'healthy' profit allows us as directors of a limited company to draw a dividend – but the same holds true whatever your business model. Money in reserve allows the business owner to draw a salary/dividend/bonus.

A reserve will safeguard the business from cashflow problems if payments are slow or there are bad debts. We pay our team at the end of each month, regardless of whether the client has settled their invoice with us. We aim to build up reserves to survive for at least two months with the usual outgoings and no income, as well as having set aside the money to pay the antici-pated tax for those months. As already mentioned, the tax payable will depend on your business model and how much you earn. Your accountant will advise you about your specific circum-stances. However, if, like us, you are operating as a limited company, (at the time of writing) the corporation tax payable is between 19% and 25%. So this is, in theory, the amount you would need to set aside. To avoid any nasty shocks at the end of the tax year we do this on a monthly basis (see: 'Taxation and saving for this in line with invoicing schedules').

It's also good to have sufficient money to invest in a new resource as needed.

Our online banking has two accounts: a current account for everyday use and a linked saver account where, on a monthly basis, we put money aside. This account pays a very low rate of interest but that is incidental. It's good practice to keep the tax 'pot' separate.

By allocating a realistic sum to the director/ owner, there is then the flexibility to draw less over a period of time if things become difficult. Surviving the financial impact of COVID-19 in this way is a good example. Conversely,

> Your accountant can help with all this.

when times are good, the salary/dividend etc. can be increased (although be mindful of the tax thresholds which will vary according to the latest budget set by the government).

Invoicing arrangements

We invoice our clients on a monthly basis. We don't ask for payment in advance of work being done. The only possible exception to this happens sometimes at the end of schools' financial year, some settings want to pay ahead of the date they close their books.

Read more about timetables in Chapters 12 and 15.

This is fine as SLTs will have put the dates in their diary already and, in the event that a date doesn't go ahead for any reason, adjustments are made on the next invoice. Invoicing works most effectively if timetabling arrangements are robust.

In the rare event that we have not been able to deliver an agreed contract, we refund the unspent sum. Occasionally a client has erroneously overpaid us. In this instance, we offer the option of either a refund or off-setting the money against future invoices.

That said, however, we do think that, in some circumstances, it's reasonable to ask for some money on account. This is routine in other areas of business, e.g. law and accountancy, until the client/provider relationship has become established. The sum paid in advance is then offset against the first invoice. In some instances, where a family has asked for an assessment and some treatment, their expectations as to what this will cost are unrealistic. You will make a decision about whether or not there is a degree of risk involved and whether the report which follows an assessment, for example, would not be handed over until that initial payment has been made.

Everyone, including single-handed practitioners, should include terms and conditions as a toolbox essential.

Go to Chapter 9 to find out more about contracts.

Templates are available on the ASLTIP website.

What to include on an invoice

There are obvious essential pieces of information to include and there may be other require-ments from the clients themselves – such as purchase order numbers (PONs) or, if payments are made through a big public entity such as the council, as is the case for a number of our clients, then there will be a unique vendor number (UVN) to include. It's always a good idea to get to know who processes the invoices – whether this is the finance officer in a particular setting or a finance officer employed by the council. These people are invaluable in helping us understand how things work and are usually more than willing to chase things up when payments are slow.

Some clients may claim their treatment costs via a health insurance company. It's a question to be asked at the outset (when you are discussing fees). The client should always check with their insurance company ahead of making the assumption that the speech and language therapy costs will be met by health insurance. There will be a process. For example, the company agrees to the costs to be incurred, provides a claim number perhaps and the client will either already know (or be advised) as to the maximum amount that the claim will fund. The company may pay the invoice directly or refund the sum to the client. One practitioner we asked said that she reduces the risk of non-payment (and delayed payment) by ensuring clients retain the responsibility for claiming from their insurance company after settling their account personally.

Design your invoice format to be as clear and straightforward as possible. Stick to the same format. Your invoices will become familiar to clients and are likely to raise fewer queries (which goes some way to avoid unnecessary delays in processing!).

When to send your invoices

Our advice would be to do this as soon as you can after the service has been delivered (unless of course the client has/will be paying in advance). For us, this is on a monthly basis – when the last planned date in any given month has been completed, off goes the invoice.

For some practitioners, a specific number of sessions might be agreed and payment requested at the end of that.

When we first started, we used to send all the invoices out on the last day of the month – in a way this made for a designated time set aside rather than tackling the task in dribs and drabs. However, it became apparent that we were being paid more quickly if we didn't wait until the end of the month – when our invoice would be one of (sometimes) many to be processed.

This is important to consider because cash flow is crucial to keep your business running smoothly. We had a few months where the cashflow was an issue and money had to be taken from our reserve to top up the current account. Chasing late payments is very time-consuming, and the time you spend doing this eats into the profit you have made delivering the service.

Naomi shares her experiences of potential cash flow problems.

> *In medico-legal cases, where the case is still in the process of settlement, payment is coming via solicitors who have an initial 'pot' of money available to begin rehabilitation. It's important*

to be aware that the pot may run out before a course of intervention is completed and invoices will remain unpaid until the next tranche of money is available.

Naomi advises that it is well worth asking pertinent questions about funding and timescales at the outset – not only in order to not leave the client in the lurch at a crucial moment but also to be able to earn a living. Large companies can withstand the break in funding, but for a sole practitioner this is not sustainable.

The initial package in such instances would be assessment, report and then up to six months of ongoing intervention. This has to be costed and it is essential that all costs are considered, including liaison time with other members of the MDT, making resources, travel time and travel costs as well as the time spent with the client. I have learned over the years not to under-estimate costs. It might well be worth considering asking for this sum in advance so as to ensure the client is not left in limbo (or the therapist out of pocket).

There are also financial implications where outcomes are not good and intervention has gone as far as it can at a particular point. The client (child or adult) may be on a lengthy NHS waiting list but there are occasions when it's the right thing to do to advise against further expenditure until or unless circumstances change.

It's important to know who to invoice. In this way the medico-legal invoice will get paid far more quickly if it goes to the right person in the solicitors' practice – who may not be the person who commissioned your service. With individual adult clients, it's wise to ask at the outset whether the person asking for the service (possibly a son or daughter of the client) is the person to whom the invoices should be directed or whether this should be the client themselves.

Late payments and non-payments

It's a good plan to make it clear on your invoice (and in your contract/terms and conditions) when you expect payment and what the consequences are if payment is late. We identify a late payment fee which will be added to the outstanding invoice.

Make sure your process and timescales are quite clear. Once the invoice is out of time (for example we specify that payment is due within 30 days of receipt of the invoice), we usually resend the invoice with a polite reminder. If necessary, this is then followed up by the invoice being sent again with an email stating that payment is required by a given date or late payment fees will be added. If this has no result, we resend with the late payment fees added.

You don't always have to enforce this (things do get overlooked from time to time), but it gives you the discretion to do so if required – and also sends out the message that you are serious and professional in the way that you conduct your affairs. This is the guidance that we refer to.

https://www.gov.uk/late-commercial-payments-interest-debt-recovery [2].

Unpalatable as it might sound, at some point you *will* come across someone who isn't going to pay. There are also businesses and individuals who will make a judgement that you are a less threatening option in terms of late payment than someone else they owe money to, and they will defer your payment for as long as they can. It is then at your discretion as to when you proceed to the small claims court.

It isn't difficult to pursue a claim in this way. There are fees, but you are able to do everything yourself without the need for a lawyer. This website is really useful, including guiding you to how to redeem money owed to your business.

https://www.gov.uk/make-court-claim-for-money [3]

We have heard from some independent practitioners who have problems with debt, where individual clients fail to pay within the time identified in the terms and conditions. The longer these debts remain, the less likely it is that the client will pay. It's worth considering investing in a card machine and expecting payment at the end of the visit. Bear in mind that with other goods or services purchased, payment is either required in advance or at time of delivery. Why should the delivery of your service be any different?

In the same way, if a client books with you and then fails to attend for whatever reason, you are unlikely to fill that slot at short notice. Consider asking for either the whole amount in advance or at least a non-refundable deposit which is deducted from the final bill.

No one sets out in business to mistrust their potential clients, but the reality is that there will be issues with late and non-payers. Think in advance how you can protect your cash flow. Genuine clients who value your service should not take offence. More about debt issues in Chapter 15.

Taxation and saving for this in line with invoicing schedules

At the time of writing corporation tax (limited liability companies only) on profits is payable at the rate of between 19% and 25%. This always has the potential to change, which is a reminder to keep a close eye on it. Again, this is another good reason to engage the services of an accountant.

Profits made by a sole trader become part and parcel of that person's personal tax calculation – i.e. the more you earn the more tax is paid. Where people are employed, tax is deducted at the source in the same way it is in the public sector.

As mentioned earlier, we calculate the tax payable on our profit at the end of each month and put this money into a separate account. Whatever your business model, it's essential to ensure that you are on top of income and expenditure so that you are able to save towards your tax bill as you go along.

Table 8.3 is an example of the summary we produce on a monthly basis. It means that we know exactly where we are at any given point. We can spot trends or changes quickly and also have the clients' budget information at a glance (which is also included on their invoices) so that they too can keep an eye on how their money is being spent.

Our business model is about days commissioned usually over an academic year. Where the commission is on a termly basis, or where the client works to a financial year, we would note that.

How to take money from your business

Our specialist contributor Jenny Marks from (MBJ etc.) advises as follows:

> *There are a number of ways of taking money from your business and the choice of how to do this will depend on your business structure, how much money you need, how much tax you are prepared to pay and your personal circumstances. For example, making pension contributions*

If no days are delivered that month, the client remains on the summary sheet as NSTM(no service this month) and the remaining days and budget value will be the same as last month.

Table 8.3 Monthly summary sheet: income and pay expenditure

[year and month] SUMMARY

A	B	C	D	E	F	G	H	I	J
List of clients	Number of days commissioned that academic Year (or specified period of time)	Value of the commission: daily charge to the client X number of days	Number of days/ sessions left at the end of the month in question	Value of remaining budget	Invoice number/ NSTM. We list our clients alphabetically and invoice numbers follow that order, irrespective of the date they are sent out.	Income: daily charge to client X number of days	Expenditure (cost of sales): number of days X daily rate paid to associates.	Dates service delivered	Notes: an aide memoire if, for example, a date was omitted from the previous month's invoice and needs adding to this one
(Add rows as required)									

The end looks like this

Income	
Add up column G	Total £
Income from training*	Total £
Expenditure: Number of days delivered X therapists' daily rate, + directors' drawings (or salary/ bonus etc	
Profit before tax (total income minus total expenditure)	£

Breakdown of expenditure	
Number of days/sessions including any other fee variations (different commissions, one-off assessments for example)	Total £
Overall Total income	Total £
Total expenditure (cost of sales)	£
Tax (profit multiplied by % payable) NB: Ltd company model	£
Balance (profit minus tax payable)	£

*Training is recorded separately because there is a VAT threshold for income from training at the time of writing this is £85,000.

can be a tax-efficient way of 'paying' yourself, but it does mean the funds are tied up for some time.

For company directors, having dividends rather than salary from your business can be a cheaper way of taking money depending on how much you need. Alternatively, for directors, certain benefits like a mobile phone contract can be paid tax-free as long as the contract is set up correctly in the first place. For some businesses, it may be possible to pay spouses or children if they have a legitimate role within the organisation or, if not, paying dividends to spouses who are shareholders can work instead.

Having a good accountant is so important when it comes to drawing money as they will be able to advise on all the reliefs available, calculate which are the most efficient for you and ensure that the recordkeeping and reporting complies with the tax legislation.

Preparing for the end of your financial year

You may decide to submit your own tax return – see HMRC's website for lots of guidance about this. Or you might decide to employ an accountant to do this for you. The benefits of using an accountant include access to advice relating to *you and your business*, rather than the generic guidance available via HMRC. There is also the 'peace of mind' aspect – after all, just as we are experts in our profession, they are experts in theirs.

That said, many people do their own accounting and tax returns with no difficulty, so the choice is yours.

Systems

There are many accounting software products available now – not so when we first started out.

We started with a very basic system and, because it works for us, we have stuck to it and decided not to shift to a software product (yet!).

A simple spreadsheet system works well, and if you are starting small this may be all you need.

Monthly income and expenditure should be entered onto the spreadsheet with some details such as invoice number, name of company and type of expenditure. This record needs to tally with any (paper or electronic) invoices, receipts and orders you have relating to your business.

Keep on top of this, and update your spreadsheet or software system at least monthly – leaving it for too long can cause headaches. It is a huge piece of work, under pressure, as the end of the year approaches, which can lead to mistakes in your accounting.

A monthly finances update also means you can check that your invoices are being paid on time, and conversely whether you have missed any that are becoming overdue.

If using an accountant, ask how they want information presented to them at the end of your financial year. It may be that you can save some money by doing some of the work yourself, leaving them to submit the relevant documents to HMRC and tell you how much tax you will need to pay.

At the end of the financial year it is helpful to ensure you have the following information:

- Invoices owed – who still owes you money (debtors) and how much?
- Invoices owing – who do you owe (creditors) and how much?
- Copies of bank statements for your business accounts (current and savings account if you have one)
- If you use a room in your home as an office you will need to provide details such as how many rooms and your broadband and utility bill costs for the year.

Here are the simple formats that we use.

Sample income spreadsheet

e.g. BACS/ direct debit

We keep training and therapy separate as, over a certain sum, income generated from therapy attracts VAT

Date	Method	Invoice no	Client	Training	S & L therapy	Other	Running total
Jan							
2nd	BACS	001	Starfish primary		£xxxx		
9th	BACS	0012	Northway High	£xxxx			
Feb							

Sample Expenditure spreadsheets

Sheet 1: pay

Sub-contractor	Jan	Feb	March
(list of names)			

Sheet 2: non-pay

	Jan	Feb	March
(List all the items from your non-pay budget plan)			
Bank charges			
Stationery			
Resources			
IT			
Subsistence			
Hospitality			

You can keep your petty cash record in a similar way

B = balance at month end

	Jan	B	Feb	B	March	B
Petty cash in	£50	£37.80				
(List all the areas where petty cash might be spent)						
Subsistence	5.50					
Client/visitor refreshments						
Cleaning materials	6.70					
Travel/parking						
Stationery/postage						
Equipment						
Other						

Make sure you keep receipts or make a note if there is no receipt available (for example, equipment bought at a car-boot or similar sale). These should be stored with your accounts.

Other things to consider

Asset register

This is a list of non-disposable items your business owns and could include office equipment such as furniture and technology such as computers, laptops, printers, tablets etc. and assessment or therapeutic materials. You can put together a simple table with headings as follows:

Purchase date	*Item*	*Replacement value*	*Notes*
			E.G: on loan to (name)/in storage

Income protection insurance

Whatever your structure, give this serious consideration. As with any type of insurance, you choose the policy and content depending on your personal circumstances. Basically, income protection insurance covers most illnesses and injuries that stop you working either in the short or long term – however, it doesn't pay out if you're made redundant. Here's how policies usually work:

- It replaces part of your income if you suffer a loss of earnings due to becoming ill or injured and are unable to work
- Income protection covers you until you have recovered or until retirement, death, your policy ends or until the limited claim period on your policy ends – whichever is sooner
- You can claim as many times as you need to – while the policy lasts

A word to the wise!

Think hard before deciding not to invest in employment protection insurance – *especially* if you are the sole earner. One practitioner we spoke to, with responsibility for two quite young children, was diagnosed with an aggressive, life-threatening disease. Thankfully, she is now well, but she was unable to work for almost two years. Income protection cover meant that she was able to survive, provide and focus on her recovery. Read her story in Chapter 16.

We conclude this chapter with a section with more useful information from Jenny.

Accountancy services

There are many ways that hiring a good accountant can add value to your business. Not only will they ensure that tax and financial deadlines are met but they will have a thorough understanding of tax legislation to ensure you and your business claim all the reliefs and benefits that you are entitled to. This on its own should pay for their services but will also remove the stress and worry from you leaving you to focus on running the business.

An accountant will provide personalized advice throughout the lifecycle of a business from choosing the right operating structure, obtaining funding, employing and rewarding staff, being able to spot opportunities for cost savings and efficiencies, advising on ways to develop the business and draw the profits in the most tax efficient way, help with budgeting and forecasting and ultimately how to pass on your business on through a sale, retirement or other succession plan.

Many accountants themselves are business owners so will have firsthand experience of the challenges of running a business and will know what is important when working for yourself. They will have knowledge of many different sectors and structures of varying complexity and size and will be able to draw on that experience to provide tailored advice which will save you time and money and provide invaluable support.

References

1. Bloor, C. and Finney, J. (2023) *7 Steps to Talking More Openly About Money.* Good Housekeeping. Available at: https://www.goodhousekeeping.com/uk/consumer-advice/money/a28897308/how-to-talk-about-money-taboo/.
2. GD Service. (2016) *Late Commercial Payments: Charging Interest and Debt Recovery.* GOV.UK. Available at: https://www.gov.uk/late-commercial-payments-interest-debt-recovery.
3. GD Service. (2015) *Make a Court Claim for Money.* GOV.UK. Available at: https://www.gov.uk/make-court-claim-for-money.

9 Contracts

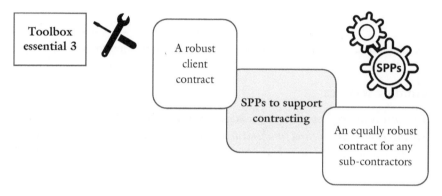

In this chapter, we discuss the kinds of contracts which will support your business activity. The contracts you have will be dependent on your business model. The essentials here are:

A. Contracts with your clients/customers
B. Contracts with your staff team: whether employed or self-employed, practitioners should have a contract with you

Again, depending on what *external* services you use, you may be subject to contracts with providers of specialist services to your business. For us these include accountancy, IT and website design services and our archivist.

The importance of having a contract

Contracts are firm commitments. They should be transparent and clearly identify what is expected (and required) from both parties – the contractor and the contractee.

(A) **contracts we have with our clients**
- we are the contractor, the client is the contractee

DOI: 10.4324/9781003382928-9

(B) **contracts we have with our team** (employed or self-employed)
- the practitioner is the contractor and we are the contractee

A contract is an agreement that involves at least two parties. It makes clear your terms and conditions of business. All parties involved have to agree on certain terms and conditions and sign the contract in order for it to be legally official.

> https://www.upcounsel.com/contractee-legal-definition [1]

We recognise that for some practitioners who set out intending to be entirely responsible for their business (either as sole traders or single-handed limited companies), the concept of contracts, formality and legal commitment sounds daunting – maybe even off-putting. The initial thought is that contracts are seen as potentially punitive: 'what if I don't manage to do what it says I have to in the contract?'

Our advice is to turn that thought completely on its head and consider a contract as a safeguard and support. Contracts are about responsibilities and expectations: a contract will protect both contractor and contractee. If, for example, a team member does not follow procedures as expected and these are set out in the contract, you can legitimately raise issues and be clear about what action you may need to take.

Clients receiving your service are absolutely clear on what to expect – and, by definition, what *not* to expect. They are also clear about *their* responsibilities. One example of a contracting essential is to do with finance. What will your client pay for your service, when will that payment be expected and what steps will you take if payment is late (or not forthcoming at all)?

Practitioners you use, (again either as employees or sub-contractors) are clear about their responsibilities as representatives of the work they are undertaking on your behalf. They are also clear about notice periods, payment and all the other things which are important when undertaking work for someone else.

It's worth mentioning here (again) a point which readers will soon recognise as a recurrent theme. Somehow people find it easier to talk about money when purchasing goods or services such as groceries or hairdressing. Bear in mind that a business is a business, whether it sells car parts or speech and language therapy.

Nothing available to us comes without a cost: public-sector/NHS services aren't free, they are funded by taxpayers. We receive what is delivered and any element of choice is very limited.

Blunt words – and for some they will touch a nerve. For now, suffice it to say it's worth remembering that altruism neither pays the mortgage nor feeds the family.

> *Right from the beginning, master the skill of being comfortable talking about money.*

Talking about paying for healthcare has the potential to open some heated debates. Views can become quickly polarised. In chapter 3 we make the observation that there are people who will happily pay for chiropody but baulk at paying for dentistry!

Contract toolbox essentials

Again, we are providing guidance as to what to include rather than a set format – which works for us but may not accurately reflect what *you* need. The client contract below reflects the type of business we are and the services we provide. However, the key components are easily transferable to most other models of delivery.

Client contract

It's good practice to insert a header which describes the document and the date it was last reviewed or revised. You would be surprised how quickly the time goes by and older versions are superseded.

Include your company registration number and registered business address as these must be displayed on official documents, company stationery (including letterheads, compliment slips, emails, invoices, order forms and receipts) and on your website.

If you have a logo, include that too. Sole traders are also required to display an address on their paperwork.

Our client contracts have nine sections. We always start with a summary of what is being commissioned (remember this is for the kind of service we provide and the customers we have – not all will be relevant to your business).

Header

(*Business name*)/client/agreement for the provision of speech and language therapy/*date*	
1) General information	
Period of agreement	
School/setting	
Value of budget	
How this service can be delivered	*(X days or: a combination of regular days and training options)*
NB: Please see section 7 (Payment) which refers to the fact that there is a *difference* between daily rate and training rates. You will be asked to fill in a training request form which will be followed by a formal quote.	*Transparency is important - we let clients know this very early on.*
Identified day	*(If already known. It's fine to put TBA)*
Responsible officer for the school	*(Head or Sendco)*
Director *(Signing on behalf of your business)*	
Named therapist/s for the school	
Date to review	*Allow at least half a term. For annual contracts we are renegotiating at the end of Spring 1*

2) **Service provision** (*a summary of the key points of the service you will provide*).

3) **Organisational information**

This section summarises accommodation, the sharing of information, how any 'additional requests' for activity might be managed.

4) **Quality and safety assurance**

We provide the setting with the assurance that the therapist we subcontract will provide evidence of enhanced DBS clearance, HCPC registration, membership of the Royal College of Speech and Language Therapists (which includes insurance) and continuing professional development (if/as required by the school).

5) **Consent, confidentiality and data protection [General Data Protection Regulations (GDPR) compliant]**

This section is divided into three:
- **Personal** (*the company requests and retains essential information in order to deliver contracted services to our customers*)
- **Commercial** (*information within the contract is commercially sensitive and should be treated confidentially*)
- **Professional** (*consent for treatment, records storage, data processing, data sharing, accessing to the internet, shared file storage in a setting, where school provide computer access, hardware compliance*)

6) **Procedures**

Referral process, prioritisation (if needed), assessment and report writing

7) **Payment**

Daily rate and length of day, how and when invoices are submitted, terms of payment, what happens if the therapist cannot deliver a planned day for whatever reason, what happens if the client cancels a day at no/very short notice. If the therapist is cancelled and cannot rearrange work for that day, they lose a day's income. Clients would be expected to pay a percentage of the daily rate. You will usually only need to enforce this once for the message to be received and understood.

8) **Alterations and termination**

*Identify the number of weeks' notice to be given by either party for significant or permanent changes to this agreement. For example, the setting wants fewer (or sometimes more!) days or the service provider decides to put up the fees – absolutely **not** to be recommended part-way through the life of a contract. Go to Chapter 8 where we talk in more detail about why establishing your price is important.*

Identify the notice period both the provider or the setting need to give to terminate the contract. In our model, half terms work well. From the provider's point of view, it gives time to close the caseload and inform parents/others about discharge. From the client's point of view, it indicates that therapists need adequate notice to find alternative employment.

If there is a breach in the terms of the contract either side has the right to terminate with immediate effect. Go to Chapter 15 to find out that this does sometimes happen.

A minimum of one half-term's notice to terminate this agreement must be given by either party, unless the terms of the agreement have been breached.

NB: Where changes are made to agreed visits *without communication and agreement at least 24 hours in advance, (your business)* reserves the right to charge 50% of the fee.

9) **Safeguarding checks**

In our contracts, the Safeguarding checks appear as appendices. Settings are obliged to either carry out or seek assurance that checks have been carried out on external contractors. We explain what checks we carry out (and what is not applicable). This information is then provided as a letter of assurance as and when the service to the setting gets underway.

Additional appendices We include our data sharing agreement 'for information' and the consent and data privacy form (as an editable document) in preparation for the commencement of service.

Signature page	(on behalf of your business)	(client/responsible officer on behalf of the client)
Name/s		
Job title/s		
Date		
Signatures		

Our contracts are emailed to the client as PDFs. We require only the signature page to be signed, scanned and returned to us for our records.

Contract extension

What happens if the client either wants an extension or an increase in terms of input (a *decrease* in input would require the six-week notice as per the contract). Again, a header (or footer) is a good idea, and remember to include your business address (and registration number if you are a company) somewhere on the paperwork.

We use a simple proforma as follows:

New commission	(logo)
Extension to existing contract *(For all other information – please refer to your existing contract)*	
Period of agreement	
Client	
Number of days	
Identified day	
Responsible officer for the school *(name on behalf of your business)*	
Therapist	
Date to review	

	(On behalf of your business)	(Client/responsible officer on behalf of the client)
Name		
Job title		
Date		
Signature		

Contracts we have with our team

Some of the team are associates and some are self-employed therapists. Both operate independently and autonomously, the distinction being that the associate operates as a limited company. These are defined in Chapter 5.

If you employ or subcontract to other roles, administrator/book-keeper for example, that person will also need a contract. We have shared our therapist contract below.

As with the client contract, it's good practice to insert a header which describes the document and the date it was last reviewed or revised. Ensure your registered business address is on the contract somewhere and if you have a logo, include that too.

Our associate/self-employed therapist contracts have ten sections. As with the client contract, we always start with a summary of what is being contracted.

	(*Business name*)/associate/self-employed therapist agreement for the provision of speech and language therapy/*date*		
Period of agreement	(dates to and from)		
Location/s of work			*A column for each setting*
Number of days per week			
Identified days			
Start date	(*week beginning…*)		
Anticipated end date	(*week ending …*)		
Date to consider renewal	(*at least six weeks before the end date. Ideally at the same time as the client contract is discussed*)		
Associate			
(Business owner/s)			

N.B: here we would insert one the definition of either an associate/self-employed therapist or a self-employed therapist.

1. Service provision

The associate/self-employed therapist will deliver the agreed programme of work on these days when school is open for staff *and/or* pupils. The programme can be modified to meet the needs of the client; however, a core service maximises the time available during the day to work with children and includes:

List the activity to be carried out

2. Organisational information

Associate/self-employed therapist hours, maximising the time available (if working in a school setting), some activities (paperwork) may be undertaken off-site (negotiate and agree this in advance)

What to do in the event that a setting wants additional work undertaken,

during a holiday period for example)

What you as the business owner will have discussed and agreed with the setting prior to the service starting. For example:

- *Appropriate accommodation (quiet area with minimal distractions) for children to work with the therapist*
- *A named person/people with whom the therapist will liaise on a regular basis as agreed*
- *The therapist to be aware of all relevant policies to enable them to carry out the role, including child protection procedures*
- *The sharing of any information reasonably required to deliver the service*
- *Familiarisation with school policies and procedures (with particular reference to safeguarding and health and safety)*

3. Quality and safety assurance

The associate/self-employed therapist will provide evidence of enhanced DBS clearance, HCPC registration, membership of the Royal College of Speech and Language Therapists (which includes insurance) and continuing professional development as required by the school.

4. Consent, confidentiality and data protection [General Data Protection Regulations (GDPR) compliant]

i)   **Personal:** *The associate/self-employed therapist knows what personal information is required by (your business) and for what purpose and understands that this is held securely, electronically and accessible only to the directors.*

ii) **Commercial:** *The associate/self-employed therapist acknowledges that information contained in both this document and others pertinent to the business of (name), is confidential and must be treated as such. It must not be shared with any third party (including individual clients and schools). The associate/self-employed therapist also acknowledges and confirms that they will not, without prior permission of the (business owner/s) contract in any capacity with the clients who have been introduced by (your business).*

iii) **Professional:** (*your business*) outsources work to associates who, as data processors, have data protection responsibilities.

    a.   *(your business), as data controllers, will make parents and carers of children referred to the therapist aware of how the company complies with GDPR*

    b.   *Schools will be responsible for ensuring that parents/ carers understand the content and implications of the (business name) consent form and privacy notice, prior to obtaining written consent for the speech and language therapist to see a child. In exceptional circumstances, verbal consent may be gained as a short-term measure with written consent to follow.*

    c.   Protection of service user personal data: *to cover record-keeping, who has access, storage (what and location). Associate compliance with security conditions (note only protection of records but also computer security requirements.*

        Access to the internet (and the school server if this is appropriate). The establishment of a secure data transfer system. Data processing agreement. Data sharing agreement.

5. Procedures

Referral process, liaison with any/all agencies involved, with specific reference to NHS colleagues). Provision of reports (when) and what reports will cover.

6. Resources

The associate is responsible for the provision of appropriate day-to-day materials and equipment necessary for the delivery of the service.

7. Insurance

The associate is responsible for the provision of appropriate insurance.

8. Health, safety and security

The associate understands their responsibility to:

- *Take all reasonable precautions to minimize risks*
- *Report incidents (including near misses)*
- *Abide by the policies and procedures of the schools and settings where services are delivered*

9. Payment

Daily rate, when to submit invoices, length of working day, what to do in the event of late arrival or illness, keeping a timetable and ensuring amendments are up-to-date. Days not worked are not paid (in the event of self-employment).

10. Alterations and termination

- *Six weeks/one half term's notice to be given by either party for significant or permanent changes to this agreement, e.g. number of days to be provided, fees etc.*
- *A minimum of one half term's notice to terminate this agreement must be given by either party, unless the terms of the agreement have been breached*

On behalf of (business name)		Therapist
		I have read and agree with the terms of this contract
Business owner/s	*(name/s)*	*(name)*
Job title	*(role)*	Speech and Language Therapist
Date		
Signature/s		

Associate/self-employed therapist contract amendment

In the same way that the client contract can be amended for whatever reason, the same is true for an associate or self-employed therapist. Again, a header (or footer) is a good idea and remember to display your registered business address (and registration number if you are a company) somewhere on the paperwork.

We use a simple proforma as follows:

Please see below amendment/extension to previous and most recently signed agreement between the person named below and (*business name*).

School/setting	
Period of agreement	
Number of days	
Identified days	
Start date	
Anticipated end date	
Date to consider renewal	
Therapist	
(Business owner)	

The terms of this amended agreement are identical to the original.

On behalf of (business name)		Therapist
Name		
Job title		
Date		
Signature		

Reference

1. Contractee legal definition: Everything you need to know. (n.d.) UpCounsel. Available at: https://www.upcounsel.com/contractee-legal-definition.

10 Governance

This chapter will define what we mean by governance and discuss why it's important. Again, following the principle of 'taking the best and ditching the rest', we identify what we consider to be the essential policies, procedures and processes to have in place to (a) operate safely and transparently and (b) be able to assure clients that services delivered are underpinned by policies and guidelines and therapists are 'fit for purpose' in the widest sense (qualified, registered, vetted etc.).

We talk about developing a governance framework which reflects the way you work. The framework is about *your* standards of quality and safety and how this is evidenced: your assurance to clients. It also supports and protects you (and the team around you) as a practitioners.

We consider each aspect and provide the details of what to include.

Later in the book, we talk about 'trouble-shooting' and in (almost) every example included, a successful outcome relied on robust governance systems being in place and communicated to everyone involved.

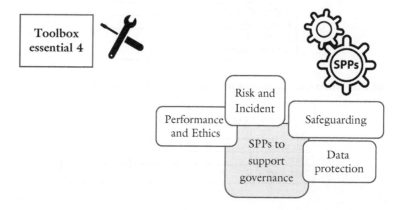

What is 'governance'?

Governance in healthcare, sometimes referred to as 'clinical governance', will be a term familiar to everyone who has worked in the NHS.

> *'A system through which NHS organisations are accountable for continuously improving the quality of their services and safeguarding high standards of care by creating an environment in which excellence in clinical care will flourish'. It involves monitoring systems and processes to provide assurance of patient safety and quality of care across the organisation'.*

DOI: 10.4324/9781003382928-10

www.england.nhs.uk/mat-transformation/matrons-handbook/governance-patient-safety-and -quality/ [1]

As independent practitioners, whatever our structure or configuration, it is immediately clear that we need to think more widely than 'just' the clinical element.

There are numerous models available: some talk about 'the seven pillars of governance', others six or four. Some include a human resources element, some don't. The first important point to identify here is that yes, your business *will need* a governance framework (for all the reasons we are about to discuss), but don't be seduced into just searching for an existing model on the internet, adopting that and trying to fit your business into it!

Here is a typical model

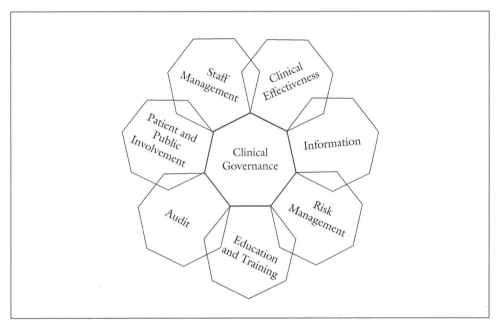

www.radarhealthcare.com/news-blogs/what-is-clinical-governance-and-what-are-the-7-pillars/ [2]

At first look it seems that each of these 'pillars' have equal importance. In our world, this is *not* the case and valuable time and resources shouldn't be diverted into activity which is outside the 'core business'. In Chapter 7, we refer to *mission creep*: learning to spot activity which is potentially idiosyncratic and will not generate income. Unless you have agreed a charitable or altruistic strand and built it into your business plan, we would strongly advise against undertaking an activity because it 'seems like a nice thing to do'. Everything you do should be a service the *client* wants, an activity which will generate income: it needs to tick both of those boxes.

So … what *should* we include? There are good examples to draw upon from the world of business. In fact, we particularly like the guidance which advises a business to build its own framework and include the things which are not only **important** (the toolbox essentials), but also the things which are relevant to your specific business or profession. At the same time, be clear about what the priorities are and who has responsibility for what. This second point becomes important when applied to the various structures and relationships that exist in independent practice.

Governance arrangements will be different for employed and sub-contracted individuals. For example, where independent practitioners are *employed*, the responsibility for identifying and providing access to education and training rests with the employer. For practitioners who enter into *sub-contractor arrangements*, the responsibility of keeping up-to-date rests with them as individuals. HCPC (and RCSLT – although not mandatory) registration is our assurance in terms of governance. We ask our team to assure us that they have supervision arrangements in place, we check the dates of safeguarding refreshers and we also host two CPD days annually.

When starting out, with a blank slate, it's a good idea to be clear about what we mean. Terminology can mean different things, depending on the context.

Governance [n]: the action or manner of governing

The definition extends to include *control or influence* and *constitute a rule, standard or principle for something.*

This is moving in the right direction and leads us to start to think about governance much more widely and apply the principles across every aspect of our business – not just the clinical work undertaken.

Let's return to the 'typical model' and begin to make some changes, reshaping it so that it reflects our business priorities.

Model 1: our *business* governance toolbox essentials

In preparation for looking at each area in more detail, let's decide where the other aspects fit, adapting the terminology to better illustrate what we mean.

- What should be in place?
- What does it *look like* (what will you see)?
- How do the pieces of the puzzle fit together? They most certainly need to as no one aspect operates in isolation

Model 2: *clinical* governance toolbox essentials

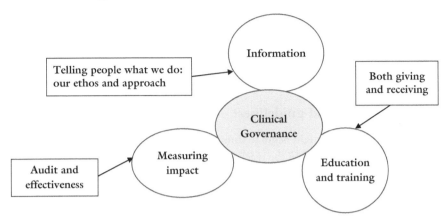

The eagle-eyed reader will have spotted that patient and public involvement (PPI), now known as co-production, doesn't feature in either model. During our days within the NHS we remember well the challenge of getting service users to engage: to tell us what they thought about the service and to offer suggestions as to how things might be different (i.e. better).

In the independent world, by the very fact that clients have (sometimes with increasing desperation) searched and searched for support and help, they are *already* engaged. We *ask* people what they want regardless of whether they are the service user directly or proxy users such as schools, settings or parents, rather than giving them what we *think* they should have and then asking them if that was okay. Of course, a client may have a narrow view of what it is they want and by negotiation and over time, it's our job to expand those horizons so that users at every level get the very best value and positive outcomes from their investment in SLT/our service.

We routinely gather feedback from those who commission us – this is all part and parcel of the measuring impact strand (discussed in far greater detail in Chapter 14).

Where (if at all) do the Care Quality Commission (CQC) 'fundamental standards' fit into our model?

NB: The CQC operates only in England, the devolved countries have their own regulatory bodies.

The CQC standards are those against which the inspection team will rate a range of health and social care provision.

- Are they safe (are service users protected from abuse and avoidable harm)?
- Are they effective?
- Are they caring?
- Are they responsive to people's needs?
- Are they well-led?

Some services fit well into a medical model but others do not (the bulk of paediatric speech and language therapy fits far better into a social or educational model). However, IP services are not subject to CQC (or its equivalent) inspection – whether they should be is an interesting point which we have touched upon in this chapter and return to in Chapter 16.

At the very beginning of our journey towards independence, we did use the CQC standards to evidence the quality and safety of what we were providing but it soon became clear that whilst obviously important, these standards were not a good fit for us. Of course, the general principles have relevance but are better incorporated into models 1 and 2 described earlier.

Do we need policies and guidelines?

It's at this point that readers might begin to think that the whole concept of a governance framework is huge, unwieldy and beyond the reach of most of us!

Take heart! *Yes*, we do need some policies and guidelines but we don't need many and, once done, they will stand you in good stead going forward –only needing review on an annual basis – unless something very significant happens.

Policies and guidelines underpin every aspect of your business: they assure clients; they support, guide and direct practitioners.

Getting started

Keep things simple and tackle the essentials. If you find that something is missing and needs to be included, you can do this as and when it occurs.

We didn't have many policies and guidelines when we first began our journey. If truth be told, one of the positive aspects of leaving the NHS was that the interminable paperwork, reporting, and seemingly onerous burden of bureaucracy could be left behind and left behind for good! Liberating indeed. In the early days, we did a lot of thinking 'on the hoof' in response to searching questions from our customers, and as the business grew, we developed a set of tools for governance that has served us and our customers well.

In the same way, as our little team of SLTs began to come together, they too needed to know what to do – particularly in the areas of risk, safeguarding and data protection.

Team and clients alike needed the reassurance that, as a business, we knew what we were doing, and were professional and rigorous, with a governance structure and framework in place to deliver a well-run, effective and safe service.

Therapists leaving the public sector at management level should be well-placed to get to grips with writing a policy or guideline. Clinicians less so. If the words of advice in this chapter can demystify the process then all to the good! When we started to put our documents together, we drew on the expertise of anyone who would help – it's so much easier to start with something and adapt it. We drew upon the comprehensive format of NHS documentation, looked at websites, spoke to colleagues in IP and used the HCPC, ASLTIP and RCSLT websites – all mines of information. The general principle of 'take the best and ditch the rest' stood us in good stead.

Policy, procedure, protocol or guideline: which one should we choose?

There are differences between all four of these types of documentation.

A **policy** is a means of guiding an organisation to a desired outcome.

> *Policy [n]: a course or principle of action adopted (or proposed) by an organisation or individual*

A **procedure** is a written set of instructions that describe the approved and recommended steps of a particular act or sequence of events (HIQA, 2008) [3]. Procedures supplement policies and describe how the policy will be implemented and met.

A **protocol** is a written plan that specifies procedures to be followed in defined situations. A protocol represents a standard of care that describes an intervention or set of interventions. Protocols are more explicit and specific in their detail than guidelines, in that they specify who does 'what', 'when' and 'how' [3].

A **guideline** is defined as a principle or criterion that guides or directs action.

A little later in this chapter, we discuss why some of our governance toolbox essentials are policies and others are guidelines.

You will see that in terms of our routine governance essentials, procedures and protocols do not feature. Why? In attempting to answer that, it's worth saying that none of the interventions we deliver would require a rigid set of instructions as to what to do and how to do it. Therapists draw on evidenced-based practice (EBP) within the context of understanding what needs to happen (or happen next), identifying realistic and achievable aims and the anticipated outcomes, whilst enjoying the flexibility that creativity brings to the role.

At various points on our journey, as dictated by circumstances, there has been a need to develop protocols and procedures. For example, during COVID-19. Also, we do have a protocol for closing down a service in a setting where the service is coming to an end. This ensures that everything is done in a similar way and no stage in the process is omitted. This is a good example of how checklists are useful tools within protocols and procedures.

As appropriate, protocols and procedures will form part of a policy, probably as an appendix.

When we talk about 'getting started', we advise keeping things simple and going for the essentials. If, at the outset, you try to cover all eventualities (some of which might never happen) you will quickly become bogged down and the anticipated joy of the brave new world of actually being able to deliver therapy might never become reality as you cannot escape the tyranny of your keyboard!

Over time, you can always develop material as and when it becomes clear that you need it. Interestingly, for seven years we managed perfectly well with documents 1 to 3 below. Naively perhaps we had shied away from the rather heavy-handed behavioural aspects of staff performance – the kinds of transgressions which see the Healthcare Professions Council (HCPC) getting involved.

Our team operate as limited companies or sole traders and are not employed. They have contracts which stipulate a six-week notice period but for behaviours which are deemed to be serious, we would (and have) moved to end their contracts with immediate effect. We have encountered therapists in the past who turn out to be unfit for purpose for a variety of reasons.

Over the years we have become wiser at recruitment and firmly believe that it's better to have to turn down work than it is to deploy someone who is not delivering in the way that we expect/want.

Our team are ambassadors for our service – as well as for the profession and if they cannot deliver the service in a way that represents our ethos and work ethic they are, in effect, doing damage to our reputation – and no business needs that.

Recent events have made us realise that to introduce conduct guidelines from the outset is a better way of making it clear to new arrivals what is expected of them. Our conduct guidelines are based on the requirements of HCPC and for most practitioners, they hold no terrors whatsoever and are accepted as being part and parcel of professional behaviour.

In the same way as policies underpin our practice, the conduct guidelines provide a reference point if behaviour falls short of what is expected, such as poor recordkeeping, lack of confidentiality or unreliability. In Chapter 12, we talk about what to look for when taking on an associate (or looking to employ a therapist). In Chapter 15, one of the examples we give looks at conduct and performance issues and how to tackle them.

Our governance toolbox essentials (as per model 1)

1. Confidentiality and Data Protection

> **Data Security and Privacy Policy**

2. Risk and incident

> **Risk Identification, Assessment, Management and Incident Reporting**

3. Safeguarding

> **Child Safeguarding Guidelines (children and young people)**

4. Conduct, performance and ethics

> **Standards of Conduct, Performance and Ethics Guidelines**

Let's revisit the difference between policies and guidelines.

> *Guideline [n]: a general rule, principle or piece of advice*

> *Policy [n]: a course or principle of action adopted by an organisation or individual*

What makes a good policy?

1. **Clear and unambiguous**: this is why a good policy will contain a list of definitions near the beginning so that the reader can be in no doubt as to what is encompassed in the content
2. **Comprehensive:** for example, a data security and privacy policy should cover every aspect of data security and privacy which pertains to the delivery of 'the service' and within the parameters of current legislation
3. **Explains the rule/s,** not how to implement the rule/s (that would be contained within a procedure or protocol)

4. **Accessible:** staff should know where to find the company policies and be able to refer to them
5. Represents a **consistent, logical framework**
6. Is **regularly reviewed** and **revised:** we review ours on an annual basis and then direct the team to the updated version. Anything new is high-lighted so that getting everyone up to speed is less onerous

It makes sense to use a similar format for each policy – it helps readers to find their way around more easily. In the appendices, you will find a policy framework which has worked well for us (Appendix A).It will give you a starting point. We have deliberately chosen to avoid the wholesale provision of our own documents verbatim. To do that runs the risk that the content is slavishly followed rather than the focus being its application to your own individual circumstances. So, by all means, use the headings but populate each section according to what is pertinent to *you*.

How do the governance tool-box essentials in model 1 translate into the practical aspects of running a business?

Here we look at the four key areas and begin to break them down further.

Model 3

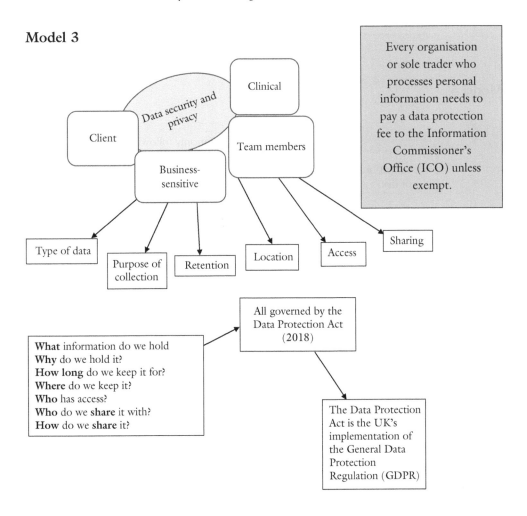

www.gov.uk/data-protection#:~:text=The%20Data%20Protection%20Act%202018,Data%20Protection%20Regulation%20(GDPR) [4]

Model 4

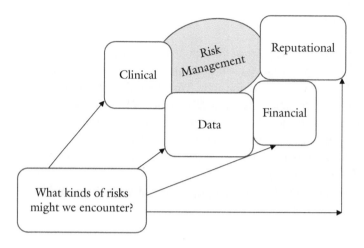

Model 5

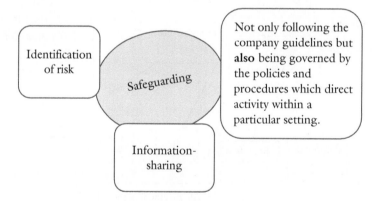

In terms of our model of working everyone needs to:

- Be aware of what safeguarding policies and procedures are already there within your settings
- Find out who the safeguarding leads are
- Know what to report and who to report it to

Model 6

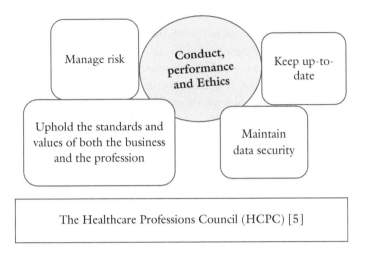

The Healthcare Professions Council (HCPC) [5]

Note how very clearly all four areas are interlinked. Similar themes continue to appear but with slight differences as toolbox essentials become, in turn, the focus of discussion.

Now let's revisit each of the four areas and look at some practical examples.

Data security and privacy

Let's consider the seven points we have identified in model 3. These points are *not* identical to the seven principles of GDPR although there are similarities. The points we list here are the things we need to think about in order to be legally compliant with GDPR but also when managing data on a practical basis within our business.

A good way to summarise the way our data is managed is to complete a **data flow mapping** exercise. This will 'anchor' the first six points. The data sharing aspect is covered in a data sharing agreement. This is a formal contract which clearly documents what data is being shared and how it can be used. It prevents miscommunication on the part of the data provider and the receiving agency by ensuring that any questions about data use are discussed.

Headings on a dataflow map:

Data	*Source*	*Purpose*	*Access*	*Storage*	*Retention/disposal*
(What?)	*(Where has it come from?)*	*(Why do we need it?)*	*(Who can access it?)*	*(Where is it kept?)*	*(How long do we keep it for and how to we dispose of it?)*

See Appendix B for a data-flow mapping example

Don't be put off by the rather grand title *data flow map*!

1. Make yourself a table
2. Write down the types of data in the left-hand column (team, client, business, clinical)
3. Add the key points across the top
4. Now write down what you actually **do** (with reference to the numerous sites which guide you through GDPR compliance). The following sites are a good place to start www.gov.uk/data-protection and www.ico.org.uk

We finish this section by talking about **data sharing** and **data sharing agreements (DSAs)**.

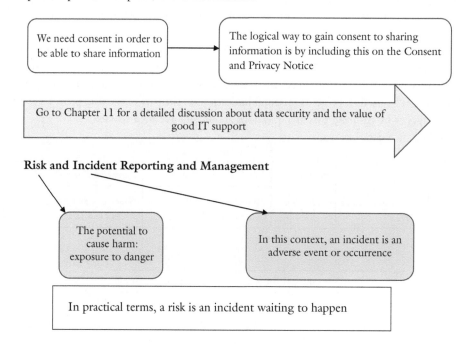

> The disclosure of data from one or more organisations to a third-party organisation or organisations, or the sharing of data between different parts of an organisation

> A formal contract which clearly documents what data is being shared and how it can be used. It prevents miscommunication on the part of the data provider and the receiving agency by ensuring that any questions about data use are discussed

The data sharing agreement is included in the contract we have with associates and self-employed therapists who undertake work on our behalf. They sign up to the data sharing agreement in the same way as they sign the contract. We also append a copy of the DSA to each client contract so that our schools and settings know what data might be shared, why it is shared, and the restrictions placed upon the recipients of the information.

> We need consent in order to be able to share information

> The logical way to gain consent to sharing information is by including this on the Consent and Privacy Notice

> Go to Chapter 11 for a detailed discussion about data security and the value of good IT support

Risk and Incident Reporting and Management

> The potential to cause harm: exposure to danger

> In this context, an incident is an adverse event or occurrence

> In practical terms, a risk is an incident waiting to happen

Let's revisit model 4. Here we have identified four categories of risk. Here are some practical examples of potential risks.

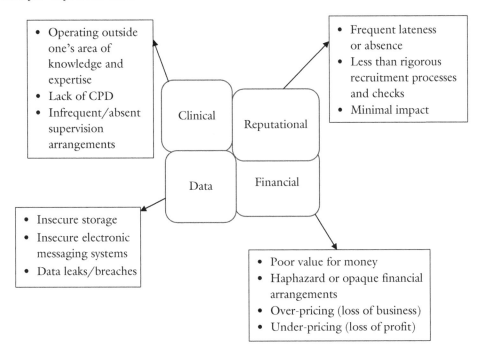

This model clearly illustrates how the categories of risk are all interlinked:

● A team member who is not fit for purpose poses a clinical, reputational and ultimately a financial risk
● A data leak or breach poses a reputational and financial risk

Manage one risk and this will reduce the impact of associated risks.

How to decide whether something is a risk, how great a threat it poses and what to do to try and reduce (or mitigate) the risk

This is sometimes called risk mapping.

There are lots of templates and matrices available and the use of RAG (red, amber, green) rating is a useful way of enhancing the written descriptive elements of risk mapping. In essence however, reliable risk management needs to carry out the following:

1. Define what is meant by risk. If there has *already been* an adverse event (an incident) this is an obvious one for your risk register
2. Identify the risks which could affect your business. Categories of risk help to make this a more manageable exercise: we have included two examples as Appendix C
3. Assess the *probability* of the risk (how likely is it to actually happen?) and the *severity* of the risk (what would be the impact?). Use a risk scoring tool such as the one in Appendix D

4. Risk control (identify what steps you can take to reduce the impact of the risk)
5. Keep a record: we use a risk register
6. Monitor and review (Does the rating of a risk change? Do you need to add anything new?)

Risk register

The register is developed in a spreadsheet format. It has the individual risks down the left-hand side and the 'mapping' along the top.

For each risk we need to ask the following questions:

Source of risk (i.e. how did you find out about it?) continuous assessment, incident etc.
Summary description of risk
Summary of risk management plan (mitigating the risk)
Anticipated resource implication (will managing the risk cost anything?)
Who is responsible for implementing the plan?
Expected date of completion (when will the actions to mitigate the risk be completed?)

Safeguarding

Revisiting model 5, we can see how safeguarding relates to data security and risk management in particular, and it's probably safe to say that these will be pertinent to independent practice as a whole.

It's important to remember, however, that the priorities and processes that support *our* business may not necessarily be the same for professionals in other clinical areas, different business models and client groups.

Readers may already be alert to the fact that we have guidelines rather than a policy in support of safeguarding. Earlier we said: *Guidelines are general recommendations. Policies are more formal documents: following them is mandatory.*

Our company (exclusively) delivers services into schools and settings. Those organisations are governed by a comprehensive set of policies and procedures, of which safeguarding is one. As and when visitors arrive in a school they present their safeguarding documentation and should receive a leaflet outlining the school's procedure. They are then bound by the policies which operate in that setting.

Any/all external visiting professionals are subject to the policies and procedures which govern activity in a particular setting. This is not the same as delivering services in premises owned or rented by the company – in those circumstances the company would have the primary responsibility for the policies and procedures which underpin a specific area of governance (including safeguarding).

Our guidelines are more about *information* rather than *direction*. The guidelines are about the team as individuals rather than a Soundswell team. In the arena of safeguarding, our team need knowledge, awareness and guidance To that end, they receive training and have regular refresher updates.

We need to be aware wherever we are.

However, when we go into a particular school (or enter the world of Scouting, lifeguards, junior soccer, Sunday school etc.), we will take on board their guidelines and specific processes.

When writing your own documents, whether policies or guidelines, always identify the date the document was developed and then the frequency with which you plan to review.

| *Title of policy/guideline* | Initiated (date) | Review schedule: annually (month) |
| | Launched (date) | Date of next review: |

This shows both the team and the clients (sometimes we are asked for evidence that our documentation is robust – and we really welcome those enquiries) that the paperwork which underpins our approach to governance is contemporaneous and relevant.

You can find the contents page for our *Safeguarding Guidelines* at Appendix E. Again, to share the whole document verbatim discourages people from thinking about their own circumstances and local arrangements.

Conduct, performance and ethics

Again, we see how some of the key points are similar across the board. However, they may assume different priorities and include different examples.

The final section in our governance toolbox essentials looks at team behaviour in terms of conduct, performance and ethics. The guidance we have developed relies for the most part on what is contained within the guidance issued by the Healthcare Professions Council (HCPC). In order to continue to be registered to practice, speech and language therapists and the other professions which it regulates, sign up to abide by the code. To fall foul of HCPC standards is to risk sanctions or – in extreme circumstances – removal from the register.

Clearly, therefore, there are good reasons why *individuals* should comply with the expected professional and personal standards. However, there are also obvious reasons why *businesses* like ours, contracting or employing others to deliver services, should expect and ensure high standards of conduct, performance and ethics.

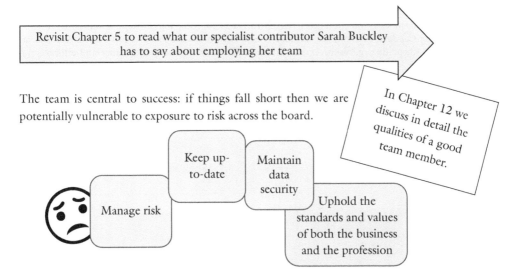

Revisit Chapter 5 to read what our specialist contributor Sarah Buckley has to say about employing her team

The team is central to success: if things fall short then we are potentially vulnerable to exposure to risk across the board.

In Chapter 12 we discuss in detail the qualities of a good team member.

Manage risk

Keep up-to-date

Maintain data security

Uphold the standards and values of both the business and the profession

Key points

- All therapists are bound by the standards of conduct, performance and ethics of the Health Care Professions Council (HCPC). These can be found at: www.hcpc-uk.org/resources/standards/standards-of-conduct-performance-and-ethics/ [5]
- A number of the standards are covered in other policies, procedures and guidelines (see 3.0 below)
- Standards which are pertinent to 'behaviour' are the primary focus of this document
- *Any and all* standards are *equally applicable* when working remotely (for example delivering teletherapy)

Here are the headings to our conduct, performance and ethics document.

Contents		Page
1.0	Introduction and scope	1
2.0	About us	2
3.0	Other policies, procedures and guidelines to which this document relates	2
4.0	The standards	2
5.0	The standards in more detail	2
6.0	Glossary	5
7.0	References	6

References

1. *Governance, Patient Safety and Quality* (n.d.) NHS Choices. Available at: https://www.england.nhs.uk/mat-transformation/matrons-handbook/governance-patient-safety-and-quality/.
2. Whitehead, A. and Hartley-Large, D. (2023) *Radar Healthcare's Solutions for Clinical Governance*. Radar Healthcare. Available at: https://radarhealthcare.com/news-blogs/what-is-clinical-governance-and-what-are-the-7-pillars/.
3. Yelluk. (2022) *Understanding the Difference Between Policies, Procedures, Protocols, and Guidance*. Bettal Quality Consultancy. Available at: https://www.bettal.co.uk/understanding-the-difference-between-policies-procedures-protocols-and-guidance-pppgs#:~:text=A%20procedure%20is%20a%20written,will%20be%20implemented%20and%20met.
4. GD Service. (2015) *Data Protection*. GOV.UK. Available at: https://www.gov.uk/data-protection#:~:text=The%20Data%20Protection%20Act%202018,Data%20Protection%20Regulation%20(GDPR).
5. *Standards of Conduct, Performance and Ethics* (n.d.) Health & Care Professions Council. Available at: https://www.hcpc-uk.org/resources/standards/standards-of-conduct-performance-and-ethics/.

11 Technology

Technology can support every aspect of your business (advertising, training and clinical interventions).

In this chapter, we look specifically at how technology can support and protect your *business* structures, processes and procedures.

We talk about what works for us and what is more of a challenge in terms of managing and maintenance. We advocate good IT back-up and support and invite our specialist contributor Chris Blunt (IT expert and cyber security specialist) to share his advice here.

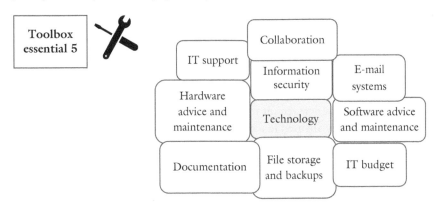

Let's start our discussions about technology by reiterating why we need any and all of the toolbox essentials in the first place – to manage and minimise risk in all its forms. This helps to establish the context for how crucial technology is, not only for our security but also for reaching the people we hope will become our clients.

Good IT back-up and support will have remote access to your machines and be able to fix things for you. The usual way that this is done these days is via a 'managed services contract' where your supplier agrees to look after specific services for you for a fixed price, with anything outside of this agreement being paid for on top.

In addition, you need your IT support to be responsive. For example, in the event of a document you want to retrieve, you need it to be done as close to 'now' as possible!

DOI: 10.4324/9781003382928-12

Hardware advice and maintenance

What kinds of computers do we need? A regular family desktop might be okay to start with, but will it be able to swiftly and continuously do all the things you need it to do? Chris's first piece of advice here is 'don't go cheap'.

> *I am often asked what's the difference between – say - a £300 laptop and a £1,000 laptop (and the same applies to a desktop). At first you won't spot much difference – possibly for the first six months if you're lucky. Machines degrade over time and niggles and little issues will start to appear. The cheaper machine will develop a lot more issues over a shorter period of time.*

By implication, therefore, you will be changing your cheaper machine more often and when you do, it's not just the cost of the machine, it's also the cost of making the change – in terms of your time and effort if you do it yourself and financial cost if you get someone else to do it.

Plan for a 3-year life cycle, depending on what you purchase.

Consider the impact on your business if your machine is out of commission for whatever reason – and particularly if it has to be sent away for repair.

Chris says on a frequent basis he is asked about the difference between a Windows machine and a Mac – is one better than the other? Sensibly, he says choose what you are comfortable with using but – if you do opt for Windows, then spend as much on that machine as you would if you were buying a Mac (i.e. buy a decent machine). If you are an employer and provide machines for your staff, consider what a new recruit might be familiar with and how much adaptation they might have to make if they are used to a different type of machine.

It's not the best plan to use the same machine for business and leisure activities. Apart from the obvious risk of damage or loss of information, there are best practice rules under GDPR about what software should be retained on machines used for business purposes.

Laptops are increasingly important as more and more clinical processes become digital. Tablets are also widely used for business – and also as clinical 'tools' in therapy sessions.

Depending on what your paper-based requirements are, it's worth investing in a printer which also copies and scans and will cope with double-sided printing at speed. In addition, consider the cost of the ink; cheaper printers often have more expensive ink or print fewer pages per cartridge. Look for printers that use liquid ink – it tends to last longer. Modern ink printers tend to be almost as good quality as a laser printer and consume far less energy to run.

Software advice and maintenance

What routes are available?

- Microsoft: most people go down this route
- Google apps: they offer a full office suite

- Open Office: (a free office suite). More maintenance might be needed if you choose this route as there can be compatibility issues

Most people choose either Microsoft or Google apps – we return to this a little later when talking about email.

Chris says there are the standard office software packages (Word, Excel, PowerPoint) but you might want to consider whether you need any specialist software (some of which might have specific hardware requirements – so have it in mind when choosing your machine).

The obvious additional software needed is security software; consider how you will protect yourself from malware and viruses. These days machines have built-in security software, such as Windows Defender and Mac Xprotect or Gatekeeper, which do a very good job. However, depending on what you do and what you are exposed to, something additional might be necessary. Take the lead on this from your trusted IT provider.

*... they purchase too many different products and services which overlap and do similar things. Pick one tool and make the most of what it can do. Microsoft 365 suite includes lots of good products which cover **most** things that **most** people need.*

IT support

This might well be a way to get set up at the beginning but then, when they are not available and things go wrong, you could be in difficulties, including having to pay an ad hoc charge for whatever help was needed.

The authors engaged the services of an IT company very early on and it was the right decision for them. Chris advises everyone to consider what is their role in the business. Where is their time best spent? Is it in setting up computers and dealing with niggles when things aren't running as they should? These issues are frustrating and they eat into the time which should be spent on the core role.

> *When things go wrong, we want to make a call and know that someone will jump onto the machine (remote assistance) and take all the hassle away.*

Here are the authors' IT provider 'must-haves':

- Accessibility
- Responsiveness

- Value for money
- Good communication skills (to be able to understand and explain things to novices!)
- An understanding of your business and what systems and processes it needs
- A sound knowledge of the General Data Protection Regulation (GDPR) and what your business needs to be compliant

In addition, Chris advises that reliability and responsiveness go without saying – and these can be hard to judge so look at Google reviews. What do existing customers have to say? A good package should include security software, an allowance of time for sorting problems, the availability of online training so that customers can increase their own skills, security awareness training and software package licences.

Consider your relationship with your IT provider as a partnership

- Are they right for your business?
- Do they understand your business?
- What sized organisations do they usually support?
- Does your business fit that profile?
- Are they geared up to recognise when your business is growing and can help you manage the challenges?

Costs will vary significantly, which is why it's important that you know what you are getting. Chris says some providers may charge as little as under £10 per hour per user – and he would question the value of that as they just wouldn't have the budget to provide any value-added services or to keep their own staff up-to-date.

An average cost at the time of writing for around ten staff would be between £50 and £60 per user per month and should include the security software, Microsoft 365 licences, training and an all-inclusive package for fixing problems.

Just be aware of what you will be getting for the money you're paying.

Knowing all these things are in place is a huge weight removed and leaves us to get on with our core business – delivering speech and language therapy services to our clients.

E-mail systems

A fundamental mistake that organisations make is around email choices.

Because a certain number of free email accounts are available with web hosting, people assume this is what they need. But it can cause so many difficulties and issues further down the line that it just isn't worth it.

A proper professional business needs proper business-grade email. Chris says that people who are serious about their business use either Microsoft 365 or Google Gmail. Whichever one you choose, your IT provider will support you and train you on the system. Then, 'embrace their products' – get the most out of the services available.

A word to the wise!

If you decide to go with Gmail but then want to use Microsoft Office 365, you are essentially paying twice.

A final piece of advice from Chris: make sure your IT provider understands the following three terms: SPF, DKIM, DMARC. These are important configuration items that need to be set up on your email. You don't need to understand the technology – but your provider does! Essentially, these items will maximise the delivery of your message (so it doesn't end up in the recipient's junk) and will help to ensure that your email can't be faked. This is particularly important if you are using CRM (mailing list software).

File storage and backups

Most modern businesses these days store files in the cloud.

Be aware of what you are storing and where and design a good folder structure. Again, regardless of the route you choose (Microsoft's SharePoint and OneDrive or Google's Google Drive), make sure that the permissions are properly set up.

This enables the sharing of some folders with particular team members and also ensures other folders remain confidential.

Your IT provider can help you with this.

Be aware of where your data storage is located. GDPR requires that all data collected on citizens must be either stored in the EU, so it is subject to European privacy laws, or within a jurisdiction that has similar levels of protection. Nothing has changed post-Brexit as current UK data protection law was amended to include all the GDPR regulations.

Both Microsoft and Google will tell you where your data is stored. Both these providers manage the storage *infrastructure* (not the files themselves) and they recommend in their terms and conditions that you use a third party to provide backups. Again, this is something your IT provider will manage for you and there will be a monthly cost for a back-up service.

Test your back-up. It isn't a back-up until you have checked. Chris recommends you test your back-up on a monthly basis by asking your provider to restore one or two files. Choose different files each time. These would be files you have changed in the last month. The point of the exercise is to retrieve a previous version so you can check if your back-ups are working. You wouldn't expect to pay anything additional for this service. The restoration cost should be included in the package from your provider.

Anything which is being stored elsewhere will also need back-up.

Are you storing files on your device?

This carries risk if your laptop is lost or stolen, or simply breaks down. If you are using SharePoint or Google Drive, there is a process whereby work is saved directly onto the drive and not directly onto your machine and you can access your files on another device or on your iPhone.

NB: Mobile phones used for work purposes also need high levels of security and adequate back-up.

Collaboration

This is about using technology for meetings, working together remotely on documents etc. Both Microsoft (Teams) and Google (Google Meet) have collaboration software. Again, Chris advises making use of these products rather than spending money on another system.

There's nothing more frustrating than poor sound quality and blurry visuals!!

To get the most out of remote meetings, purchase a decent microphone. Whether you opt for a microphone or a headset depends on how many calls you are making and where from.

Think about your camera angle and any lighting issues/reflection. Ideally the light should be shining on your face and not be behind you – which will make you difficult to see.

Set a professional background to avoid people passing to and fro behind you or jumbled/messy shelving or personal information being on show. It's worth remembering that some cheap laptops don't support virtual backgrounds.

Documentation and policies

Chris recognises that people might not feel these are required right at the beginning, but advocates that organisations which 'do it well, *do* start their documentation from the beginning'.

Some kind of documentation is needed to describe your IT system and how it works. It sets out what to do and how to do it. Whilst there is only you – and for some readers there will only be themselves as individual providers – there isn't an issue, but as soon as others join the team, idiosyncratic ways of working will inevitably creep in. At the very least, the team should be naming and saving files in the same way, using the recommended software, following cybersecurity guidance and complying with GDPR.

Whether you develop a policy or a guideline is up to you and the advice we give in Chapter 10 will help you decide.

A word to the wise!

Keep abreast of specialist advice in a rapidly changing sector

(Developing more formal documentation around IT processes is on *our* action plan for the future.)

A budget for IT

There are three key points to make here.

1
When you set your budget, think of it as a 3-year budget i.e. what's your spend going to be over 3 years?
The outlay in year 1 is likely to be quite hefty as hardware purchases are made, then less in years 2 and 3 and then to rise again in year 4.
This needs to be on your asset register – see Chapter 8.

2
Keep a spreadsheet of all your monthly recurring costs (your IT provider, licences etc etc). Review this on a 6 monthly basis and see if you still use/need all the things you are paying for. Dispense with what you don't need. Be ruthless, you can always pick something up again in the future.

3
Set an IT budget for each person in the team. If/when you employ someone, there will be additional costs (hardware, software, maybe a mobile phone). Know what extra costs are being incurred and think about the budget per individual as a % of what you pay them. Decent kit and services will make them more efficient and effective and feel more valued in the long run.

Before we move on to talk specifically about cyber security, a final general comment about IT from Chris: the IT world changes quickly – make sure you have someone you *trust* to keep you up-to-date with what's relevant to **you** and **your business**!

Cyber security

Chris has divided his expert advice into seven sections.

1. Introduction

The first point that Chris makes is that IT and cyber security are not the same. This is important to know, as most of us are likely to assume that our IT provider will also be looking after security. To some extent they will – in that IT companies will talk about the technical aspects of security (such as malware protection, running updates and configuring firewalls). These are all the technical things many of us don't really understand but we need to know enough to ensure we can ask our IT provider the right questions and seek the right assurances. Cybersecurity is more about the *non*-technical considerations.

How do we define cyber security? Chris says that a panel of five cyber security advisors would give five different answers – which is confusing and doesn't help us to understand what needs to be in place at a basic level. He acknowledges that this is a problem for the industry as a whole, let alone a small business!

> *Cyber security is how to protect your digital assets from internet-born threats.*

In the UK, we have access to the National Cyber Security Centre (NCSC) – a government website, which amongst lots of other useful information, makes recommendations about what businesses should have in place.

www.ncyber securityc.gov.uk/ [1]

Chris strongly recommends a visit to the *cyber essentials* part of the NCSC.

www.ncsc.gov.uk/cyberessentials/resources [2]

He describes this as reasonably accessible for the novice – 'it will give you a good basic "feel" and should prompt you "interrogate" the people who look after your security'.

2. The role of people in the cyber security process

This is primarily about training. How do we educate both ourselves and our team about what they should and shouldn't be doing? Do we access any training? What should training include?

> *Most breaches are down to human error.*

To tackle this in a phased way is a good idea. Start with general cyber awareness training for everyone. Depending on the size of your organisation (or, if you are a sole practitioner, by joining forces with others), you can set up a more in-depth focus group/team discussion.

This idea fits well into the non-clinical supervision model and also the emerging ASLTIP non-geographical groups which are emerging in response to areas of particular interest.

Chris advises businesses to ask their IT provider about specialist training they have in terms of cyber security. This is a field which is changing very quickly, and we should bear in mind that keeping up-to-date will have a budget implication.

Chris has produced a video guide which looks specifically at passwords. Find it here www.youtu.be/sXLy3nXJDO8 [3].

3. Planning

Plan for things to go wrong. Think in terms of 'when' rather than 'if'. What could go wrong and what action will you take? Write your plan down and exercise it regularly: '*treat it like a fire drill. The more you practice, the more you will learn and be better prepared to deal with the real thing when it happens*'.

If like us you have read the last few sentences and are at a loss as to where to start, visit the National Cyber Security website and search for 'exercises in a box'. This is a free online tool that provides exercises for any organisation to test and practice their response to a variety of cyber-attacks. All you have to do is register (which is free).

www.exerciseinabox.service.ncyber securityc.gov.uk/ [4]

There are resources with scenarios which encourage people to consider how they would respond in particular circumstances. As you go through the exercises, you rate how you feel about each scenario and then it gives you an action plan to improve afterwards.

I haven't a clue where to start...

Document what you do – this is the basis of your plan. Again, if you are a sole practitioner, joining up with others to work things through is a sensible option.

Now is a good time to revisit your risk register and make sure IT and security have a presence there. Your 'disaster' plan will go a long way to mitigating risk.

Documenting your IT procedures in general is a good plan – including how you do things on a day-to-day basis. For example, what is your process for adding a new user or for authorising someone to have administrator access to your system? Does your IT provider know what your processes are and how they operate?

4. **The importance of technical controls**

Passwords: Chris is the first to acknowledge that passwords are 'a pain'! He advocates that we should have different passwords for every single system – and whilst there is nothing wrong with writing passwords ◄───── down, there are alternatives.

> In a high-security environment, writing down passwords would be frowned upon – encouraging break-ins to access the passwords. For most of us the threat comes from people outside our organisation – from the internet, so writing them down is not such a big risk.

Password awareness managers or 'vaults'
These are 'bits of password-protected software' which sit on your computer or on the cloud and help you manage your passwords. In simpler form, they integrate into your browser and whenever you go to a website you have visited before, the 'vault' will automatically populate the username and password for you. When you go to a new website and have to set a new password, the 'vault' will often auto-generate (and remember) a password for you.

The vault has the capacity to generate and store hundreds of passwords. Is this system secure? Yes, generally so, and it's far more secure than using the same or similar password for every system! The few incidents that do occur are usually because the password for the vault itself is weak.

Multifactor authentication: this is a fundamental technical control to have in place. This involves a requirement to put in two different types of information in order to be able to log into a system (two of the three options below):

- Something you know: e.g. a password
- Something you are: e.g. a fingerprint or facial recognition
- Something you have: e.g. an app on your mobile or a code sent to your phone

Multifactor authentication means that even if the password is compromised, intruders can't access the system because they don't have the other component.

Knowing a little about the technical controls allows the novice to seek the right advice to move forward with increasing security.

Updates: these are important and failing to update will compromise security. Cyber essentials advise updates to happen 'within 14 days'. Seek confirmation that your IT provider is doing this. After weak passwords, the second most common reason someone compromises your systems is through a vulnerability that already had an update which hadn't been applied.

Culture: Chris advises that we should encourage open discussion about cyber security. By regular awareness raising, it will stay at the forefront of our minds.

The impact of cyber criminality has made people reluctant to talk about it – many just 'sweep it under the carpet'. Because they don't share what happens to them, the criminals are able to use the same techniques over and over again.

Find ways in your team or support groups to talk about cyber security – to share experiences – your own and those of other people.

5. Trusted advice and frameworks

> The National Cyber Security Centre (NCSC) has become the primary go-to resource in the UK.

Alongside the 'exercises in a box' resource, there are blogs for small businesses and additional services if you are a charitable organisation.

Cyber advisors: launched by the UK government in April 2023, a qualification for both individuals and organisations which confirms that they are competent to advise small businesses about cyber security. When sourcing advice, look for the official badge from the NCSC.

Looking beyond the basic cyber security, there are various frameworks for cyber security 'good practice'. Cyber essentials is the entry level. For readers who want to develop a deeper understanding, there are other frameworks.

The next step up for small businesses is IASME Cyber Assurance.

www.iasme.co.uk/iasme-cyber-assurance/free-download-of-iasme-self-assessment-questions/ [5]

Using cyber essentials is the single most important piece of advice I would give.

This is a good framework to use if/when you are ready to move on. It offers a step-by-step plan to implement cost-effective cyber security. It looks at the technical side but will also help with policies and procedures.

> Chris advises that when tendering for contracts, businesses are asked if they have an 'information security management system' in place. Tenders often ask for systems '*like; ISO27001 – which makes people think that's what they need … usually though it's just because that's the most well-known one. IASME Cyber Assurance is far more relevant and manageable for small businesses*'.

At the time of writing, the IASME for small businesses costs about £5K.

There will be readers who already have experience of submitting tenders for contracts. Others will be frustrated by the fact that independent providers rarely get close to tendering. For some, the idea will be a world away. In Chapter 16, we talk about 'levelling the playing field' in terms of commissioners being willing to consider a *range* of providers for delivering services … so maybe not quite the pipe dream some may think …

The final word from Chris

Cyber security is constantly evolving, constantly changing.

Cyber security is a journey not a destination

There will always be more that we can do as the bad guys are on a mission to get around the controls we put in place. Get started on the cyber essentials and if you need help, look for someone with cyber advisor status.

There is an excellent blog available to members on the ASLTIP website; it very closely reflects the advice just given on cyber security, so we haven't repeated it here. What we *have* included, however, is the personal experience of one of the blog authors.

A very convincing phishing email with an attachment was sent from my business email address to more than 1,400 people. I was alerted to this by a vigilant colleague. My advice would be:

- *Don't panic*
- *Prepare for many phone calls, texts and emails from people telling you that you have been hacked. For me, this included some clients, relatives, the ASLTIP Chair, ex NHS manager and IT managers from solicitor firms, to name a few*
- *Act quickly. Fortunately, our IT team (who we had employed just three months previously) were sent the email so called me straightway to shut my email account down and make it secure – this made a big difference*
- *Be prepared for companies to refuse to communicate with you via email until you can demonstrate you have investigated your cyber-attack and can identify the extent of your data breach. This happened with three firms of solicitors I worked with, and it was terrifying*
- *Don't be afraid to call the ICO. They were very helpful, and I was able to talk to an actual person who helped me consider how data may have been breached. Because the hacker had accessed my inbox, they also had access to any email attachments which may have had unprotected client data: reports, minutes of meetings, therapy plans and so on. The ICO confirmed that I needed to report the breach and I was required to complete an online form, regarding what had happened, actions taken and how I was going to*

prevent further attacks. They then considered the case and four long days later concluded that I had done all I could and gave some further helpful links and advice regarding cybersecurity

- *Make sure you are registered with the ICO*
- *Keep your inbox to a minimum. Save attachments safely and delete unnecessary emails. My inbox was overflowing at the time of the attack*
- *Reassure people after the event. Some of my clients and relatives were very upset by this event and I took time to talk to them about what had happened and how we were increasing security to keep their data safe*
- *Talk to your team. We were only a small team of three with four email addresses, but it was important to talk as a team about how to keep the company email addresses secure*
- *Write a policy*

Naomi Saul: www.communicationrehab.co.uk/ [6]

References

1. National Cyber Security Centre. GOV.UK. Available at: https://www.gov.uk/government/organisations/national-cyber-security-centre.
2. *Resources*. NCSC. Available at: https://www.ncsc.gov.uk/cyberessentials/resources.
3. Blunt, C. (2022) *Password Awareness Training for Cyber Essentials*. YouTube. Available at: https://youtu.be/sXLy3nXJDO8.
4. Exercise in a Box. (n.d.) *Exercise in a Box*. Available at: https://exerciseinabox.service.ncsc.gov.uk/.
5. *Free Download of IASME Self-Assessment Questions* (2022) Iasme. Available at: https://iasme.co.uk/iasme-cyber-assurance/free-download-of-iasme-self-assessment-questions/.
6. Saul, N. Communication Rehab. Available at: https://communicationrehab.co.uk/.

12 The team

In this chapter, we discuss what skills you might recruit to your team. Here we are talking about *roles* and not whether you decide to employ or sub-contract (we talk about this in Chapter 5). We will also think about how, having identified the roles, you might recruit and retain the right people who will fit your team ethos. We will also list outsourced functions you might need.

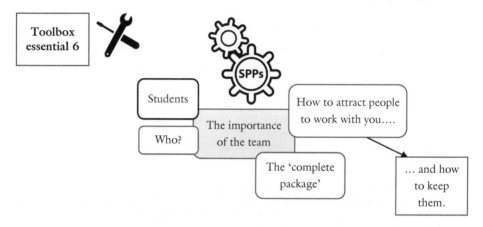

The 'functions' you need will depend on both business and your clinical service delivery models. Let's make an assumption that, like us, you are 'starting small'.

Identifying the skills you will need: here are some key actions.

A (i)**List** your **business functions**. The toolbox essentials will provide you with a ready-made list to get things underway. You can always add to it – but be sure to keep that word 'essential' at the forefront of your mind. The business functions support the clinical service delivery, not the other way round

(ii) Now think about the **frequency** with which you will have to carry out these activities

- Some things will be one-off pieces of work to get something in place which will then only require some maintenance (or review). Policies, procedures and guidelines fall into this category, as do most of the documentation in toolbox essential one (the day-to-day stuff) and refreshing or reviewing the formats of your contracts

- Other things will be busier at particular times of the year. Examples here would be preparing for the financial year end, renewing client contracts and adjusting the financial forecast – this is especially busy for services like ours that deliver into schools with contracts running for an academic year

DOI: 10.4324/9781003382928-13

- Other activity will be cyclical – such as invoicing and (for us) regular check-ins with clients to see how their service is running.

(iii) Now think about the **scale**. Obviously the more clients you have, the more client-focussed business activity there will be – and the more team members you will need. The one-off jobs and maintenance will stay the same but the invoicing, keeping team details up-to-date, contract re-negotiation, check-ins with clients and with team members will all take more time

Having identified the 'functions', the frequency and the scale, decide who can do what. At the beginning it is very likely to be you doing it all! As your business grows you may decide to recruit someone into a book-keeping or administrative role. If you do, thought needs to be given to where you will site that person. Do you have premises for example? In Chapter 13, we talk about clinical models of service delivery and that includes *where* your service will be delivered. You might rent space to establish a clinic (or use accommodation on your own premises). You might rent office space from which to run your business and store equipment. You might work from home – but inviting an employee to work from your personal space may not be the right thing for everyone. In the case of our business, we have no premises, and just rent a storage unit for equipment.

At what point might you decide to seek the support of an administrator and/or book-keeper (better still if that person has the skills to undertake a dual role!) or an archivist?

We store our discharged files electronically and the archivist's job is to scan paper files and arrange the shredding of the paper copies, to add the electronic files to the store and update the database.

The decision about additional posts you might recruit to is driven primarily by finance – i.e. can your business afford to maintain a role which, in essence, generates no direct income? What do you need to add to your fees in order to offset this overhead?

Another important consideration is which tasks that person can undertake in order to free *you* to protect your work-life balance, which, after all, is one of the great attractions of working independently.

Also, there are some aspects of running a business which you might find more challenging than others and having some help might greatly relieve the pressure. Partners, friends and wider family have lots of skills they share either on a formal basis or more informally. We know one clinician whose husband runs the financial side of her business, leaving her free to concentrate on the clinical service.

There are pros and cons to using these kinds of informal connections. Assess the risks involved. How rigorous and sustainable are they? What happens if events in personal relationships adversely impact the business arrangements?

B (i) Revisit your **clinical service delivery model**. Let's use speech and language therapy as the example here, although the roles are easily transferable to other professional groups. You will need speech and language therapists and you may also decide you need a therapy assistant role.

The skills and expertise you require will depend on the type of work your business will do and the number of 'bodies' you need will depend on the amount of work you have.

At the outset it might just be you, but over time, if your long-term plan is to grow your business, you will need team members. Whether you decide to employ or sub-contract will be entirely a matter for you. There are pros and cons to both (discussed in more detail in Chapter 5).

Recruitment

Whatever the role you are looking for, you *must* ensure that person is 'fit for purpose'. In our own experience, and from conversations with others whilst researching this book, it's better to wait for the right person than settle for someone who becomes a liability because they take up a lot of your time managing/coaching them. In a previous life, Diana had shares in a small bus company where an administrator role was filled with no application process and no interview. It clearly exposed the risk of recruiting 'a friend', someone who is 'nice and local' or someone you don't feel you can challenge (never mind dispense with, should the need arise) for whatever reason.

The bookkeeper/administrator role is easier to recruit in a formal way. You know the tasks you want fulfilled, you can write a job description and a person specification and set up some scenarios at interview. Don't forget to ask for references! Depending on your set-up, this person might be the first point of contact for your business.

Consider whether they are efficient, effective, empathetic and trustworthy and able to fully function in your absence – because, for much of the time you *might* be absent delivering your service. Even if this isn't the case and you are co-located in office-type accommodation, if you find yourself micro-managing that person, the impact on profit is obvious.

Therapists

The right skills and experience for your business model	You are looking for therapists who can deliver as per your clinical model and client groups. Within our team of paediatric therapists, we have people with a variety of special interests (fluency, autism, AAC) and some preferred age groups and settings. However, everyone is able to assess, diagnose and treat a wide range of paediatric SLCN.

They are able to deliver training for parents and a range of other professionals involved with the client groups. The variety of backgrounds, experience and skills brings a richness and strength to the team as a whole – there is always someone to call upon if others feel they need someone to talk things through with – in addition to the clinical supervision arrangements they have outside of the team.

Recruitment	There are various ways you might recruit people to your team: advertising, trawling for new graduates at HEIs, offering taster opportunities and word of mouth (existing team members will spread the word amongst people they know).

At the time of writing, therapists are in short supply and those with established skills and experience even more so. People hear about our team almost always by word of mouth. We have advertised in the past – and this can work, but can also be hugely expensive, with limited (or zero) return depending on where the adverts are placed. In the past, we have recruited new graduates (with varying degrees of success), and this may be the solution for you. If you do decide to go down this route, don't underestimate the levels of support that person will need in order to become fit for purpose (able to operate autonomously and represent your business). You will need to invest to accumulate. With the right person, this can be not only a great opportunity for a new graduate but also part of building your team going forward.

Recruiting and supporting a new graduate can future-proof your workforce.

Calculating the cost of supporting a new graduate

Newly qualified speech and language therapists will need to go through the RCSLT competency process irrespective of where they work. You/your team will need to provide the support, supervision and coaching required as the new recruit works towards competency, gathering evidence and seeking the experiences and opportunities needed to fill any gaps. Team members should be realistically remunerated for supporting the new graduate. In our business, where clients are offered a combination of experienced team member and inexperienced new recruit, the costs would reflect this.

Other professions may have different systems but regardless of the job role, all new graduates need a properly planned and long-term support plan in place.

In *our* business model a new graduate working towards competencies may well be able to accelerate the process, as the range of requirements is likely to be narrower than those identified in public sector roles.

However, it would be sensible to budget for between six and nine months of support (and potential reduced charges to settings).

> Make sure that the competency framework reflects the environment in which your business operates.

New graduates and independent practice

New graduates may be wary of joining a team which sub-contracts rather than employs its team – and this is completely understandable. In Chapter 5, specialist contributor Sarah Buckley talks about why she employs rather than sub-contracts her team.

Self-employment is not for everyone. The amount and type of information available to final-year students from their HEI varies (see Chapter 4). Some report being actively discouraged from considering the independent sector (quite why this should be is a mystery). However, being self-employed and working *alone* as a new graduate is definitely not something we would advise!

That said, there are other options somewhere in the middle of these two extremes. If sub-contracting is your business model, you can go a long way to inform and reassure your potential new recruit, pointing them in the right direction as to where they can find out much more and get the support they need. You can also encourage more creative ways that they can embark on their new professional life. More than one final-year student we spoke to was undecided whether to work with adults or children – mixed posts are almost extinct these days. To consider taking up two part-time posts is a possibility, one of which could be in the public sector and the other in independent practice.

If you are an independent practice and an employer, new graduates should be asking exactly the same questions as they would if applying for a post in the public sector.

Our toolbox essentials talk about …

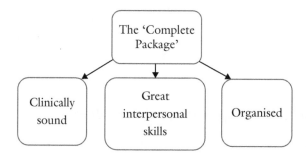

We can all make allowances for a degree of eccentricity and some quirkiness can add to a team. However, sloppiness, laziness, disinhibition and any/all things late just don't make the cut!

A word to the wise!

Unless your team can perform across all three of these parameters (clinical, interpersonal and organisational), they *will* cost you time and, eventually, money.

We mention some of the mistakes (some our own and some that other people tell us they have made) in Chapter 15.

We really can't over-emphasize this. Your team represents *you*. On our website, the following is how we introduce our team to the world. This message is there for potential customers as well as therapists checking us out as a possible source of work.

Soundswell therapists come from a variety of back-grounds, but they all have one thing in common, they want to make the biggest possible difference to outcomes for children and young people with speech, language and communication needs.

Our therapists are the face of Soundswell – they are talented, personable and good communicators.

Induction

There are good reasons for spending a bit of time on planning what kind of induction you might need for new members to your team. It's difficult for anyone to get swiftly and confidently up to speed if no one explains about processes and procedures! You need new people to settle in fast, as that is to everyone's benefit. Also – from your organisational viewpoint, it is far more difficult to monitor compliance if individuals are thrown in at the deep end and expected to just pick it up as they go along.

What team members need to know will vary according to your business model and the way you deliver your clinical service (and the role you are expecting them to undertake). With that in mind, it's useful to divide your processes and procedures into things that fit well together under different headings. In effect, you are creating an induction checklist to ensure that nothing is overlooked.

There will be things the new recruit needs to provide *you* with and vice versa. Our checklist is part of a broader document, Section A of which identifies more information which will help the new recruit. The information is divided into three categories:

- Required
- Recommended
- For information

Personalise the document (and checklist). You might, for example, identify who to go to or where/how specific information can be found. Then give ownership to the new member whose responsibility it is to ensure they have familiarised themselves with the requirements in Section A and provided the information in Section B.

Remember to keep it *simple and restricted to what is necessary*. If you are employing the individual, you will probably be paying them to manage their induction checklist – in which case they won't be producing income.

If the individual is self-employed, you won't be paying them at all!

> NB: Our associates and our archivist are self-employed.

Here is our induction checklist

It includes items that both the team member and the directors need to action and is a shared document passing between us until all boxes are ticked.

This document includes information from ASLTIP's 'Setting up in independent practice checklists'. However, Soundswell does *not* require therapists to be members of ASLTIP.

The items on this checklist include some which are requirements, some are recommendations and some are for information only.

	Required/recommended/for info only
Section A	
Professional bodies	
You are required to be registered with HCPC and RCSLT.	Required
Read RCSLT guidance sheets. Non-speech and language therapists would seek guidance from their own professional body.	Recommended
Membership of ASLTIP, committing to abide by code of conduct available via this link: https://www.flipsnack.com/helpwithtalking/code-of-conduct-2020.html [1].	Information
Information Commissioners Office (ICO)	
You must be registered with the ICO.	Required
You must comply with Soundswell's data security and privacy policy and GDPR procedures (further information will be given).	
More information and training around information governance at https://ico.org.uk [2].	
Record keeping	
Paper or electronic notes are acceptable.	Information
Paper records must be stored in a secure filing cabinet either in the setting (cabinet supplied by Soundswell), or at therapist's home with agreement.	
Electronic records must be held within Soundswell Team cloud storage.	
Records are audited periodically.	
Further guidance and templates can be found in cloud storage.	
DBS	
Enhanced DBS check (children's workforce) required and sign up to the auto-renewal system (preferred).	Required
If adult workforce is required therapist will be notified.	
Tax and national insurance	
Register with the Inland Revenue that you are running a business.	Required
HMRC (Inland Revenue) www.hmrc.gov.uk 0845 915 4655	Information
You will be taxed as a self-employed person.	
You can, if appropriate, have dual status and be taxed as both employed and self-employed.	
You must register as self-employed within three months of setting up.	
National Insurance contributions will reflect your self-employed status.	
Pension	
For advice about setting up a pension www.dwp.gov.uk [3].	Information
Business model	
There are a variety of business models available; HMRC is a good place to look for more detail.	Information
Soundswell needs to know what your business model is for our own accounting purposes.	Required
Personal safety	
As an independent therapist you will be travelling into schools and people's homes – ensure that someone is aware of your home visit locations and at what time you are expected back at http://www.suzylamplugh.org [4].	Recommended
Soundswell holds next of kin details.	Required
Insurance	
Membership of RCSLT provides professional indemnity and public liability.	Information

CPD and supervision	
You are responsible for your own CPD and supervision arrangements, see RCSLT guidelines. Soundswell host a twice-yearly CPD day for which there is no charge to attend.	Required
Safeguarding	
Soundswell's Safeguarding guidelines will be provided at induction and updates circulated as required. Level 3 (or equivalent) safeguarding training is required every 3 years. Members of ASLTIP can access this as part of their membership via educare.co.uk [5]. Team members who are not ASLTIP members can find training guidance in our safeguarding guidance document in the team cloud storage.	Required
Equipment	
You are expected to have your own equipment and assessments, with the exception of some of the more expensive items which we are able to loan to therapists as required. A full list is in the team cloud storage folder.	Information
Timetables and invoicing	
Team members complete a timetable in team cloud storage. This is used to generate invoices to settings and therefore must be accurate. Invoices are submitted at the end of each month and are paid within the first week of the following month. Invoices must match timetables in order for payment to be made promptly.	Information
Risk and incident	
Soundswell's risk and incident policy will be provided and updates circulated as required.	Required
Section B	

Completed

Meet director	Taster sessions completed
CV (inc address and mobile number)	Info and photo for our website
Next of kin	Data security and privacy policy [read/sign]
DBS number and date	GDPR compliance document [read/sign]
DBS letter for schools prepared	Safeguarding guidelines [read]
RCSLT number	Risk and incident policy [read/sign]
HCPC number and name	Data sharing agreement [read]
Safeguarding training date	Data processing agreement [read]
ICO number and date	Contract issued
Passport seen and page copied	Cloud storage access
Utility bill seen and address copied	Rates of pay shared
References x 2	ID badge

Retention

Having built your team, you need to keep them! In Chapter 1, we speak about the importance of the team, without which there *is* no service. Because our team is made up of autonomous self-employed professionals, we are mindful of the restrictions imposed by IR35 (HMRC: Understanding off-payroll working) [6]. We must demonstrate how we value them in ways more qualitative than quantitative (apart from paying them of course!). Our philosophy is nurture without nannying. To support but not dictate. We are non-hierarchical; no one team member is more important than another.

We keep in regular touch with the team either in person or via a video call as well as email. We actively encourage them to keep us up to speed with how things are going with their settings – this means we can be proactive if there are any issues as well as positive developments.

One of the reasons why therapists opt for independent practice is because they want to *enjoy* what they do, to be able to get up in the morning and actively look forward to their day. To be able to use their skills and expertise to make a difference.

When we contract with a client, it's a two-way process. Yes, we have responsibilities, but the setting *also* has a role to play in ensuring that the therapists can do their job.

We source the work, i.e. make the decision as to whether we accept a setting or renew a contract. In conjunction with the therapist, we will also make the decision to withdraw if, despite everyone's best efforts, things are not working out as they should.

> Read more about how and when things go wrong in Chapter 15

We put on two continuing professional development (CPD) days a year. Opportunities to network and enjoy food together are an integral part of a programme which contains clinical elements but also well-being components and fun (a sense of humour should perhaps be an official part of the 'complete package'). The team are involved in deciding and delivering the topics for the day, but we also try to invite speakers – perhaps from one of our client settings or someone with a more strategic view of the provider landscape.

After one particularly difficult year for a number of us in the team, we focussed more on well-being and ways for individuals to cope with the stresses of life in general. None of us is immune to the ups and downs which are routine in all our lives. There are ways to help each other over crises without being overly intrusive. Our team are particularly good at mutual support on a number of different levels. It is this kind of ethos which takes time to build but once it's there it weathers most storms.

Outsourced functions

Outsourcing means paying someone else to do pieces of work for you. You cannot do everything yourself and so, if the business is to grow and thrive, it's wise to outsource some functions.

Again, depending on your business model, how big you plan to grow and the skills and expertise you may have access to on an informal basis.

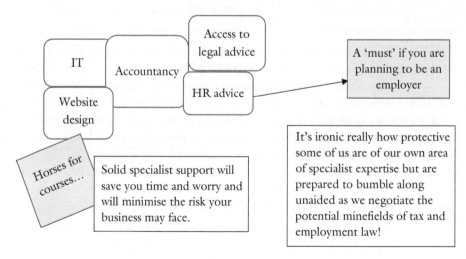

There are companies which may provide several specialist skills under one roof and also companies which specialise in particular industry areas.

Students

References to students are made in various places in the book. In Chapter 4, we talk about their contribution to one of the focus groups, and in Chapter 16, the importance of placements and employment are discussed. We mention them here too as, in essence, they *should* be members of our team and, if some of the barriers to offering placements in the independent sector could be overcome, there would be more opportunities to include them.

> The sole practitioner and students

Laura is firmly committed to training the next generation of therapists and would take students if this was reasonably easy to do. She has links to three HEIs. The checklist of compliance requirements from one was lengthy and beyond the reach of a sole practitioner. Some of it assumed that placements would be within the NHS:

'*Educators promote and demonstrate values and behaviours that reflect integrity and current NHS Constitution*'.

> *One thing I have learned is you can only access the student placement IT system for feedback and assessment if you have an NHS email address … this has been a big barrier for me as a clinical educator in this role.*

In another, unrelated instance, Laura had a plan to involve students to support the delivery of some aphasia groups. However, there were barriers to this: the students could only be recruited as volunteers, but the experience wouldn't count towards Laura's required hours as a placement tutor or count as a placement as far as the students were concerned.

Sarah's company offers student placements – they are a key part of her recruitment strategy We asked Sarah what barriers, to recruitment in general, she had come across and how had she overcome them.

> *Recruitment is a challenge for all speech and language therapy providers, NHS, IP or others* (at the time of writing). *Think about your recruitment strategy for the short, medium and long term.*
>
> *I offer a work experience package for individuals thinking of studying SLT and have just recruited my first new graduate who did the training after attending the work experience programme five years ago. Long-term!*
>
> *I have good links with local HEIs and regularly offer placements that network me with graduating SLTs. I offer incentives for student SLTs to engage with my practice. I attend jobs fairs and RCSLT events to promote my business.*
>
> *I have also invested time and money in getting a sponsorship licence and am now in a position to recruit and sponsor overseas SLTs who want to work in the UK. There is a cost implication here, but it is not as high as using agencies who typically want 25% of starting salary plus VAT.*

> *Network with other local SLTs – it could be that they interview someone who is not a good fit for them, but may work well for you.*

In terms of offering student placements, there is variability across the nations. In her role as ASLTIP chair, Sarah advises willing independent practitioners to seek support from ASLTIP, which works strategically with RCSLT and is networked with HEIs.

Read more about Sarah's approach to being an employer in Chapter 5.

References

1. *Code of Conduct 2020*. Flipsnack. Available at: https://www.flipsnack.com/helpwithtalking/code-of -conduct-2020.html.
2. *Information Commissioner's Office (ICO)*. Available at: https://ico.org.uk/.
3. *Department for Work and Pensions*. GOV.UK. Available at: http://www.dwp.gov.uk/.
4. *Live_Life_Safe Suzy Lamplugh Trust*. Suzy Lamplugh Trust. Available at: https://www.suzylamplugh .org/.
5. *Making Online Learning Simple*. EduCare. Available at: https://www.educare.co.uk/.
6. HM Revenue & Customs. (2023) *Understanding Off-payroll Working (IR35)*. GOV.UK. Available at: https://www.gov.uk/guidance/understanding-off-payroll-working-ir35.

13 Clinical service delivery

Simple steps to launch your (clinical) model

This chapter examines key aspects of clinical service delivery which are closely linked and lend themselves to discussion sequentially.

The different ways therapists might choose to deliver their services, within the context of their chosen business model (the 'offer'). We discuss different options and examples from within our own experience and as a result of discussions with a number of colleagues.

The offer

The details you will need to consider when delivering a quality and effective clinical service – things which are relevant regardless of the type and size of your business model.

Toolbox essentials

Finding (and keeping) clients – getting yourself 'out there' and getting your name known.

Engagement

Let's begin by reminding ourselves of the clinical toolbox essentials by revisiting model 2 from Chapter 10.

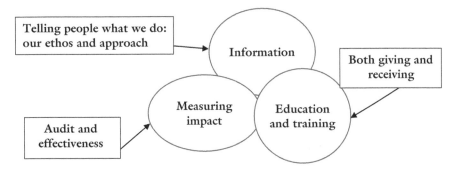

DOI: 10.4324/9781003382928-14

The context

It's worth bearing in mind that you might have a vision for the future which, at the outset, isn't feasible as you are working to get established. Whatever any of us aspire to when we take the independent path, in terms of the work we are prepared to take on, many of us (ourselves included) have initially accepted almost everything that comes along and then, as demand has increased, been able to focus in on the areas of greatest interest and satisfaction.

Never lose sight of your dreams – whether you are a sole trader or running a company, aspirations are one pretty good reason for putting together a business plan. ('This year I/we am focussing on … so that next year I/we will be able to …)

A business plan reminds you where you want to be and helps keep you on track (and helps avoid the dangers of Mission Creep; more about both of these in Chapter 7).

If your business model changes, remember to keep any advertising (including website information) current so that people looking for services do not have expectations raised which you cannot fulfil.

Business models versus clinical service delivery models

Before we look in detail at delivery models, it's worth reminding ourselves of the difference between *business* models and models of *clinical service delivery*. The former talk about how your business is configured and are covered in Chapter 5. Here we are looking at ways therapists might **deliver** their services. The two aspects are closely linked, however, because those therapists might be sole traders, company directors or direct employees (of a limited company, school or setting etc.).

As a *sole trader* you have the freedom to be the decision-maker and have complete control over what you do (and don't do). This applies whatever your source of work. If you opt to take on some work as a contractor, you can choose the work (or contractee) which best fits with your own interests and approach to delivering speech and language therapy.

As a *company director* you also have control over the decision-making and what work is taken on (including the sub-contractors which best represent your ethos and approach).

Limited companies with more than one director rely on a *shared vision*, as do partnerships. Sharing the load can only be beneficial; however, there can be pitfalls too. In Chapter 7, we talk about having an agreement in place if you and your business partner/s or co-director/s want to go your separate ways. Read Holly's story in Chapter 16 for first-hand experience of alliances that fail for whatever reason.

As a *direct employee* (of an independent company perhaps, or a school/setting), you will have less control over decision-making and the kinds of activity you will be required to undertake. That said, as with *any* post applied for, the therapist would soundly research what is involved before opting in or looking elsewhere.

In our experience, there is potentially more risk involved in taking up a post as a single, *direct employee* in a non-health related setting such as a school (whether public sector or an independent group or single establishment).

It's more important than ever to understand (and be prepared to insist upon) what you need to fulfil your professional registration requirements. To avoid becoming stale, out of touch, demotivated or unsafe, you will need access to other therapists for education, support and supervision opportunities. In terms of your workload, be clear how you will ensure that your employers are realistic about the role of the therapist, and that you are in agreement with (and can deliver) what they want.

> Independent therapist directly employed by a special school

I adapted the school's contract with me so that it reflected my role and what I need in terms of support, supervision and CPD. They accepted that I wanted the contract to be formally reviewed every year (to avoid any slippage …).

This possibly poses less of a risk for therapists employed directly by companies providing services for adult clients for example, as the very nature of their business is offering a multi-disciplinary approach to, for example, rehabilitation or voice difficulties.

Let's move forward with the assumption that you have already decided upon your business model – certainly initially and for a reasonable period of time. This will allow you to get underway. If you take on board the advice to put together a business plan (even if this is quite rudimentary), this would be the place to record future aspirations or intentions to develop and evolve your business model.

Whatever your business model, **be clear about your offer**. This piece of work needs to be complete before you can begin to engage with clients (or contractees) – so you have joint and shared expectations of what will be provided, how and why.

| Step 1 | Start by mapping what you will deliver – which is just another way of saying 'what you are going to offer'. |

- **Who** (will you work with)?
- **Where** (will you opt for the setting where the client is, or invite people into your own home or perhaps rent a consulting room)?
- **What** (difficulties do you work with)?
- **How** (what will you actually be *doing*?)

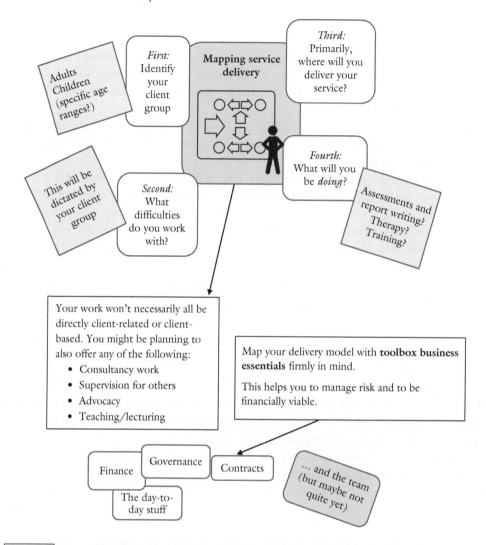

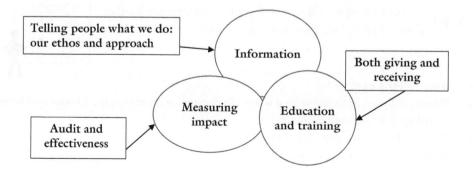

Your offer

Provide information

Telling people what you do, how you do it and share your values in a way which is

- Clear
- Transparent
- Unambiguous

Measure impact

How will you demonstrate that you are effective (so that your clients know they are getting value for money)?

Information

What is to be shared?	**Your offer:** • Client group • What you will do • The difference it will make and the importance of measuring impact **Values and ethos:** • (for us, for example,) The importance of universal strategies for managing SLCN whatever the aetiology • Liaison with public sector services **About you/your company/your team:** clients want to know you are qualified and registered and that you are skilled and experienced in the areas encompassed by your offer
With whom?	**Clients:** individuals and families **Commissioners:** schools, settings, private companies (and on occasion) public sector entities. It isn't unknown for the public sector (NHS or local authority or other) to commission a service from an independent contractor to fill a gap or meet a need. This is widely recognised in terms of medical procedures outsourced to private companies to operate on cataracts, manage knee or hip surgery for example
Some information is more of a priority for certain audiences	Individual clients want to know what you will do and whether this will resolve their difficulty. Clients such as schools and settings want to know what you will cost and what they can expect to receive as part of the package they are paying for
Where audiences differ, how will you make your information accessible?	As speech and language therapists this should be second nature to us, but this is where you may benefit from the support and knowledge of a website designer, marketing expert or social media guru. It's about ensuring the audience you want actually sees your offer, as much as it is about making it easy to understand what that offer is

Client engagement

Step 3

As we reach this point, the importance of getting step one right (the mapping exercise) becomes clear:

- What service (or services) you plan to deliver
- Identifying the recipients
- Location/s for service delivery

Map this out first and then the steps you take to attract business – and the right kind of business for you – will be more effectively targeted.

So, what can you do to get yourself known? Here are some things we have tried.

Internet presence

When looking for a product or a service (or to check what other people think about it), we all head to the internet. Remember – a website doesn't need to be all singing and all dancing from day one in the life of a fledgling independent practitioner. It's well worth taking time to look at what other people do and whether you think it works.

After over ten years, we are now on our third-generation website. Our first attempt was all we could afford in the early days. Looking back now it's probably fair to say that the first Soundswell website was feather-light, pale and one-dimensional and the impact it had was broadly commensurate! In those early days, we (rightly or wrongly) deemed an internet presence to be less of a priority as a way to attract business. We had more work than we could manage and didn't really see much need for a website.

Back then we were more in favour of personal contact – which we'll come back to later as the results of our efforts in that direction proved to be a valuable learning experience.

We would certainly advise visiting lots of websites – not just for speech and language therapy services but for other services too. This is time well spent as it will prevent possible pitfalls. Katie, our specialist contributor (website design), would agree. Here are some obvious considerations:

- Is the site easy to navigate?
- Do things link together in the same way as all the different aspects of your delivery model link together?
- Is it easy to find out what, where and how services are offered?
- Is it clear who *you* are – whether you are a sole practitioner or part of a bigger organisation?
- It's nice to see photographs too – though important to try and avoid those where informality supersedes professionalism
- Do you make it clear that you are regulated and registered and fit for purpose – with a little biography perhaps which establishes your track record?
- Is it easy for visitors to contact you?

A site has to be attractive so that visitors want to spend time – so colour is good and some animation, but not so much that things move so fast that it's hard to keep up and access the information. Think about how much text you use – break it up by varying font size and colour perhaps – but also explore other ways to get the information across (models and diagrams for example). Photos and graphics break up text and lend warmth. 'Real people doing real things' bring something that people can relate to on a personal level.

The market for offering website construction and design seems fiercely competitive – there's lots of choice out there. Cost is important but so is the relationship you will build with your designer. Can they explain the technical aspects (preferably without making you feel like a dinosaur), and will there be the right balance between what you want and what the designer thinks you need? A good designer takes the time to understand your business.

Once your site is live, someone will need to be responsible for making sure it stays current and is carefully proofread. The site content is edited via a CMS and it's worth taking the time to get to grips with a system which will do what you want it to do. For us, Jo and our administrator make changes and additions to our website – this hasn't been without its challenges, but is well worth it as it saves money and also means we can post contemporaneously.

> Make sure your website 'go-to' person can help train you to use the content management system (CMS).

The more complex the site, the more work involved. That said – if you are a sole practitioner working in a specific area and have minimal changes to make – a blog is a great way of showing you are reviewing your site regularly and adding to the information there. Social media sites are a useful source of trending topics – which can then be reshaped and posted on your site, to include your particular angle/focus.

Katie Leedham has been working as a website designer for ten years and she has the following advice to offer …

*Your website is all about marketing. Marketing isn't just about generating more business … It's about how you are perceived by existing customers, potential new customers **and** competitors! As well as highlighting your company ethos and creating your 'business personality', marketing is about influencing what people think about your company.*

Don't *try to overcomplicate things! One of the biggest mistakes I see in branding and marketing is businesses over-complicating their offer, often using fancy jargon, or a business name that doesn't give you any clue about the services provided. Companies can fall into the trap of trying to seem impressive or describing their services as 'business solutions' but not actually telling people simply … what it is they actually do!*

Before you meet someone in person, the website makes that all important first impression of you and your business. What kind of first impression do you want to make?

Katie advises us to think about our website from the user's point of view; clearly state **who** you are, **where** you are and **how** you can be contacted. In plain and simple terms – say **what** it is you do and **how** you can help people.

Always do your research. Take a look at any branding, websites, marketing and social media profiles of your competitors and businesses in your industry. Have these questions in mind:

1) List the things that you think they do well
2) List the things that you feel they don't do well
3) What impression of the business does their website give you without knowing the business? List some words of the feeling you get from these businesses. For example: modern,

professional, height of their industry ... or bad spelling, unprofessional, old posts, poor grammar

4) Do they look like the kind of professional business you would want to work with?
5) Can you find their contact details quickly and easily?
6) Do they clearly explain their services and who they work with?
7) What do you like (or not) about their style? Do you like the colours, do they make good use of photography? Do they use 'real pictures' or 'stock photography', and what impression does that give you?

This is a really useful exercise. Katie says you will be surprised at how much you can learn.

Think like your target market

When *you* shop for a service, what are you looking for?
What information do you need?
How can you ask for more information such as costs and availability?

> *Get in the mind of your target market and think like your customer*

What keywords would you want your target market/customers to think about when they look at your business? Brainstorm these words and use them to guide your marketing.

Maximise your website and your offering

> *It's great having a website that also acts as a brochure, which is informative and builds credibility for your business – whatever you decide, it needs to work for* **you.**

Q: What extra services can I offer my customers/audience via marketing?
Q: What business processes could I streamline through my business?

Whether you are building your audience through email marketing, offering content or resources in return for paid money or contact details, or whether your website is an 'information hub' for your customers/audience – you can use it to house downloads and create areas that specific users can log into.

You can streamline some of your business processes through your website ...

Q: Do I have any forms customers will need to complete?
Q: Could these be housed on my website?

A word to the wise!

Website technology is advancing all the time so always use the expertise of your website designer/developer and marketing associate (if you have one) to find solutions which would work for you.

Social media

Don't just jump on the latest social media platform.

Just because it's the latest trend…doesn't mean your business should be on it!

> *Think about where your target market/audience 'hang out'. Are you targeting businesses and business professionals? Should you be on LinkedIn … are you a visual consumer business, selling a product? If so, perhaps you should be on Pinterest or Instagram instead. Don't just sign up to the social media platforms you like to look at yourself … sign up to the platforms your target audience are going to be looking at.*
>
> *If you're not going to use it … don't have a profile – there's nothing worse than a social media profile that hasn't been touched for a couple of years. All that says to the user is 'are these folks still in business … is this an old profile?'*

Don't have a profile just because you think you ought to!

Keep things professional

> *Social media can be great fun, but on your business profile do your audience want to see photos of your pets or what you were doing at the weekend? Just bear in mind the message that sends. As a general rule, keep your personal and business profiles separately.*

Katie has a caveat to add here:

> *People buy from people and it's good to build rapport and convey a sense of personality. Social media can be a great way of doing this! So there could be times to bring in snippets of the personal into your business profile – such as a behind-the-scenes shot, or some relatable content about having your children or dog in the office. Always aim to tie it into the business in some way and keep it little and not too often.*

A word to the wise!

Remember – things work both ways. Make sure you only follow appropriate accounts and, when commenting (as the business you are representing) on any posts and platforms, think about any potential negative impact.

Think about your comments and the accounts you follow

One final observation from Katie – she makes no apology for appearing to state the 'blindingly obvious'.

> *Think about someone having road rage in a branded vehicle representing a company. Consider the effect that could have on the business – used carelessly, social media can have exactly the same effect!*

Advertising

Where to advertise, **what** to advertise (and will the reward be worth the investment)?

Clients

Generally, people advertise for two reasons. They are looking for

Associates

Make sure you have a presence where people will look. Clients will search the internet, visit the ASLTIP website and ask other people. The majority of our business has always come via word of mouth. Most customers like to visit a website and look for positive reviews or testimonials before making purchase – we can all relate to that.

Potential associates, including final-year students, will look online. They will hear about opportunities from friends and colleagues. Again, we spread the word when we are looking for people to join our team and we have been known to headhunt!

Be aware, almost invariably →Advertising = Expenditure

> Don't forget to include a budget for marketing in your financial forecast (more in Chapter 8).

However, there are other ways to get your name out there – it will cost you little or nothing but will require a bit of effort and ingenuity!

If social media is your thing, you can be active here but also think about guesting on various blogs and offering contributions to publications which appeal to the clients you want to attract - and to associates who can see that you are progressive and advocating for your profession and the good it can do. Contacting magazines and offering something topical *does* work – we know because we've done that ourselves. It's even better when *they* call *you* – and that has happened too!

Another thing we *have* done – a number of times – is to either take a stand at a specific exhibition or conference and/or apply to do a guest speaker slot. If you take a stand at an exhibition – again – think carefully about how much business it will need to generate in order for it to be worthwhile. Sometimes this has led to us making very useful contacts and more business, and sometimes it has felt like an expensive and wasted day.

The key is to know what you want to achieve by being there and checking whether that conference/event can *really* help you achieve that goal. Is it about raising your profile in the profession or in the marketplace? Or is it about gaining new associates or customers? How will you know if it has worked and whether time and money spent was worth it?

Here's a simple way of looking at things:

Calculate:

Time for planning, preparation, travel and attendance

Number of people going

Now add on:

> Cost of any display materials, fliers and 'give aways'
> (such as pens and post-its)

Finally:

> Divide the total by your daily/sessional rate

This equals the *minimum* amount of new business your attendance will need to generate if you are to break even.

The other thing to take into consideration is that if you do take a stand, make sure you *maximise* the networking opportunities. Visit other stands where there might be common interest. Get names and emails, or leave a flier. Step away from your stand and as people pass by, engage them in conversation. Ask what interests them and has brought them to the conference/exhibition. If they are geographically remote from where you are delivering services, focus on any service you are delivering remotely or a training package you may have which travels to groups in their own locality.

Here's another idea we have tried and which can work well, depending on your business model and client group. Deliver a half-day training session as a speculative venture. Find a venue where you can book a room at little cost – we have used local community buildings. They are usually reasonably priced and generate income for the centre. All you need is space, toilets and somewhere to offer refreshments. You then advertise low-cost places to local schools. In an area where you might already have a foot in the door, negotiate a room at no cost in return for the promise of two or three free places. Then encourage the school to advertise the course to other schools in their cluster group or locality.

A slightly more ambitious plan involves offering a training course to a school at the commercial price you would normally charge and, in return for making accommodation (and refreshments!) available, the school can then 'sell on' as many places as your course will allow.

We know of colleagues who work with adults who have visited the local groups and networks supporting stroke and head injury patients – groups such as The Stroke Association and Headway. Sometimes there may be opportunities to do some joint work with NHS colleagues with particular clients too. It helps staff and volunteers to be aware of what is out there to provide continuing care and intervention for people – particularly when NHS intervention begins to reduce.

Getting your message across

How you present yourself and your information is not just about colours, logos and a catchy name (although those can be fun to do). Of equal importance is making sure your 'advertising' materials are cohesive and convey a similar *message* – on your website, in any possible pack to make available to new clients and also in terms of any posters or fliers you use. The messages will be the same – the amount of detail and quite how it is presented should be the only thing that differs. This helps to clearly identify what you *do* (and by implication what you don't).

It also helps to use the language and terminology used in the setting/s you are targeting. If you work in schools – or are visiting schools and settings as part of your management of an individual child, for example, do your homework. Understand the Early Years Foundation curriculum, and be aware of what is delivered and expected at the various key stages. Make it your business to know about specialist vocabulary. Again, getting this right saves fruitless enquiries which waste time and energy for everyone.

Having those discussions in person

It's worth bearing in mind that this conversation may well happen at different points in the relationship. For us (almost) without exception the debate takes place *before* the initiation of a fee-paying arrangement. We talk about our model of service delivery and what outcomes a school might expect. In other circumstances and with other types of models, this might not necessarily be the case. To reach the point of discussing clinical outcomes for an individual client (child or adult), the clinician/client relationship will now be a contractual one. An assessment will have taken place and these findings will contribute to what is reasonable and achievable.

What does the client want (or *think* they want)? What do they want to achieve? What are their priorities? Always find this out first. Sometimes this will be unrealistic, and sometimes it will be very narrow – people often don't know what they don't know, but they do know they need help and support.

Work through this first before beginning to weave in your offer. Have broad-brush information to hand but with flexible options – you can adapt, omit or expand, according to what you hear.

At some point, it is helpful to know *why* the client has identified the things they have in terms of what they want to achieve. For us, this means what is the anticipated *impact* if 'x' happens? How will things be different (or better)? What will it look like (how will we know)? Now is not the point to ask the 'why' question – it can be tricky at the best of times and could sound confrontational. We will come back to *impact* in Chapter 14.

Presenting your model/s clearly and preferably with graphics to support is vital. Bearing in mind that we deliver services into schools, we use a representation of the well-known 'pyramid model' with its three tiers of intervention. Our customers are familiar with this model in their own fields of expertise and can relate to it quickly and easily.

Some clients have a particular and often set idea as to what service they want, which is (in our experience) usually focussed on how much time they will receive and how often (and what can be delivered in that timescale). It usually relates to the service they have received previously, and they are not aware that there are other ways things can be delivered, so they ask for 'more of the same please'. Letting them know that you, as an independent provider, are able to offer a different range of services can be a revelation.

More often than not (and for various reasons), there will be something of a discrepancy between *aspiration* and *reality*. Be prepared to demonstrate bridging the gap. Here are some simplistic examples from our own experience.

Aspiration

What would be better value for money and almost certainly more effective ...

We've decided we want ...

- Half a day a week for our EHCP children
- Tier 3 activity (i.e. direct one-to-one therapy sessions)
- We have put together a timetable so that as many as possible can be fitted in
- We want you to work in this side room
- Whole days are better value (how about a day a fortnight?)

- What are your anticipated outcomes and how will you know they have been achieved?
- There needs to be carry-over into the classroom and some time for us to explain what we're doing and why
- If a TA is alongside, they can support the carryover (and pick up lots of new skills to use with other children who are struggling)

As fewer and fewer NHS SLT services are able to deliver the recommendations made in EHCPs, it's worth mentioning that both writing and (perhaps more so) *delivering* recommendations in these plans have the potential to become a growth area. Both aspects of this work require the appropriate clinical skills. However, the practicalities of costing recommendations are also important to consider.

Independent practitioner Tom has experience of both writing and delivering recommendations. He worked for a number of years in an independent specialist school, working with multiple local authorities and delivering EHCP provision. His expertise may help others.

He offers two key pieces of advice:

1. **Detail** recommendations so they are comprehensive and explicit and identify *all* the different aspects of what will be involved and where the activity will take place (such as face-to-face interventions, liaison and report writing, training components, transition, parent/carer participation and attendance at statutory reviews) for the purposes of doing what is required to support the child or young person concerned.

For every need I attach a recommendation and then cost these explicitly and thoroughly

Tom matches provision to need, using a table format in his report so that this stands out and is not lost in a body of text. Recommendations also need to be realistic and cost-effective for the setting where the child is placed. Only when this information is clearly and transparently available can costing be realistic.

2. **Applying realistic costs** to the delivery of recommendations safeguards both the authorities funding the plan so they can be assured how the money is being spent and practitioners so that they charge fairly and realistically for the work they have agreed to undertake. When tendering for a new contract, costs will be required; '*it helps to have mapped these out in advance*'.

This is an opportune moment to return to the subject of *outcomes*.

You will have some idea of what the client wants to achieve and what timescales they think are reasonable. Whatever you are doing clinically, think about what your client has said and what you know from your own experience.

Again, our examples come from our own area of service delivery. From our own point of view, outcomes are not always about the progress of individuals. Our offer includes *objective-focussed* activities where the aims are around universal (pyramid tier 1) approaches to benefit *all* children. This might be about changing the environment, for example, or delivering training for staff. Sometimes objectives are about whole cohorts; supporting staff to implement universal screening in Early Years is a good example of this.

As you broaden the range of options as to what is achievable and also necessary, based on what your (prospective) client has described, the moment arrives to introduce the concept of *impact*. Impact should always be about the benefit to the 'end-user' – the child/children, the adult, the carer, the family, the educator. So, for example, if an Early Years Foundation Stage (EYFS) setting has an audit of the communication environment, what will be the impact? Longer-term, how will things be different? If care home staff receive training on nutrition, texture modification and safe feeding, what will be the impact for the vulnerable residents?

Alongside impact will be the need to be able to ***measure*** that impact – i.e. how you will demonstrate the achievement of outcomes.

Demonstrating success should be a critical part of what we do. In essence, it's the whole point of why we do what we do and why anyone should invest valuable (and often scarce) resources in speech and language therapy – and in you! This is a big subject all on its own and, for that reason, we have devoted the following chapter in its entirety to *measuring impact*.

We are almost at the end of this section. We have discussed at length the importance of getting across the quality and effectiveness of what you are aiming to provide. We will conclude with a couple of obvious – but important – practicalities.

So often, at the outset, cost and quantity are at the forefront of the client's mind.

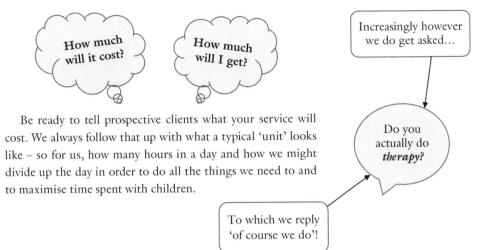

Be ready to tell prospective clients what your service will cost. We always follow that up with what a typical 'unit' looks like – so for us, how many hours in a day and how we might divide up the day in order to do all the things we need to and to maximise time spent with children.

Sadly, this illustrates the level of expectation that the client has, based on their previous or current experience with predominantly consultative SLT services.

If different *aspects* of your service are costed differently, be ready to say that too. For example, an initial assessment and report package might differ from a regular session; training might differ from a regular day in a setting.

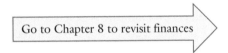

Go to Chapter 8 to revisit finances

Quantity and timescales

Try to avoid open-ended arrangements. It is much easier to manage expectations if you are able to say how much time will be spent (duration), over how many sessions/days and for how long (the period of the agreement).

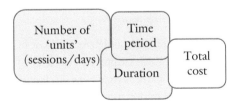

Alongside the 'what' and 'how' discussed earlier, this information will be written into the contract you have between you and the client.

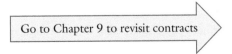

Go to Chapter 9 to revisit contracts

At what point would a contract be renegotiated? This is discussed in step four which follows.

Step 4	This chapter is **not only** about attracting business in the first place **but also** managing the ongoing relationship with clients. This second strand is important for all sorts of reasons which we will go into in more detail here and you will find it is a recurrent theme throughout the book.

Keeping in touch is crucial to the success of the client/provider relationship. If you, personally, are the provider, i.e. delivering the service in the setting yourself, you will see the client regularly and the channels of communication should be easy. There are frequent opportunities to informally check how things are going – as well as the more formal review milestones in intervention.

If you are the contractor, delivering the service on behalf of someone else, then you are 'between' the contractee and the client – as the associates are in our business model. If you are the owner of your business, the client is one place removed from you by the team delivering the service on your behalf (whether they are employed or self-employed).

For the purposes of this section, we will focus on the models where you might be one place removed from the client because you don't deliver the entire service yourself. The first and routine port of call to check on how things are going is with the therapist responsible for that particular client. Encourage a proactive approach: you want to know about the success and any challenges as they occur – things are much easier to sort out in the early stages.

That said, the onus is certainly not all on the person at the coal face! We in-build regular reviews with all our settings – in the early days these were as frequent as termly. Now we make decisions on an individual and needs-led basis. It is very tempting to pick up the telephone or have a video call. Remote calls have become the norm. Both have their place.

A word to the wise!

Nothing can take the place of a face-to-face visit. You are able to get much more of a feel for the issues and your point of contact in the setting is often more relaxed and forthcoming. It's also a chance to look at any practical issues such as accommodation and to meet other key staff. It provides an opportunity to reinforce messages that the associate has been struggling to get across, and to hear how the associate is perceived within the setting too.

When we touch base with our clients, whether it's remotely or in person, we write a brief summary afterwards (which we also send to the setting) – to help us remember the issues as time goes on. It also helps to make a note of any actions and information requested.

Making notes on initial contact is also important.

Such an idea may seem onerous but more than once we have said 'thank goodness we made some notes!'.

More about notetaking is in Chapter 7.

Assuming your contracts are not open-ended, there will be a point at which it's time to consider renewal. Depending on your business model and client group, this point could be within a few weeks or not for a number of months. For us, the time to think about commissions for the next academic year is around Easter. When demand is likely to outstrip capacity, it's important to know whether your existing clients want to renew and on what terms.

On occasion, clients will ask to reduce their commission and there is always the possibility that some won't renew. More often, they want to at least maintain their current level of support or to increase it. Whatever your model, any/all changes will impact on your planning and if you employ or sub-contract work, the changes will require some reconfiguration within the team.

The sooner you know what your client-base looks like, the sooner you can begin to ensure that there is enough work – and work that you *want* to take on – to meet your financial commitments.

> Don't forget to update your financial forecast (budget plan) to take account of changing circumstances.

If your relationship with your clients is good and you establish and maintain good channels of communication, any changes shouldn't take you by surprise! Where a client decides not to recommission, it's important to understand why – there may be learning to take from the end of the partnership.

14 Measuring impact

In our book *Supporting the Development of Speech, Language & Communication in the Early Years* (Jessica Kingsley Publishers, 2022) [1], we say that 'everything we do should be because we know it will make a (positive) difference. Otherwise – why would we do it'?

The trickier thing is to be able to measure the changes we make. The reasons why are obvious really but are worth repeating here:

- Justify why we do what we do
- Make a case for 'more' (time, opportunity, funding)
- Share good practice more widely

In this chapter, we look in detail at different ways professionals can evidence the impact of what is being delivered. The ideas here can support your advertising, the evidence of your effectiveness and demonstrate to clients and team members alike your commitment to high-quality services, which **really do make a difference.**

Before we begin to look in detail, however, let's consider what we mean by 'impact'.

The terms 'outcome' and 'impact' are sometimes used interchangeably but it's important to note that they are quite different www.futurelearn.com [2]. While outcome refers to specific and measurable short-term effects, impact can adopt a more comprehensive viewpoint, looking to broader and long-term effects.

In measurement terms, outcomes are usually predefined and can be measured objectively using quantitative measures. Impact, however, can be quantitative, qualitative, subjective and based on people's feelings or experiences, making it harder to quantify as a result.

Impact has been defined by the Council for Allied Health Professionals Research as 'an effect, an influence, a significant change or benefit to health, quality of life, society, policy, services, the environment and the economy' (CAHPR, 2015; Hayhow, Wren, Deave, 2019) [3].

I think for many of us the terms **are** probably used interchangeably – and certainly dictionary definitions and thesaurus research would indicate that if not interchangeable they are certainly close relatives!

DOI: 10.4324/9781003382928-15

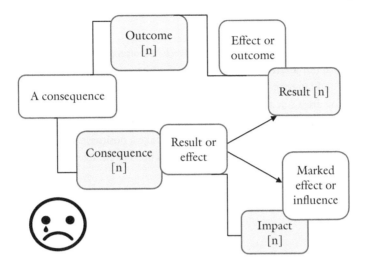

We would refer speech and language therapy readers to the Measuring Outcomes Framework and guidance notes produced by the Royal College of Speech and Language Therapists (RCSLT) [4]. These documents provide lots of information, context and definitions to support practitioners to feel confident in measuring outcomes. It is particularly useful that a distinction is made between 'individualised outcomes' and 'non-individualised outcomes'. This is a differentiation that we make in our own 'Measuring impact' document.

The RCSLT use the terms above, and we point to measuring impact for individual clients and for objective-focussed activities (such as any one of a number of examples of universal (tier 1) strategies in a school or setting). A similar parallel could be an objective-focussed activity in a care home or day centre, for example, or a raft of behaviour management strategies implemented in a specialist setting.

The most important thing here is not to get so bogged down with definitions that we lose sight of what we are trying to do – which is to show that speech and language therapy (or any professional activity) makes a difference to the people receiving it.

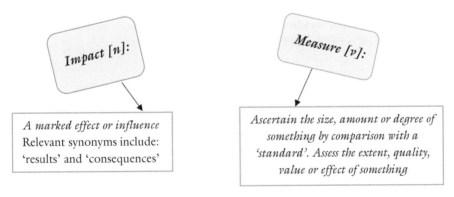

A. **Rationale**

In our book *Supporting the Development of Speech, Language & Communication in the Early Years* [1], we talk about a raft of important things to have in mind when considering commissioning a speech and language therapy service. This is applicable to *any* service, and it doesn't matter whether you are a sole trader or a company employing a number of other people.

The decision-makers need to be confident that the provider they choose will meet a range of essential criteria – **including** whether or not it will make a positive and lasting difference to the people for whom it is being commissioned. Providers need to be able to **demonstrate** that what they do makes a positive difference.

It's equally important for both the service user (or proxy user in the case of the schools and settings receiving a service) **and** service **provider** to understand what we mean by 'measuring impact'.

B. **From number crunching to quality outcomes**

In the early days of Soundswell, as one of a range of parameters, we used to report on the amount of activity undertaken in a setting. Numbers on the caseload, new referrals, assessments, treatments, reviews and discharges were all there. The number on the caseload was important because it needed to relate realistically to the amount of time a school commissioned.

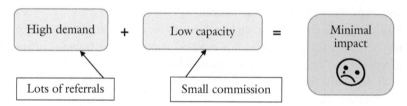

By counting the numbers of new referrals and discharges, we were at the very early stage of trying to identify *throughput*.

This was the start of Soundswell as a service provider, beginning to critically appraise what we offered – initially asking ourselves *why* we were doing it, *what* would be different (i.e. impact) and *how* would we measure that difference.

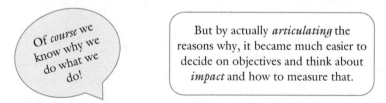

This was followed quite quickly by ensuring that we *routinely* asked our clients what *they* would like and *why*. What did they want to achieve and how would they know it had been successful?

As any independent practitioner knows, our activity is led by the priorities and concerns of the *client* (with input, advice and guidance of course) and not vice versa.

Once the service had become objective- (i.e. outcome) focussed, the next logical step was to consider the range and type of activity we might deploy in order to achieve those objectives.

Lateral thinking: as the range of activity increased, so did the challenge of measuring impact – but more about that a little later.

C. Why it's important to understand the difference between 'impact' and 'activity'

'Activity' is about what happens; it implies something dynamic like *an action in pursuit of an objective*. 'Impact' is about the outcome of that activity. Traditionally, speech and language therapy activity has been predominantly measured by 'contacts' (a communication of some sort between the therapist and the recipient). This was by no means unique to therapies. Services have been judged (and commissioned) based on their contacts: how many, how often, how long? Are they face-to-face or on the telephone? Are they intervention-based, liaison or review?

The modern service provider knows that capturing activity alone (i.e. thinking about activity in terms of *amount*) is a crude one-dimensional measurement which won't capture the impact of what is delivered.

It *is* quite useful, however, to make sure that the size of the workload is realistic in terms of the amount of time being commissioned. It is also useful to develop your own notional case/work-load formula which will support decision-making about what specialist level (pyramid-tier 3) activity is/isn't possible (if what you do is going to make a positive impact and show throughput).

(For more about the pyramid model: Gascoigne M. (2006) 'Supporting children with speech, language and communication needs within integrated children's services' [5].)

D. Getting started

With apologies in advance to non-speech and language therapy readers, the ideas which follow are speech and language therapy based but try thinking about the framework in terms of your own profession.

Everyone loves a checklist … here are a few things to think about.

Speech and language therapy activity makes a difference to staff and parents too	Do you plot your activity against the pyramid model (universal, targeted and specialist interventions)?
	Begin to think about activity in terms of *type* rather than *amount* (remember the pyramid).
	List the kind of activity you offer your settings. It's a good idea to think about *measuring impact* in its widest sense. Start by looking at what activity is being delivered in your setting and with what kinds of needs.
Training for staff benefits every child	Does what you offer meet the needs in the setting (or do you nearly always offer the same thing/s)?
Well-equipped staff at universal level can reduce the need for expensive input later	Are there other things you could do that might need a bit more thinking about (whilst still achieving the desired outcome and maybe more economically for the setting)?
	Do you ask your clients what *they* want (in terms of what they want to achieve)?
	Do you offer suggestions? New clients are often non-plussed when *you* ask what *they* want (they have probably never been asked before) and almost invariably say they 'want therapy'.
	Bring the conversation back round to outcomes. Ask what they want to **achieve** …
	… but be ready to offer some guidance …

You can actually do a surprising amount with just 10 days…

Parent workshops will certainly help more children to be ready for Nursery…

Therapy for tier 3 children is a good idea but how about some adding in some training for everyone at universal level…?

E. Getting into detail

Hopefully Section D will have kick-started your own lateral thinking process. These ideas are by no means an exhaustive list; yours might be similar, but they can be adapted to other professions, different clients and what they want to achieve.

Keep the fundamental questions in mind.

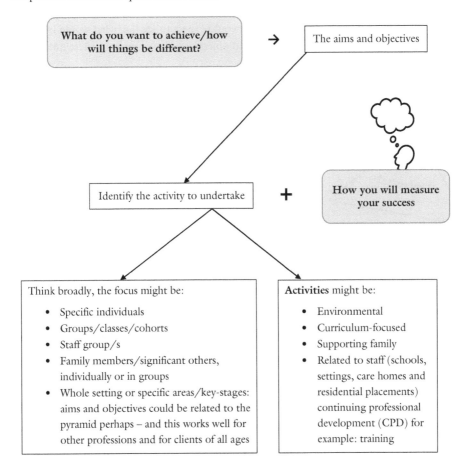

F. **Ways to measure**

A range of measures are possible:

A. *Quantitative*: measures of values expressed in numbers e.g. 'how much, how many, how often'?

Examples here would be formal and standardised assessments which show progress across a range of skill areas. These might be carried out by the therapist or by others involved with the client – school staff for example.

B. *Qualitative*: things which can be observed but not measured or things which are descriptive and based on characteristics.

Examples could include increased participation, reduced absence, client/family well-being ratings, staff rating of an individual's participation and well-being, attention and listening gains, non-verbal communication indicators, social interaction indicators – friendship groups etc.

If you are working regularly in one setting, a useful training/workshop topic could be to generate a list of possible ways you could measure the impact of the activities you are supporting in the setting. It's always useful to ask staff what they would expect to see (i.e. what would be different) as a result of the successful completion of agreed objectives. The answers to these questions very often indicate what could be measured and how.

G. Using the pyramid model to set objectives

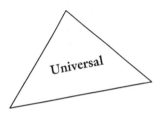

At universal level there are a number of tried and tested approaches which we routinely recommend. There will be similar universal 'go to' approaches recommended by, for example, behaviour support specialists, educational psychologists and other therapies.

N.B. at the universal level *you* are training (and supporting) *others* to implement these strategies and approaches. You will also be training them to be able to make these data comparisons (and thus measure progress for themselves).

At targeted level there are more tried and tested approaches and interventions which are routinely implemented in our settings. Again, think about your profession and what you will usually recommend.

At the targeted level you might be showing school staff how to measure the impact or perhaps doing this jointly.

Approaches and strategies here are likely to be far more specialized. You might receive support to implement the strategies and approaches: there may be varying degrees of involvement from someone else (a teaching assistant for example) but the delivery will be lead by you, the professional.

At the specialist level, the measuring will be bespoke as every client is different and measurement will be tailor-made around the specific outcomes you want to achieve.

H. What to choose and where to start

Objective 1: find out the training priorities

Carry out a staff knowledge and skills audit, which is useful in identifying where staff feel reasonably confident (or not) and can help prioritize training needs.

We have used this tool in a number of settings as a starting point.

What to do:

1. Make a list of the areas staff need to know and understand to support the needs of your clients
2. Break down each area into six to eight 'descriptors' which cover the main (key) points staff need to know for that topic
3. Ask staff to rate their confidence for the key points or each topic on a scale of one to five
4. Analyse the results to see which topics are a priority for training

Here are examples of training courses from speech and language therapy.
- S & L development
- Attention and Listening
- Using questions
- Vocabulary
- Narrative
- Visual supports
- Phonological Awareness

Objective 2: demonstrate the impact of your training

Carry out pre- and post-training evaluations for your courses. How much did participants know before the course and how much they felt they knew afterwards. This gives an immediate comparison and measures the initial impact of your objective.

I. **Small commissions**

This is probably a good place to make a few pertinent points about 'small commissions'. This is usually when there is an extremely limited budget and expectations may exceed what can realistically be provided. *You* know what your services cost. It can be a good idea to develop some ideas as to what you could offer in terms of limited packages.

Alongside asking our potential customers what they want, we always ask how much budget they are able to allocate. This is a good way of introducing ways that the budget can be maximized; identify objectives together and what impact the activity will have. If your model of service delivery involves working with individual clients, something as simple and obvious as an introductory package (assessment, report, suggested next steps and some strategies to be undertaken by the family) makes it clear who will do what and how much it will cost.

It is particularly helpful to settings if the activity can be discussed in terms of the pyramid. For a relatively small outlay, a range of activities at universal level – focussing on a specific cohort or key stage – can make a significant impact. Or, at specialist level, an agreed number of EHCP plans can be reviewed and updated. In our experience, small commissions often lead to more work as the benefits of what has been delivered become apparent.

The trick is to be explicit and to write down what the agreed objectives are. In Appendix F, we share with you an impact report written by one of our team at the end of a school year in a setting where the commission was just nine days.

J. **Don't be afraid to do a pilot or 'trial run'**

You might come up with a new and different approach to solving a problem. Give it a trial run, look at the successes and make any changes to make it even more effective and then offer it again. An example relating to speech and language therapy, but could easily be transferred to other professions, occurred when we mentored a specific member of staff to skill them up in a particular area. This enabled that member of staff to reliably and accurately carry out a communication environment audit so that the setting could manage this in-house.

Think about possible instances where *you* can see a more unusual solution to a problem or to meet a priority need – and a valuable opportunity to deliver something truly bespoke may present itself.

A word to the wise!

Once you become a regular part of the life of your longest-running settings, they are just the right place to try something a little bit different. In our experience some of our best ideas have been developed as a result of a Special Needs Coordinator somewhere saying 'I wish we could...'

K. **Advertise your successes**

Always include examples of measuring impact as part of your information for potential new clients. Put it on your website; write about it and talk about it. Share with others so that schools and settings know how to recognise a high-quality and effective service.

References

1. Mcqueen, D. and Williams, J. (2022) *Supporting the Development of Speech, Language and Communication in the Early Years.* S.l: Jessica Kingsley.
2. FutureLearn. (n.d.) *Online Courses and Degrees from Top Universities.* FutureLearn. Available at: https://www.futurelearn.com/.
3. Hayhow, R., Wren, Y.E. and Deave, T. (2019) Sharing your findings and ensuring impact. In Dobinson, C. and Wren, Y. (Eds.), *Creating Practice Based Evidence: A Guide for SLTs.* Second edition. J&R Press Ltd.
4. RCSLT Framework. (n.d.) rcslt.org. Available at: https://www.rcslt.org/wp-content/uploads/2021/06/RCSLT-Measuring-Outcomes-Framework-June2021.pdf.
5. Gascoigne, M. (2006) *Supporting Children with Speech, Language and Communication Needs within Integrated Children's Services RCSLT Position Paper.* London: RCSLT. Available from the RCSLT website: www.rcslt.org.

15 Trouble-shooting

This chapter will describe real situations from our own experience (and those of others too): events and occurrences, all of which had consequences in terms of the effect on our business – some of them serious. We talk about the lessons learned and how we used these events to help us better manage potential risk in the future.

Sharing these experiences allows the reader to be forearmed and to put things in place to reduce the potential impact of any and all of the following:

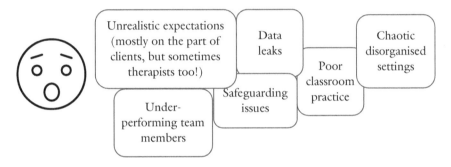

Don't think it won't happen to you – it most certainly could. The trick is to see it coming and be prepared.

Before returning to the problem solving aspects of this chapter, we'll share with you some of the characters we've come across on our 12-year journey (NB: All the incidents in the cameos that follow were eventually safely and successfully resolved).

No chapter containing what this one does is without a generous helping of humour and light relief. Although there are some absolute shockers here – clients and therapists in equal numbers – each one is a valuable lesson and, with hindsight, a source of some amusement!

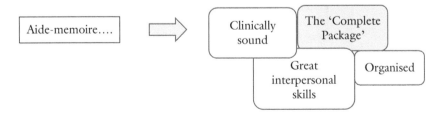

DOI: 10.4324/9781003382928-16

| The 'one out of three ain't bad' | I'm a really good clinician and that's the important thing (*but my time management, prioritisation and admin skills are non-existent*). If I think the school aren't doing what they should be, I'll certainly tell the parent this (*that went well – not*). I do struggle with the traffic but if I'm late (*which I am quite a lot*) I'll pop in another day. I'll remember to put it on my invoice though. Ok, maybe it wasn't the 20th now I think about it. Probably the 21st – well it's not a big deal as I know I went in that week. |

| The 'rose-tinted spectacles/rock up when you feel like it' | Of course I can take on that school (*20-mile bus journey with all my equipment*). Of course, I'll be able to pick it all up again after the baby is born (*due very soon*) – I *think* my flat mate will help look after it (*but she works away a lot…*). I'm sure it will all work out! |

| 'Can't quite get my act together (and does it really matter?)' | I know I look a bit down on my luck at the moment but my dog died, my partner has left me (*and taken the soap*). |

| The 'plough on regardless' | I have plenty of resources and kit for any event (*three bags full*). I do struggle to cart it all around but you never know what you might need! It can take up a lot of space in that little therapy room (*indeed it does!*)! It takes me quite a time to find what I need sometimes (*that's also true*). The TA told me to stick to my side of the room, which was a bit direct I thought (*sometimes you just have to say it how it is*). I do my very best to tell her just what she should be doing (*failing to notice that she actually rolls her eyes…*), even though sometimes (*every time actually*) we can't get through everyone we need to. |

| The 'I look good (*flirt well)* but can I *do* any good'? | My skill set is very niche (*I don't really know about much in any detail*). I've moved around a bit (*never stays long in one place*) and had plenty of experience with different companies: it's not always easy to get a reference for the next move though. I find it hard to get my head around being self-employed. In my previous (salaried) job therapists had plenty of time to catch up and liaise… there's two of us in this school and we do need to discuss the caseload (*get paid to chat*). It's jolly unfair of that Head to say we've spent entire mornings not seeing any kids! |

| The 'I know nothing much but I've (*somehow*) made it this far' | I trained abroad so that excuses any lack of knowledge … (*does it really matter if I don't know the difference between receptive and expressive language?*).
I don't need to be fully focussed on this discussion (*about the child I have been observing, so I can be checking my phone at the same time*). |

The 'even young dogs struggle to learn new tricks sometimes'	I trained abroad in a totally different system from yours, but my way is definitely correct and I do not recognise the need to adapt or learn anything.
The 'says what you want to hear'	Oh yes, that's definitely my specialist area (*and that is and that one, oh and that as well. A specialist in everything – until proved not to be!*). Yes, definitely, absolutely, want to work for you full time (*a week later it drops to 4 days, then 3 and ends up as a day a week – but not before we had taken on more work…*). I'm really comfortable with advising on the environment and on universal stuff (*happy to tell staff what to do but not over-keen to do anything much personally… or provide anything written down*).
The non-communicator	I know what I'm doing so don't really see the need to chat to anyone else about it. People think I'm under-confident so I work hard to cover it up (*by being silent and invisible*). Er no, I won't be able to deliver training if I take on any work with you. Would I like some support to take on things that are challenging (*communicating with people*)? No – I'm fine as I am (*and I'll just stick to individual sessions with pre-schoolers and I'll work in a cupboard somewhere no one can see what I am doing*).
The 'half a job with full pay'	Oh yes, I have lots of experience in specialist settings (*but I don't think I can see that client on my own or speak to that member of staff*) and no, I don't feel confident enough to do (*any*) training (*ever*) even if you support me – it's just not my thing.
The bone idle	I don't need to make any notes or write any reports, I just tell the TA and she writes it all down in her folder.
The doormat	This is my third career change but I don't think it's (*SLT*) really for me…. No, I'm not ready to deliver any training. Oh, it isn't a problem that I have been told I must work in that storeroom (*which is so small that it's a good thing there isn't a cat that needs swinging…*). I don't mind that the SENDCO just keeps referring more children but doesn't provide any TA support and won't liaise with me. I don't want to make a fuss. I'll just do as I'm told even if it is not effective.
The Miracle (I passed didn't I?)	I am quite new to the profession and love working with (*sitting watching*) X and Y (*therapists*), I can pick up some really good ideas (*take notes? No need I can remember everything I see*). I'm just observing you do this group – no I'm not ready to take part in it this time round (*or any time round in fact! Not prepared to get stuck in, have a go, or learn from mistakes*).

Calamity clients

Our examples of 'hands-on' involvement range from one extreme to the other. We are no longer shocked by the enormous difference in client approaches and their expectations of what a service can and should do. It has to be said that these examples represent a very small number of our client settings, the vast majority of which are great places to work – supportive and welcoming.

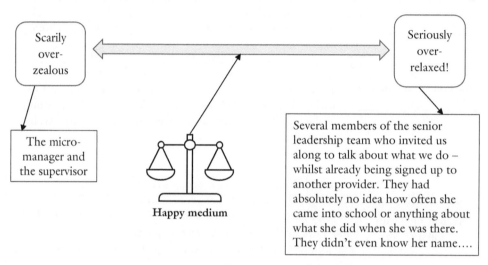

Chaotic and disorganised	'Speech and language are a top priority for us' (*but it's OK to cancel our therapist when she is pulling into the car park*)
	'And for us!' (*pre-arranged appointment pupils out on a trip*) Did we mention they are all in exams today? *(No...)* Sorry there actually isn't anywhere for you to work today (*or quite often actually*)
	'We are really committed to delivering this'! (*but are unable to support any programmes between visits*)

| Burglar Betty | In advance of going with another provider as we subsequently discovered, because they were copying the notes to pass on 'It's quite OK to open your filing cabinet and photocopy your notes (*and reassemble them in the wrong order*) because I know where you keep the key ..... |

| Out to lunch when GDPR came a-calling | Ooooops! Did we really send you all that data about hundreds of children in the Care system? Oh dear, silly me – I'm not that good with computers. Anyway, it's not a problem – just delete what you don't need. |

The micro-manager	I've got a timetable here, I'll bring the children one -by-one and take the other one back. Or they can queue up outside the room if you prefer? *That's handy (not) -no time for notes to be written, a pit-stop or feeding anything back to staff. And all day in a room with no windows....*
	We'll put the training in for a 10.30 start, it's only 90 minutes so we can slot in a few children beforehand (*no concept of any planning or preparation for the training or quality sessions or the children or liaison time with the TA*).
	What? You need time to think, eat, empty your bladder?

The supervisor

> Well, I think we need a clocking in mechanism for the therapist (*Do you? We don't!*)

> We'll have that training as 4 X 45 minute workshops. 9.15 – 10.00/10 – 10.45/10.45 – 11.30/11.30 – 12.15. *Arrrrgh! 45 minutes becomes 35 as people drift in and out. No drink break and no toilet time **again**!!*

The Debtors

> Oh, are you *sure* we didn't pay invoices A, B, C, D? (*yep*) I put the cheques in the post (*hmmm*). Well, I've put *another* cheque in the post (*we'll wait with bated breath*). I'll have to cancel all these other cheques – can't think where they must be going (*you and us both…*). Send it signed for? Well,… I suppose I could… (*jolly good! Or better still pay it by BACS!*)

> **Q**: How long did it take a NHS Trust in the north west to pay for training we delivered to EYPs?
> **A**: 11 months and a letter of complaint to the CEO.

> **Q**: How long does X setting wait before settling invoices?
> **A**: When they have been re sent them 4 times and when the late payment fees have been added and debt recovery has been mentioned (*which prompts them to finally pay up – but without paying the late fees though!*).

The Disturbing

> Accidentally caught in the crossfire between warring factions in a setting:
> - I've given this to do *(screening all nursery and reception pupils)*, but I don't see it as part of my job (*I'm refusing to do it-so no referrals for the therapists and no intervention groups can begin*)
>
> - The TAs in this school will not work a second over their hours so will not speak to you at break times or stay for any twilight training sessions
>
> - A nursery child alone and unsupervised in a shower cubicle
>
> - Another child picking up small objects and putting them in his mouth
>
> The frighteningly over-casual approach to safeguarding:
>
> - At the height of the radicalisation and extremist issues in Birmingham, a child discloses that his big sister was 'in Syria' and hadn't been seen for months. The Head is informed '*thanks for letting me know*' and makes a pencilled note on a scrap of paper
> - Therapists think a child's date of birth looks wrong (the child is clearly older). Staff in the school office say that the 'parents' can provide no birth certificate or evidence of the child's identity
> - We have to do restraints when children misbehave. (We know all about behaviour and communication [*not*])

Can you do an interactive presentation to the senior managers in our large MAT about the various language screening tools, in order for us to choose one that suits across the trust? It's in a fancy hotel miles away and there will be dozens of us. *(Until we turn up and there are 5 disinterested people who do not want to interact and already have a screening tool in place)* Oh and then we will question the size of the invoice you sent for this work (after we have accepted the quote), was it really worth that much?

Castles in the air…

Can you do an interactive session with 'impact' to an away day for staff from the MAT *(most of whom had never seen us, didn't know who we were and what we did…)*. There will be quite a lot of us. *(interactive and impactful with 600+ delegates is a big ask)*. The venue is *(a well-known football club)* with nice facilities. Yes, bring some of the team, come for lunch and then you can go on just afterwards *(Everyone knows the 'just after lunch' slot is never the best)*.

Despite taking one of our best presenters who could earn a living as a stand-up comedian, it was really a waste of time and effort – oh – apart from the lunch perhaps…

Warning bells on an industrial scale

A stand-alone independent specialist setting school with a mixed economy *(takes anyone – a range of SEND and excluded pupils. No evident admission criteria)*. You decide what you need to do *(no idea what SLT can offer)*. We have a relaxed and informal approach *(mavericks with little obvious regulation, no clear offer and no evidence of outcomes. A strong aversion to paying invoices resulted in them being sued for non-payment)*

Come and find me if you need the toilet (yes, really)

Keep your foot against the door we're waiting to get the lock fixed

We haven't got any paper towels for drying your hands on (conspiratorial aside 'most people use the tea cloth…')

On a serious note

How to avoid some of the 'people' pitfalls

Our advice would be to keep the three key skills at the forefront when meeting with potential associates. We don't conduct formal interviews when approached by therapists with several years' experience. We rely more on word-of-mouth recommendations, meeting and talking with them. We do ask for references and carry out the usual checks required (see Chapter 12).

References are a moot point really. Having written and received numerous references over the years whilst in the public sector, we are aware that information *not* provided can sometimes be more revealing than the information that is! If we become aware of warning signs with an associate, we will revisit the references and often there is no hint of what the reality turns out to be.

Over the years we have met with lots of therapists. We are always interested in finding out what experience they have had to date and why they are looking for a change. What are their strengths and areas for development? What do they enjoy? When this is their first foray into IP, we also make a point of talking about what it means to be self-employed – as objectively as possible.

Where an individual is determined to leave their current post, we always advise making a planned exit. Decide what you want to do and then work out how you're going to do it. What needs to be in place? A fairly predictable route is to keep a foot in one camp (to continue with their existing NHS role for example) whilst exploring other possibilities and, as long as there is no conflict of interest, that seems a sensible thing to do.

At some of these initial meetings, there have been tears and evident signs of general unhappiness. In these instances, it is even more important to make a planned – and maybe phased – withdrawal. It's good to keep in mind the wise words from Chapter 2, that stress changes how people weigh 'risk and reward'.

If the initial meeting goes well we will offer some 'taster' days with us. Therapists get paid for these days (though at slightly less than the regular rate), and it is an opportunity for them to work alongside an established team member and be able to ask questions, as well as demonstrate that they can appropriately manage the kinds of clients in our settings. We need to see if they fit with us and, reciprocally, they need to feel that we are the kind of business they are looking to work with.

The taster days are a great opportunity for testing not only clinical skills but also the organisational and interpersonal skills which are so crucial. Will this person be able to hold their own with a tough SENDCo, prioritise objectives to help a new SENDCo make the most of the service and be able to show an under-confident TA what to do? Are they active partners in the experience or happy to sit back and watch? Do they confidently pick up and write the case notes … is it legible, does it make sense, do the notes meet HCPC standards in terms of record keeping? Do they ask questions, offer contributions, show empathy, see the funny side …? Be wary if you can't answer yes to most of this list.

A word to the wise!

It might be that you want to offer a trial, with the opportunity for either side to bail out after an agreed period.

Induction helps new team members to understand how things work and settle in more quickly.

Make sure you have a robust induction process. Help people to get settled in rather than hope they pick things up as they go along! We have few 'rules' as such but the ones we do have are important and make sure that the business runs efficiently and effectively. The must-do's include:

- Keeping a *contemporaneous* timetable and amending it if necessary
- Sending in invoices *promptly*
- Responding to emails in a *timely* manner
- *Communicating* with us about how things are going – good and bad
- Being *proactive* if there is an issue or a change looming
- Being able to *evidence impact* in a way that clients can understand

Client issues and how to head them off

Spend time preparing your offer and supporting information – both in written form and on your website. Make it clear and transparent. Include your ethos; if you are a specialist intervention business (i.e. tier 3 work directly with the client) or want to provide support at all three tiers, *say* that. We have settings who ask: 'can the therapist do more project-based stuff?' or 'can the therapist do more one-on-one sessions?' Yes, of course!

What you do should be in response to the needs and priorities of the client – so make that clear from the outset – and be prepared to refresh it at appropriate intervals.

The wording in your contract is also a good place to set out practical requirements such as accommodation, internet access, invoicing and what the therapist does/doesn't do (revisit Chapter 9 for more detail about contracts).

Be aware that very few people read the small print (and surprisingly some don't even read the large print), so be prepared to work on getting your message across consistently and continuously (and politely) referring the customer back to the contract when required.

Sometimes just say it how it is …

A couple of years ago we introduced a light-hearted, single-sided document which we send out with each new/renewed contract. It's called 'Help Us to Help You' and actually lists the importance of being able to make a hot drink, having a fob to move around the building independently, knowing who people are and where they are and (of course) the perennial need to be able to visit the loo as and when necessary! Clients who read it find it amusing …

Contract review meetings (face-to-face or remote) are also a valuable way of making sure that things are proceeding as they should – do them as frequently as you need to. Time spent in the early days will often smooth the way for further down the line (and don't forget to make some notes of the meeting which you can then share with the setting).

> In Chapter 7 we talk about the value of keeping minutes.

Encourage your associates to alert you to any issues so you can get things back on track at the earliest possible opportunity. Be honest and up-front; sometimes it can be misperception and sometimes perhaps the associate isn't performing as you want, but you are unaware. Keeping robust channels of communication greatly reduces any potential 'ambush' however.

Know when to call time | Sometimes things *won't* work out, despite your best efforts. For clients and associates alike; recognise when the cause is lost. If things reach that stage, terminate the contract (make sure that termination arrangements are explicit in the contract you have with clients and associates) rather than let things stagger on with no resolution in sight.

One thing is *absolutely* certain: troublesome associates and calamity clients will cost time, angst, energy and eventually money.

16 Looking to the future

Well, here we are – the final chapter!

> *Life is like riding a bicycle. To keep your balance, you must keep moving.*
>
> – Albert Einstein

Apart from the obvious sentiments, such as we hope you have been informed and entertained along the way, we also want to share some thoughts and aspirations looking ahead.

Before we do so, however, let's just revisit/pull together some of the issues/themes which have emerged.

The purpose of this book was to expand horizons in terms of opportunities to work differently and to site this within the context of the provider landscape current at the time of writing.

During the course of our investigations, the challenges facing the public sector services were laid bare on a daily basis. We met or spoke to many interesting people and learnt a great deal about the issues which are important to them in terms of their working lives.

Time and time again we were hearing the same message: therapists (and others) want to …

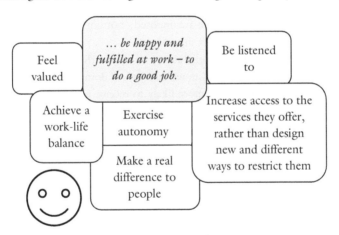

This is all about the workforce: it really doesn't seem too much to ask, does it? How do we nurture and protect our single biggest asset?

DOI: 10.4324/9781003382928-17

So- what would you do if you were still in your previous roles in the NHS?

More than once we have had to ask ourselves what would we do if tasked with effecting positive change? How marvellous it would be to come right back with useful, practical suggestions! Alas – life is never that simple. The sheer size, number and complexity of the issues involved make it almost impossible to know where to begin.

Whatever we did, we hope that we would be **kind** (a sentiment echoed by a number of others we met); that we would value and support our team and be open about the huge challenges facing us all.

> Let's not lose sight of the reason we are all here – regardless of where we work or who employs us – to improve the quality of life and opportunity for the many thousands of people who are denied the basic human right to be able to communicate to the best of their ability.

Like many things which evolve rather than are imposed, 'bottom-up' practices follow more natural pathways and are more likely to garner support.

In the same way that the park designer waits to see where the people walk before finalising his paths and walkways, a good manager knows that ways of doing things which have grown and developed from established practice are more likely to receive workforce sign-up. We make no apology for saying that any individual professional group is best placed to know what works to support the needs of their client group.

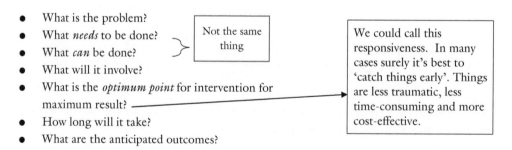

- What is the problem?
- What *needs* to be done?
- What *can* be done?
- What will it involve?
- What is the *optimum point* for intervention for maximum result?
- How long will it take?
- What are the anticipated outcomes?

Not the same thing

We could call this responsiveness. In many cases surely it's best to 'catch things early'. Things are less traumatic, less time-consuming and more cost-effective.

More money is the solution to the problems our services face.

Another common misperception... if it were true, the NHS would be the envy of the world.

Well yes, that **would** be true if there were the people out there **to** recruit.

Well, we'll increase training places at HEIs

OK, but you'll need more clinical placements. Departments already at full stretch can't support the current numbers in the way they know they should (they can't support the NQTs either...)

It takes time to train speech and language therapists and see them through their post- qualification competencies, so they are fit for purpose.

Whilst competent practitioners know what will produce results, what is **less** reliable at an individual practitioner level is what it will cost.

Cost is a critical point – which should apply across the board. Everything comes at a cost. If true costs were more transparent, perhaps the will to make money go as far as possible would become more pressing.

Arguably, independent practitioners probably have a much better idea about costs as they are closer to the action and financially more 'streamlined', as their activity isn't also funding large numbers of roles which do not generate income.

There is a common misperception that joining the private sector is 'all about making money'. In Chapter 1 we describe how, in the early days after becoming independent, we (and many others) encountered adverse reactions from some public sector colleagues. It *isn't* all about money for us, or for dentists either (remember Rohan's story in Chapter 3), or for occupational therapists, physiotherapists, educational psychologists, counsellors and specialist teachers.

Make no mistake, however, money *is* important in both the public and independent sectors. For us, the important thing is what we *do* with that money. We are transparent when negotiating contracts with potential clients. Large commissions are good – but so are much smaller commissions – as discussed in Chapter 14. The challenge is to come up with increasingly novel and creative ways to meet priorities. Think out of the box – what can be achieved within a particular financial envelope and what will be the impact?

Perhaps it's this last thought which has fallen by the wayside in far bigger organisations, where the decision-making process is remote and out of the hands of practitioners. Sometimes it can seem 'just easier' to carry on as we are rather than take time to reflect on how things might be done differently and more effectively.

In the public sector – and increasingly so now in the private sector (as in our business model), schools and settings struggle to balance what they want to commission with what they can afford.

In 2023, the gap had become a gulf. Commissioners have a budget of X and therefore commission Y. Clearly Y is woefully inadequate to meet the need. No blame is being apportioned here – it's a fact.

Valuable time and energy are spent designing pathways of care which, in essence, gatekeep access to services. We've heard this from a range of professionals – including dentists, explored in detail in Chapter 3. As we have learned, very few dentists are directly employed by the NHS (salaried). They opt (or not) to undertake NHS contracts in much the same way as our business contracts with a school or setting. It's worth remembering that dentistry has often been described as the barometer for other professions. There may well be a crisis only a couple of stops down the line for a number of other professions.

Not just in speech and language therapy, but in other professions too, staff groups are (quite rightly) involved in developing pathways or 'packages of care' – call them what you will. Many become increasingly unhappy about the constraints they are working within.

> *I spend almost all my time doing things in a way I know, and research says, to be ineffective; and not in a way that services users, education partners and parents want either.*

How do we know this? We know from the Loan-Clarke research, from the findings of Claire Ewen's research, from our own questionnaire and because people we met say so.

Operating within a system which is diametrically opposed to one's philosophy eventually engenders anxiety and stress which can reach unacceptable levels, as is evident in both Cathy and Marianne's stories.

'Nothing stays the same and nothing is forever' are words often associated with negative thoughts and a yearning for a nostalgia which will never return.

We have made various references during *our* story to the happy time we spent in the public sector, the opportunities it gave us and the passion we had (and still have) for our client group.

> Sentiments echoed by several questionnaire respondents who are happy and fulfilled in their NHS roles.

But we are pragmatists – those days of the flexibility to be a bit more creative with service design are almost certainly a thing of the past.

We prefer to see the potential for not only being able to move through (and out the other side of) times that are tough but also being able to contribute to change for the better.

Looking ahead ...

It's hard to crystal ball gaze and try to predict what will be the 'hot topics' for our profession in six months or a year. What we **can** do, though, is to pull together the things which have emerged from the many conversations we have had. Finding solutions to these problems is important – to therapists, to students and their educators and to our professional organisation and ASLTIP. They should be important to commissioners and employers too.

From the information gathered over the course of almost a year, these are the issues we return to time and again.

We make no apology for posing some pretty hefty questions – none of which we can answer ourselves, in isolation.

First of all, let's consider how to nurture and retain the current workforce and recruit and support the workforce of the future.

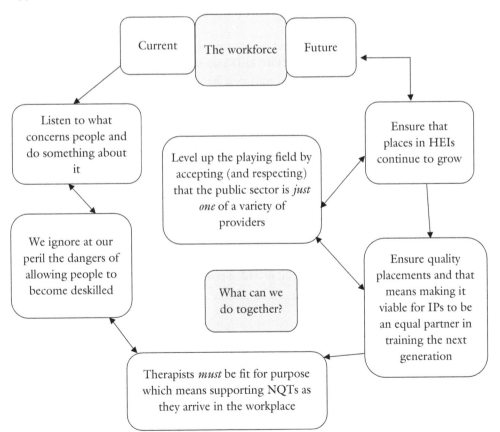

Since well before we left the NHS, our professional body the Royal College of Speech and Language Therapists (RCSLT) have recognised that members from both the public and private sectors might be operating on the same patch. Working in Harmony, mentioned at the very beginning of this book, laid down expected standards in communication and liaison.

It's time to do more than just pay lip service to *working in harmony* – and that's not meant to be derogatory in any way. We must **actively** work together and look to **ourselves** for the skills and talents to do things differently.

Remember that golden thread of optimism which permeates the personal stories? Whilst there are people prepared to stand up for their profession/s and the people they serve, there will always be optimism.

Critical friends

Co-operation, collaboration and communication are the way forward

The section which follows looks at the issues we faced (and still face) in the country's second largest city.

In the early days, we did make overtures to local services on our patch, but, apart from some grassroots liaison about specific children, our bridge-building was not reciprocated. We tried hard to be included in local initiatives about SEND but nothing sustained or substantive ever came of it.

2018 saw a very low point indeed for children's services in Birmingham and speech and language therapy services in particular. The OFSTED joint inspection report was scathing, leaving us (and many colleagues) with a range of conflicting emotions, none of them good.

> *Joint commissioning is significantly underdeveloped across the local area. Professionals were unable to identify or articulate a clear view, either individually or as a partnership, about their main priorities for joint commissioning. As service development and capacity do not match demand, the needs of children and young people are not being met. This is particularly evident within the speech and language therapy (SALT) services.* (Joint local area SEND inspection in Birmingham, 2018) [1]

Without any concept of joint commissioning, how much more remote could joint provision possibly be?

There was more ...

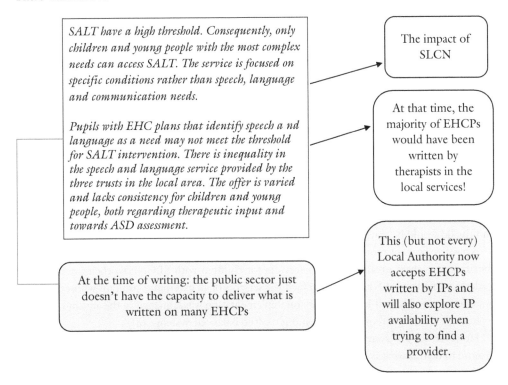

SALT have a high threshold. Consequently, only children and young people with the most complex needs can access SALT. The service is focused on specific conditions rather than speech, language and communication needs.

Pupils with EHC plans that identify speech a nd language as a need may not meet the threshold for SALT intervention. There is inequality in the speech and language service provided by the three trusts in the local area. The offer is varied and lacks consistency for children and young people, both regarding therapeutic input and towards ASD assessment.

The impact of SLCN

At that time, the majority of EHCPs would have been written by therapists in the local services!

This (but not every) Local Authority now accepts EHCPs written by IPs and will also explore IP availability when trying to find a provider.

At the time of writing: the public sector just doesn't have the capacity to deliver what is written on many EHCPs

There had to be a way forward, a way to harness the increasing variety of independent practitioners emerging from the changing provider landscape.

More than five years ago, we made an appointment to meet with the then councillor with responsibility for children's services who took on the role in the spring of 2018, 'inheriting' as she said, 'the complex issues relating to rapidly increasing demand for services following decades of poor performance and lack of government funding for SEND services'.

https://www.birmingham.gov.uk/news/article/920/statement_from_cllr_kate_booth [2]

Arguably, that has continued to happen in the intervening five years since that meeting.

Our aim was to try to explain the diversity of providers and the opportunities available for more joined-up thinking (and the potential positive impact on children and families).

To establish the context, we provided the councillor with brief notes about the dramatically changed provider landscape.

NHS services have been subject to resource constraints year on year and this trend is set to continue. Related to this, but not only driven by the NHS funding constraints, is the rise in numbers of independent practitioners, operating both as individuals but also as larger groups such as partnerships, companies and social enterprises.

Huge numbers of children in our nurseries and schools are unable to access the curriculum because their language skills are so poor. Many/most do not meet the threshold for local speech and language therapy services.

There is a role for **all** providers to work together to meet the SLCN across the city.

The headlines to the points we made were:

- The need for the council to consider taking the lead in developing a 'true partnership' *action* plan
- For comprehensive universal (tier 1) training to empower schools to manage SLCN in their settings (prevention must not be swallowed up by the intervention crisis)
- Recognition that schools, settings, children and families should have access to *timely* provision for both intervention and training, **regardless** of who the provider is
- We also drew attention to the (then) recently announced **Early Outcomes Fund** (funding for local authorities to work together in partnership to improve early language outcomes for 0- to 5-year-olds through high-quality local services)

The councillor herself was unavailable but sent a representative. We came away disappointed. The very clear message was that we had good ideas, but this was all firmly in the 'too difficult' box and the lid would be staying closed.

Now, five years or more down the line, has there been significant change? Are waiting times shorter and is there greater access to services for children with SLCN? To their credit, senior leadership in our local NHS trust engaged the services of an external consultant whose Balanced System is nationally well-known. Work on implementation was launched in the autumn of 2023.

https://www.bettercommunication.org.uk/the-balanced-system/ [3]

However, for *any* system to have the best chance of success it needs enough 'bodies' on the ground to deliver what is required.

Do commissioners really understand what speech and language therapists do and how many different types of providers are operating within Birmingham? Are independent providers invited to bid for services? Are we (collectively) any nearer looking at ways providers locally could work better together?

 From our perspective, not a lot has changed, but we are always hopeful …

Is there a directory of each and every provider in the city (public and private, limited companies and sole traders alike)? How difficult would it be to provide a resource which lends transparency to the whole process of choosing someone to deliver speech and language therapy services in a range of settings. A place where the commissioning agent – whether that is a parent or a school or setting – would begin to look for the person or people to meet their needs. The answer to that (despite schools and settings in the city thinking it would be a very good idea) is 'no'.

ASLTIP corporate membership would mean that people could search companies as well as individuals.

The ASLTIP chair says: *'What would really help is the opportunity to update ASLTIP Articles of Association for the current context. How and when we do this will be dependent on the views of the membership and legal advice to keep us compliant.'*

We know that schools and settings rely almost exclusively on word of mouth and parents are directed to the ASLTIP website. A directory wouldn't solve the problem of too few therapists, but it would be a step on the way to levelling that playing field.

To truly make progress, not just for a fairer marketplace, we need evidence of joined-up thinking at both strategic and operational levels.

For clients (children and adults alike) to become successful communicators, they need the **means** (i.e. the wherewithal), **reasons** (talking has to be motivating) and the **opportunity** (someone to listen to their voice) (Money, 1997) [4].

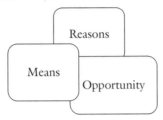

This, in essence, is what speech and language therapy is all about.

If we can do it for the clients, why can't we do it for ourselves?

Actually, we can and there are 'green shoots' beginning to appear.

From what we have learnt from our FOI findings (detailed in Chapter 4) and from anecdotal unsolicited comments on visits to schools, NHS enhanced services operate in a way not dissimilar to the core service, with a limited menu of options and often inconsistent personnel on site or long-term vacancies. Potential customers find this disheartening – on top of a significant level of frustration with such a narrow core offer.

This is endorsed in greater detail by the findings of our survey into how local schools and settings source their additional support. The responses make clear what schools and settings find disappointing and frustrating.

It seems an odd thing to offer for payment (i.e. 'sell') something described as enhanced and then, essentially, deliver more of the same.

> *Enhance [v]: to improve the quality, value or extent of*

We know from our FOI requests that some services folded because they couldn't provide the variety of interventions that schools and settings wanted.

There are lessons here to be learnt from the private sector:

- *Ask* what the client wants
- *Learn* what the client needs
- *Understand* the client's budgetary constraints
- *Be creative* and *identify* realistic, achievable and measurable objectives
- Demonstrate your *impact*

In Chapter 13, we talk about transparency and being thoroughly familiar with your product so that you know what can realistically be offered and at what cost. In the same way that any of us purchase goods or services, we want to know details and, most importantly, whether the product will do what we need and want it to do. Professional services are no different.

Before we move on to expand the themes of cooperation, collaboration and communication (with real examples and aspirations), we would like to revisit a plan we had back in 2014. We wrote a paper proposing a model whereby independent provider companies could establish a closer working relationship with NHS services.

At that particular time (as we discuss in Chapter 4), NHS services were being actively encouraged to develop an 'enhanced offer' and such services began to spring up countrywide. Few if any speech and language therapy managers could possibly be equipped to – in essence – set up and run a business (why would they be?). If that was reflected in a clinical context, it would attract all manner of criticism! It would be interesting to know how many of those early traded (enhanced) services survived. In addition, few NHS trusts had the appropriately skilled 'back room' business support available to assist clinical managers who found themselves suddenly 'running a business'.

The purpose of our paper was to recruit an NHS partner to pilot the idea. The plans allowed for a developing relationship between our company and the NHS partner – moving through three levels of engagement. Starting small and becoming increasingly interdependent, the plan identified anticipated outcomes and what activity might look like at each level.

There could be clear benefits for everyone, with the service user front and centre.

- Increased and more transparent choice
- Better relationships all round
- More effective use of resources
- The establishment of effective and sustainable traded services, working in genuine partnership with other providers
- Greater opportunities for both students and qualified staff alike

… and, of course, there would be business opportunities, not just for independent providers but also for the NHS partner.

And for the profession as a whole:

- The potential for a model of genuine and equitable collaborative working which would support the profession nationally to move towards marketplace provision

We took our proposal to two different service managers in the West Midlands – it was received quite defensively by one and was blocked by the line manager of the other.

Re-reading this proposal ten years later, much of it is still relevant.

As we discuss in Chapter 4, the FOI responses at no point mentioned income generation as a reason for selling an enhanced service. Why not? Is this a missed opportunity, as we felt it was ten years ago? Has the landscape changed again to the point where public services might be much better placed concentrating on delivering a high-quality and robust core offer?

If the latter is the case, then no one would argue, as long as the playing field is levelled (as we mentioned earlier in this chapter) and there is a recognition that the public sector is just one of a *variety* of providers.

This is certainly beginning to happen 'on the ground' as these two examples demonstrate.

A recent new setting came to us via recommendation from the local NHS therapist.

We are looking for a provider to… is this something you could do?

We can't provide that but here's someone who might be able to

Our Local Authority special needs team asks us for EHCP reports and invites us to quote to deliver some bespoke and sometimes tricky commissions. This is not the case everywhere.

Thinking more widely than speech and language therapy, if any individual or group seeks to spend money on additional/different/faster support and intervention, that is entirely up to them. Clearly many **do** want that choice: at the time of writing the range of services offered by private providers is vast and likely to continue to grow.

Example 1: In 2022, the Health Foundation published an article into NHS waiting times post-pandemic and government initiatives aimed at tackling the backlog. '… help tackle the backlog, the NHS has arranged to treat more patients via independent sector health care providers'.
https://www.health.org.uk/publications/long-reads/waiting-for-nhs-hospital-care-the-role-of-the-independent-sector [5]

Example 2: In the Spring of 2023, *The Guardian* newspaper headlined 'Record rise in people using private healthcare amid NHS frustration'. https://www.theguardian.com/society/2023/may/24/record-rise-in-people-using-private-healthcare-amid-nhs-frustration [6]

Example 3: In August 2023, a government press release announced: 'Government boosts use of independent sector capacity to cut NHS waits'. This involved 'the opening of 13 new community diagnostic centres across the country, to deliver more than 742,000 additional scans, tests and checks a year'. Who could possibly argue with that? It's an eminently sensible thing to do and it's a pretty firm bet that the 'free at the point of delivery' argument will remain silent. Why? Because, for the service user, it will be business as usual – just far quicker and possibly in more luxurious surroundings. The provision of funding is happening at a strategic level.

There is a fundamental difference between the first and third examples. The initiatives in one and three are, for the service user, still free at the point of delivery. The NHS has opted to use its funds differently. In *The Guardian* article, users are spending their own money (either via health insurance premium or directly from earned income).

As is so often the case, what looks like a hugely innovative, cutting-edge 'new idea' is second-ary care-based (i.e. a hospital-based service) and comes about because people are suffering and sometimes dying waiting for a diagnosis (let alone the treatment) which may put them on the road to recovery. People are outraged and, in some instances, in despair – and so they should be!

Is this the start of significant change? It certainly has appeal in that an initiative has got underway in response to a specific problem without first feeling the need to change the funda-mental belief held by so many that the NHS can do no wrong and we tinker with it at our peril (that has been firmly incarcerated in the 'too difficult' box for years).

There will always be people who hold firmly to the ideals of health services being *free* and as such there being an *entitlement,* and some who maintain paying a private company to do some-thing is tantamount to lining the pockets of the rich at the expense of the poor. However, human nature being what it is, new ways of doing things, with evidenced impact, will go a long way to change the hearts and minds of many.

Readers might be wondering why Example 3 has been included, but is it too big a stretch to see the potential parallels with speech and lan-guage therapy services?

There is already a model of public and private sec-tors working together where well-known private companies are used to speed up various types of health screening, thereby helping people access NHS treatment services more quickly – so why not in primary care?

By enabling budgets to be deployed to meet need – regardless of the sector best placed to do that – we have the potential for another hugely innovative, cutting-edge 'new idea', developed in response to thousands of children and young people with SLCN being denied the help which will enable them to reach their full potential and access education and life's opportunities as they grow into adulthood.

In order to move forward we must get past the resistance to 'payment' being mentioned in the same sentence as 'healthcare'.

In some quarters the resistance to change is zealous, bordering on the obsessive. The constraints and waits are resurrecting that fear that Bevan fought so hard to remove. In the case of, for the most part, non-emergency services such as speech and language therapy, the fear is more 'despair' and leaves no option for those that possibly can 'shift for themselves'.

Such resistance, according to Hardman (2023), is at real risk of '*returning to the two tiers of the pre-NHS days, where people who were rich could get excellent treatment and the rest had to hope for the best*' [7].

Of course, nothing is ever that simple but with sufficient will, it's entirely possible. There are other pieces of the puzzle to factor in as well – and we will come to them shortly.

Keeping the client and family front and centre

Each week we are contacted by desperate parents hunting for someone to help their child with 'his talking'. These are often very difficult calls to listen to. Such are the feelings of responsibility and guilt (although self-induced) from therapists who are almost always operating at capacity, that we no longer ask the therapists in our team (which is a schools-based service) whether anyone can take on yet another individual case in their own private practice. Instead, we listen, tell the parents about ASLTIP and signpost to other possible options locally that we know of. It's important not to become inured to the sad stories we are told about NHS waiting lists and children missing out on the help they need and deserve. We must turn that sense of injustice into positive steps to get people the help they need.

This question came from the father of a three-year-old who 'wasn't talking'. The father was clinging to the hope that we had seen older children who had eventually begun to talk and that it wasn't 'too late'. It's very difficult, if not impossible, to provide any kind of reassurance in a phone call.

Could you just tell me what's the oldest child you've seen before they started to talk?

Cooperation, collaboration and communication – making it happen

Earlier in this chapter, we said we made no apology for posing some pretty 'hefty questions'. Since our move to the private sector in 2012, we have spoken to a considerable number of people – all of whom have ideas about how to progress the collaboration and cooperation agenda. It's clear that no one group in isolation can affect the level of change we need.

With the service user at the forefront, this is an opportune moment to revisit the concept of a fluid model of available support and to look at how each sector could support each other.

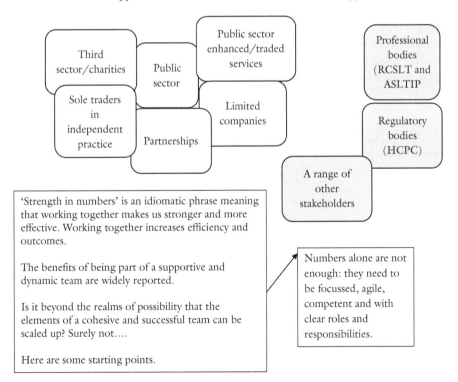

Third sector/charities

Public sector

Public sector enhanced/traded services

Professional bodies (RCSLT and ASLTIP)

Sole traders in independent practice

Partnerships

Limited companies

Regulatory bodies (HCPC)

A range of other stakeholders

'Strength in numbers' is an idiomatic phrase meaning that working together makes us stronger and more effective. Working together increases efficiency and outcomes.

The benefits of being part of a supportive and dynamic team are widely reported.

Is it beyond the realms of possibility that the elements of a cohesive and successful team can be scaled up? Surely not....

Here are some starting points.

Numbers alone are not enough: they need to be focussed, agile, competent and with clear roles and responsibilities.

Identifying priorities

These are not just *our* priorities. Common themes have emerged – shared not only by other speech and language therapists but by a range of other professionals.

Workforce

Q. How do we recruit, support and retain our most valuable asset?

There is a body of evidence in this book alone which identifies what people want and what drives them away from a profession.

Q. How do we give students the best possible opportunities both during their training and also when they enter the workplace?

As one of our questionnaire respondents observed:

> *I really welcome the mix of independent practice and working in our local HEI. I think it is vital that students are exposed to independent practitioners as well as the NHS so that they are flexible and properly prepared for the working landscape. I also think that exposure to independent practitioners as a student helps to combat some of the prejudices and preconceptions that still exist about independent practitioners. This is essential if we are to work together effectively – we are all on the same team!*

● **Job satisfaction**

This is a good place to identify what we mean by 'job satisfaction'. Closely related to 'making a difference', job satisfaction is about carrying out a role which is useful, enjoyable and fulfilling. This is a good point to say that many people tell us that taking on management responsibilities is the only way to climb the career ladder.

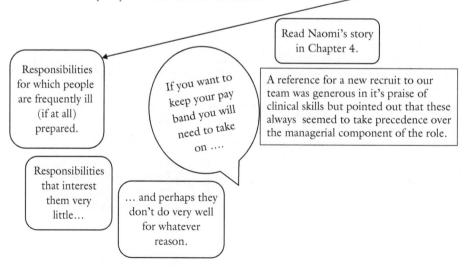

> Some clinicians become very skilled and compassionate managers, and arguably having a clinician as manager is far better than having a non-clinical manager who does not understand the service they are managing. But for those who don't have the skill set or the interest, it can be (at best) unproductive for all concerned.

How can NHS teams offer career opportunities and job satisfaction for experienced clinicians who **don't want** to take on management roles?

- **To become and remain skilled**

Core offer menus are so narrow that swathes of skills and interventions are no longer required. As Rohan our NHS dentist reported in Chapter 3, it is demotivating to qualify to be able to deliver A – Z in terms of treatments and interventions but then to only be able to deliver A – J for example.

- **Making a difference**

This is critical because it's the reason we enter vocational professions in the first place. Marianne starts her story in Chapter 4 with '*I love being a speech and language therapist – it feels a genuine privilege to do what I do*'. Things really can't get much better than that, can they? But, as we learnt, Marianne's journey to reach that point had been long and sometimes painful, largely because all the other things she wanted and needed were ultimately unavailable to her in her NHS role.

- **Free at the point of delivery**

This is important to a lot of people. It cropped up many times as part of the questionnaire and as we see from the personal stories Kezia and Holly found the attitudes of others difficult to cope with. One respondent even went so far as to say:

> *When I first joined the profession, almost the only choices available were to work in your local county's NHS, move to a different county in order to hold down a different NHS job there or be seen as a traitor to the NHS free at the point of delivery.*

Strong language indeed but it will strike a chord with some readers.

- **Feeling valued, supported and cared about**

It's very difficult to value, support and care about the people we serve if we ourselves feel, somehow, unimportant (or worse) to the people we work for or with.

Problems and difficulties in our personal lives are magnified and we are far less resilient if our working life is stressful and unfulfilling. We know a public sector service manager who spends a significant proportion of her time supporting and trying to help staff with problems, some of which are serious and distressing. She herself is in danger of suffering from compassion fatigue. By contrast, a private sector employer's approach to her team is liberating and enabling. One of *her* biggest challenges is making sure she maintains the necessary employer-employee boundaries.

> *One of the benefits of employing rather than subcontracting is the opportunity to consider what is the offer to the employee. As an employer, I can craft a work environment that heroes learning and development and provides opportunities for clinical and professional development. For example, funding whole team training on new therapy approaches.*
>
> *We use a learning and development project approach (Agile: see Chapter 5), where employees set their own objectives for development with incremental steps to achieve them, so they can really take responsibility and drive their career progression.*
>
> *I am also really mindful of well-being and the pressure on team members to provide a quality and effective service. I have set up initiatives like an employee assistance package and private healthcare to protect and support my team.*
>
> *Finally, my team are the most immediate stakeholders for my organisation. Planning meetings are an opportunity for employees to input ideas for the company's development and to put their stamp on SBT* (Sarah Buckley Therapies) *while they are part of our journey.*

To feel valued, supported and cared about is one of the strongest messages coming out of both the personal stories and our questionnaire. In Chapter 3, Claire Ewen concludes her contribution with these words:

It is therefore also the responsibility of *employers* to ensure that the well-being of their staff is supported, through the careful management of demands and the consideration of how SLTs achieve 'professional autonomy and the provision of effective support'.

It's accepted without question that clinical responsibility requires training, CPD and supervision

How widely is this reflected in mid-management roles?

Maybe not so much given the feedback from our questionnaire (which identified 'management styles' as one of the reasons why people left) and the examples which appear in some of the personal stories

This disturbing contribution was left by one of the respondents to our questionnaire.

I moved from a hospital with a toxic working environment to a different trust in a community team that is much more supportive and values teamwork. I have worked in a hospital team previously and the environment was very supportive, and I loved it, but when I made a move to a different hospital my experience was the complete opposite despite the nearly identical job role.

The respondent reported draconian 'rules' such as beverages only being allowed when on a formal break. There were no non-work-related conversations between different disciplines in the team and attempts to do so were not favourably received. An unchallenged 'bullying culture' was reported, where some consultants would belittle individuals by name on ward rounds. The respondent felt that 'quality of patient care' was less of a priority than 'numbers': *'there was a constant pressure to see more patients no matter how high your numbers were'.*

Poor well-being support was mentioned. After a 'significant incident' involving a confused patient, the respondent's manager phoned her: *'she told me that I would need to pick up the pace or stay back late without remuneration to make up for it and didn't even ask if I was okay'.*

The respondent eventually handed in her notice: *'my manager accused me of not caring about the patients and tried to guilt trip me into staying'.* The respondent reported that two people she knew went to work in the same hospital and reported similar difficulties.

Unfortunately, one colleague became severely affected by the mental pressures that work put them under and they were unable to work again. I think if I had stayed in that job my mental health would have suffered tremendously. It is amazing how different the same job can be in different environments, with different teams and with different managers.

This contributor is at the extreme end of the experiences which crop up in a number of our stories. Anyone reading this could be forgiven for feelings of shock and sadness – anger too perhaps.

Please, please, please can we, collectively, begin to look at ways that people in management roles can support and nurture their single greatest resource? Whether knowingly or unknowingly (difficult to decide which is more culpable), there are people in positions of authority who abuse the power invested in them.

What would help us along the road to genuine cooperation, collaboration and communication?

Thank you to everyone who contributed to the 'wall of wisdom' – these are *just some* of the unsolicited comments across *all* the various groups of people we have spoken to whilst working on the book.

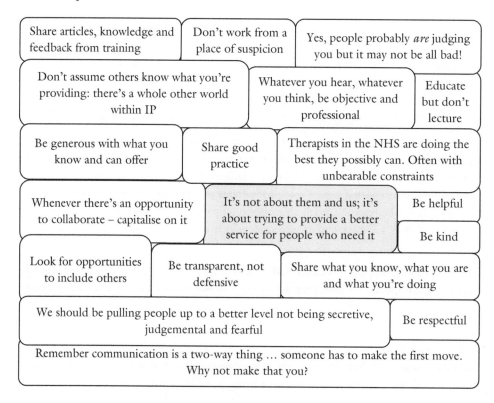

Share articles, knowledge and feedback from training

Don't work from a place of suspicion

Yes, people probably *are* judging you but it may not be all bad!

Don't assume others know what you're providing: there's a whole other world within IP

Whatever you hear, whatever you think, be objective and professional

Educate but don't lecture

Be generous with what you know and can offer

Share good practice

Therapists in the NHS are doing the best they possibly can. Often with unbearable constraints

Whenever there's an opportunity to collaborate – capitalise on it

It's not about them and us; it's about trying to provide a better service for people who need it

Be helpful

Be kind

Look for opportunities to include others

Be transparent, not defensive

Share what you know, what you are and what you're doing

We should be pulling people up to a better level not being secretive, judgemental and fearful

Be respectful

Remember communication is a two-way thing … someone has to make the first move. Why not make that you?

The majority of the examples which follow focus on speech and language therapy but, by thinking more broadly, a number of them have application to other roles and a multi-disciplinary team approach.

What is the best way to encapsulate these ideas?

We have used the pyramid of intervention model which will be familiar to a range of professionals working with children. It is a good, practical way of illustrating how actions need attention from different organisations and at different levels.

Gascoigne M. (2006) "Supporting children with speech, language and communication needs within integrated children's services" [8]

Who will start the ball rolling? Anyone can be the catalyst – wherever they work

Recent work in Birmingham to establish the Balanced System has gone a long way to identifying who is doing what in terms of SLCN.

If it is possible to scope the provision across Britain's second city then surely it is conceivable that directories of IP& NHS services in defined areas could be established

One of the participants in the CEN focus group spoke eloquently about how her role in a nursery worked in partnership with what could be provided by the visiting NHS therapist.

A degree of uniformity in terms of contracts offered would help more concerted support from ASLTIP.

No matter where you work…

✔ *Contribute* to the bigger picture by scoping what is currently happening on *your* patch

✔ *Contact* your professional (SLT) colleagues and take the initiative about working jointly with a client (is there a bigger picture you can be thinking about?)

✔ *Join* networks

✔ *Share* good practice. If you get something good going, no matter how small it is – shout about it!

✔ *Signpost* an enquiry you can't accommodate *to* someone else who might be able to help

Another good reason to find out who else is offering services on the same patch as you

Independent SLTs are proactively approaching HEIs to talk about creative placement options. (ASLTIP chair)

'ASLTIP could support the dialogue with your HEI. Once a n HEI has a sense of the amount and quality of potential placements that IPs could offer, there is a joint incentive to look at solutions for systems and process to overcome barriers'. (ASLTIP chair)

If each individual person did just one thing, think what a difference it could make.

Things that each and every one of us can do immediately.

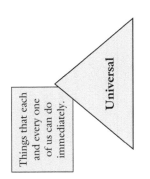

Universal

Building relationships locally

Naomi (whose story appears in chapter 4) has invested time and effort in establishing relationships with colleagues in her area. It helps to have worked on the patch in her previous NHS days but important to keep those contacts live. She always checks with new clients if they have pursued NHS services and if they are on a waiting list, encouraging them to access these free services. NHS therapists will direct enquiries from relatives of individuals on the waiting list to ASLTIP – latterly she has been recommended directly by name. Naomi also has well established links with the charity sector, local Headway and Stroke Association coordinators in particular.

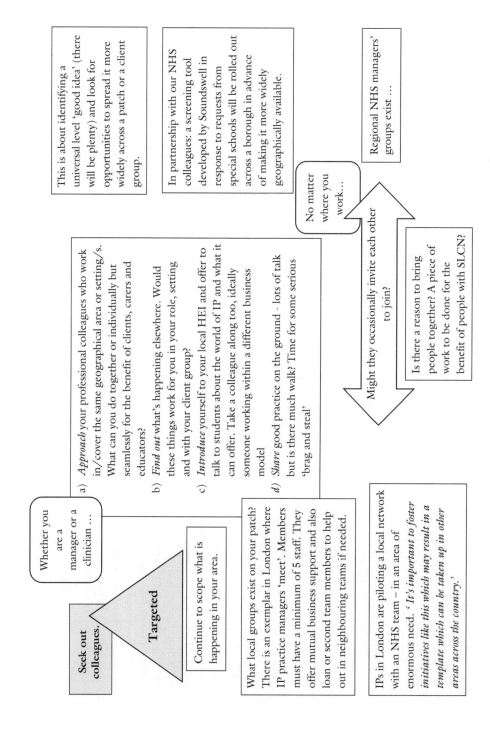

This is about identifying a universal level 'good idea' (there will be plenty) and look for opportunities to spread it more widely across a patch or a client group.

In partnership with our NHS colleagues: a screening tool developed by Soundswell in response to requests from special schools will be rolled out across a borough in advance of making it more widely geographically available.

Regional NHS managers' groups exist ...

No matter where you work...

Might they occasionally invite each other to join?

Is there a reason to bring people together? A piece of work to be done for the benefit of people with SLCN?

a) *Approach* your professional colleagues who work in/cover the same geographical area or setting/s. What can you do together or individually but seamlessly for the benefit of clients, carers and educators?

b) *Find out* what's happening elsewhere. Would these things work for you in your role, setting and with your client group?

c) *Introduce* yourself to your local HEI and offer to talk to students about the world of IP and what it can offer. Take a colleague along too, ideally someone working within a different business model

d) *Share* good practice on the ground – lots of talk but is there much walk? Time for some serious 'brag and steal'

Whether you are a manager or a clinician ...

Seek out colleagues.

Targeted

Continue to scope what is happening in your area.

What local groups exist on your patch? There is an exemplar in London where IP practice managers 'meet'. Members must have a minimum of 5 staff. They offer mutual business support and also loan or second team members to help out in neighbouring teams if needed.

IPs in London are piloting a local network with an NHS team – in an area of enormous need. '*It's important to foster initiatives like this which may result in a template which can be taken up in other areas across the country.*'

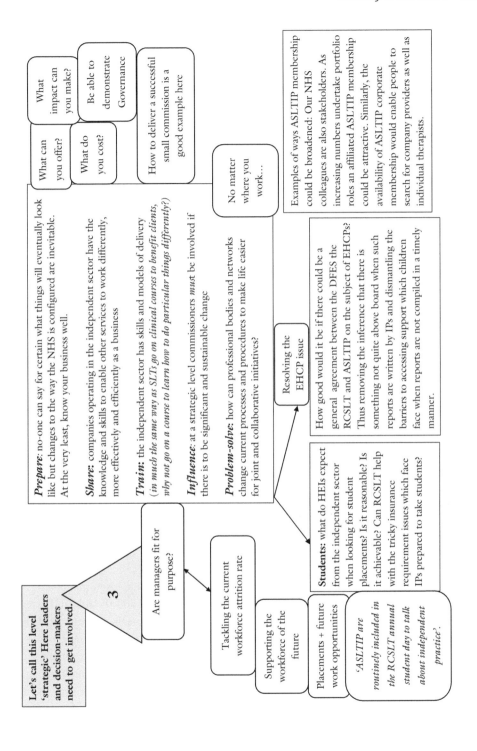

Let's call this level 'strategic'. Here leaders and decision-makers need to get involved.

3

Prepare: no-one can say for certain what things will eventually look like but changes to the way the NHS is configured are inevitable. At the very least, know your business well.

Share: companies operating in the independent sector have the knowledge and skills to enable other services to work differently, more effectively and efficiently as a business

Train: the independent sector has skills and models of delivery (*in much the same way as SLTs go on clinical courses to benefit clients, why not go on a course to learn how to do particular things differently?*)

Influence: at a strategic level commissioners *must* be involved if there is to be significant and sustainable change

Problem-solve: how can professional bodies and networks change current processes and procedures to make life easier for joint and collaborative initiatives?

What can you offer?

What do you cost?

What impact can you make?

Be able to demonstrate Governance

How to deliver a successful small commission is a good example here

No matter where you work…

Are managers fit for purpose?

Tackling the current workforce attrition rate

Supporting the workforce of the future

Placements + future work opportunities

'ASLTIP are routinely included in the RCSLT annual student day to talk about independent practice'.

Students: what do HEIs expect from the independent sector when looking for student placements? Is it reasonable? Is it achievable? Can RCSLT help with the tricky insurance requirement issues which face IPs prepared to take students?

Resolving the EHCP issue

How good would it be if there could be a general agreement between the DFES the RCSLT and ASLTIP on the subject of EHCPs? Thus removing the inference that there is something not quite above board when such reports are written by IPs and dismantling the barriers to accessing support which children face when reports are not compiled in a timely manner.

Examples of ways ASLTIP membership could be broadened: Our NHS colleagues are also stakeholders. As increasing numbers undertake portfolio roles an affiliated ASLTIP membership could be attractive. Similarly, the availability of ASLTIP corporate membership would enable people to search for company providers as well as individual therapists.

There are two further points to be made – definitely falling into the 'hefty' category.

1. The first is related to the often contentious **'conflict of interest'** issue.

    In Chapter 7 we talk about the 'public and private sector interface'.

Historically, when a therapist informs their manager of an intention to undertake some independent work, the response has traditionally been that 'it isn't allowed' to do this in the same geographical area as any NHS work is undertaken. We have perused the NHS guidance – which is summarised in Chapter 7 and cannot find any reference which specifically says this. Anecdotally this seems to be down to individual managers.

Things have moved on considerably since the quite commonly held view that anyone operating outside of the public sector was 'only in it for the money'.

We all need to keep sight of the fact that at the beginning of any search for speech and language therapy, there is an individual who needs timely help.

There **is** an argument for saying that independent practitioners (or practitioners who work in both sectors) who take on clients who have waited for an unacceptably long time are **reducing the pressure** in the public sector and improving the situation on their own patch!

Is it a bridge too far to also put forward the argument that suitable public sector premises could be available for early evening, school holiday and weekend appointments offered by IPS? Would commissioners pay for this to reduce waiting times and help children and families? If there are vacancies then there must be unused budget in establishments. Why not think about creative ways of spending (rather than losing) it?

In the same way that we advise our schools and settings to continue to refer to the public sector so that commissioners realise the demand is still there and is still very high, if the numbers waiting reduce significantly, there is the potential risk of commissioning 'atrophy'.

Our view is that we are a very long way away from any such alteration, given that commissioning knowledge and awareness of SLT in general is not well-evolved and the role and extent of independent provision even less so. Current risk is minimal and arguably offset by the benefits for individuals and families. Going forward, there is a piece of work to be done here.

Another, not dissimilar example, might be that when local NHS services are commissioned but not able to deliver what schools need, for whatever reason, could not the funding be given directly to the school, even if only on a temporary basis, to buy in what they need from the independent sector?

2. Secondly, we should raise the subject of **'regulation' or 'scrutiny'** in terms of the private sector

During the course of writing this book, the concept of 'regulation' in terms of independent providers has arisen more than once. One FOI respondent said that they had set up their enhanced service thus *'ensuring a service that has the assurances of being backed by the NHS safeguards (such as mandatory training, supervision, CPD etc.)'*. The inference here is that IP services are somehow less safe.

There are differing views on the way forward for 'regulation' and private practices. Should they be required to 'evidence a set of criteria', 'audited' in some form, or come under 'scrutiny' from some official body?

> *Scrutiny [n]: critical observation or examination*

> *Regulation [n]: a rule or directive made and maintained by an authority*

> *Audit [n]: an official inspection of an organisation, typically by an independent body*

No one we spoke to thought there should be **no** regulation. On the other hand, however, no one would want to see the weight of a CQC inspection landing on an individual practitioner or small business! If/when the time arrives when a *variety* of providers are able to tender for a range of contracts, there will be a need to evidence governance. Chris, our security and technology specialist, raised this in Chapter 11.

1. We asked two directors of private companies for their views on private SLT companies being subject to some degree of regulation.

Jo, who has her own practice in Birmingham, says:

> *I think the smart thing would be to implement regulation as soon as possible. I'm not sure what that will look like, but the ability to give some level of reassurance to those buying our services is valuable. Many of us know how tortuous the process of HCPC's effectiveness in dealing with clinicians who are not fit for purpose. I do not think it is a robust mechanism to protect the public. We are a small profession and for us to be implementing something on a voluntary basis would be an excellent idea. I do not however underestimate the additional work that this would entail and the bureaucracy of such a process is often what has chased people into IP. It would also be onerous for sole traders.*

Sarah, our specialist contributor, says:

> *As individual SLTs, we are all responsible for meeting the HCPC standards of proficiency to make sure we provide safe and effective services. Regulation of companies is a more challenging one and it is worth considering what exactly we would be regulating. We already need to be compliant with the relevant HR/health and safety/data/company law. Would we be regulating quality of services and if so, why? I'm not opposed to regulation in principle if there was a robust reason behind it.*

It is important to remember that professional accountability strengthens people. Any regulatory process should be seen as positive and a way to minimise risk and evidence quality.

Potential ways forward might include:

- Gathering views as to what might be important governance procedures to have in place
- Understanding how directors of private companies currently ensure quality within their teams (a good starting point for what 'regulation' might include)
- Considering the development of an audit tool to support independent practitioners to evidence governance
- Encouraging a 'bottom-up' approach which bases itself on what is already happening and builds on it, with guidance to support those who are new to IP

Readers will be familiar with what factors **we** think are important – described in detail throughout this book.

We asked our two directors how they ensure the quality of what happens at their practices.

Sarah said:

> *My company has a series of policies and procedures that employees are required to read and sign off on as part of induction.*
>
> *I have set up audit processes for company policies and procedures that happen annually and involve participation of the whole team. This year's audit has been about EHCP recommendations and hours (we are a paediatric practice). Recently we did a target document audit. Understanding and setting up audit has been a learning curve, but it does keep us accountable and is a good opportunity to review our standards.*
>
> *Alongside internal measures, we seek feedback from our stakeholders. We regularly invite families, schools and LA to feedback via an online survey and we take this feedback forward during service development planning and review of policies and processes.*

Jo observes as follows:

> *To some extent that is rather based on the premise that I know what a good job looks like (I hope I do), it is my opinion I know what excellent (and substandard) looks like, based on a number of factors:*
>
> - *Undertaking roles as team and clinical lead in the NHS*
> - *Supporting both undergraduate and postgraduate clinical education*
> - *Experience scrutinising the clinical practice of others through my medico-legal work*
>
> *Most of the people who work with me have come through personal recommendations. I have a therapist agreement which sets out what I expect of all my therapists. All reports that go out from my company have first been seen by myself to ensure that they meet company standards, including a clear differential diagnosis based on assessment with details of what assessment has been carried out and also a set of clinical recommendations.*
>
> *As a team, we have electronic clinical records which means that anybody within the team can observe what is being written. This gives me the opportunity to monitor the quality of information that is being written about our clients. I also have systems in place for audit, support and supervision and foster a culture of openness and sharing of clinical knowledge and skills.*
>
> *Team support and supervision are cascaded down amongst the team and I am frequently copied into queries and discussions, whereby I can see the evidence. The team is safe to be vulnerable amongst each other and all work to further develop their combined knowledge, skills and confidence.*

As a profession, we need to evidence appropriate governance in response to questions from potential commissioners. Our personal preference is to provide information as routine rather than potentially being ambushed at short notice by a lengthy questionnaire about GDPR or equality impact assessments for example.

Having appropriate governance in place is *not* about ticking boxes or being ready for any future tendering opportunities – it makes sound business sense. In Chapter 6 when we start to talk about systems and processes which need to be in place, we say '*the whole point of having systems in place is to minimise risk*'. Risk to us, to our businesses, but more than anything, risk to service users.

Being open, transparent and safe is part of levelling the playing field.

As we come to the end of our story …

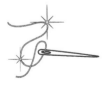 We should take heart – from the collective experiences of those who have shared their journeys with us. How they have faced (in some cases considerable) challenges, made sometimes difficult decisions in the face of, sometimes, a fair amount of opposition and managed to keep on moving until they ended up in the *right place for them*. Regardless of where they moved to or from, an overwhelming 75% said that it was.

And yes, sometimes it does help to bear in mind the wise words of Aesop (a particular favourite of ours).

> Aesop was also quite vocal on the subject of tyrants …

There's always someone worse off than yourself.

We should *also* take heart from the final story in the book. It contains examples of the 'pushes' which feature in other stories and the hurdles to be overcome, and, as with so many of us, these challenges are set against the backdrop of events in our personal lives.

However, what makes this story unique is the sheer magnitude of the serial, negative significant events. Most of us would struggle to pick ourselves up after any single one of these. That isn't to say that what happened didn't take its toll – it most certainly **did**, but self-belief and determination should never be underestimated. This is truly a story of triumph over adversity. This is Holly's story.

Things start conventionally enough: Holly was a married mum with two very young children. She had progressed in the profession but had reached the point where she felt unfulfilled. Her energy and drive for new challenges were unfulfilled as developments just weren't happening to the extent that she felt that her manager and the NHS structure at the time was 'holding her back'.

The effective manager recognises and fosters talent in others. Sadly, however, the scenario of managers feeling threatened by more junior staff is not unfamiliar. Responsibility is easily devolved, but with little or no power to influence, things can become very stressful – as we saw in Cathy's story in our opening chapter.

Holly had already dipped her toe in the water by exploring other avenues which used her professional skills, but in different ways and away from the Trust where she worked. Her solution to one particularly difficult job she was given (to move into a different service area and, in effect, reconfigure the workforce in order to down-grade staff) was to plan her exit strategy.

> *I figured that my experiences in the NHS wouldn't be unique: others would follow. I wanted to be ahead of the game and I had faith in my own abilities to make it.*

This was at a time when there were far fewer IPs around and 'mainstream' service scepticism was gathering momentum. '*I was viewed as a maverick, an autonomous provider with no accountability*'.

Holly started a company with a colleague (who was part-time in the NHS). '*We had visions of eventually establishing an MDT. The plan was that I left first and then she would follow – building up the IP work on the days she wasn't working for the Trust*'. So far, so good, but it transpired that the colleague and business partner was locuming in a nearby Trust instead of contributing to the business.

> *It took me some time to realise what was happening. She was always 'unavailable' and never returned my calls. It was as if she had dropped off the edge of the world. I was being professionally*

ghosted. It eventually came to light that she was defrauding the business we started, diverting referrals and having invoices paid directly into her personal account. I had taken all the risk when we set up the company and was devastated that I had put my trust in someone who let me down so badly. I lost a huge amount of confidence but was determined not to be defeated.

Holly closed that business, rebranded herself and started again from scratch. Luckily the associates who had gravitated towards the first business stuck with her. The business undertook work in schools as well as holding clinics for individuals (both adults and children).

Like most of us, Holly found herself saying 'yes' to almost every enquiry, with a view to becoming more selective further down the line.

*The team grew organically. Probably 90% of them were people I already knew or were recommended to me. It **wasn't** about the money – the associates consistently over-performed and under-valued their skills. My aim was to nurture them and pay them well for the work they did.*

It was the right approach and to this day, the team experiences very low turnover.

It looked like the 'bump in the road' was behind and the time was right to purchase premises which would be a permanent clinic base. A mortgage and complete renovation plan followed. Work was well advanced when the second catastrophe occurred.

I discovered that my husband was living a double life. Almost overnight I found myself with sole responsibility for the children who were still young, the business to run, a hefty mortgage for the clinic premises and the devastation that arises from a relationship breakdown.

The priority was to divest herself of her husband's interest in any shared assets and to hang onto the property at all costs. Holly had sound business advice from her solicitor, accountant and support from a mortgage and financial advisor. Eventually, over a period of five years, she succeeded in getting divorced, severing all financial ties and remaining independent and solvent. Her personal and professional life were back on track and there was everything to look forward to.

'*At this point, I was working all the hours I could in order to maintain my home and business. I was literally mortgaged up to my eyeballs but I was free and trying to establish some equilibrium*'.

This was to be a short-lived period, as less than a month after the decree absolute was served, Holly became very acutely unwell and during exploratory surgery she was diagnosed with a very rare form of cancer.

Apart from the acute and obvious stresses of not being 100% sure if she would survive or not, there was also the stress of needing to continue to make a living. A year of difficult and painful and traumatic treatment was followed by two years of recovery.

*Thankfully, I was well insured and had both critical illness and income protection insurance in place. This meant that during the very difficult period of fighting for my life, I wasn't worried about keeping a roof over my head and food on the table. If you do **nothing else**, make sure you have insurances in place – income protection insurance, insurance against critical illness!*

It was when I started my graded return to work, I decided to invest in a business coach. I needed to work smarter – I couldn't work as hard as I had been because I no longer had the physical capacity. I needed to have a plan and develop a business which would sustain me and my children, which would continue to grow so that at some point in the future when the time was right for me to wind down, there would be an asset there I could sell. I wanted to be able to take prolonged periods away to travel and in order to do this, the business needed to function without me. I needed to establish processes for all aspects of the business to make this a possibility.

Fast forward to the present:

My illness made me realise that life truly is precious. Yes, I continue to have aspirations for the business and plans to develop. The business coach has taught me so much about valuing what we do – money is definitely not my strength! I'm better at the financial aspects now.

Holly continues to run her business and has lost none of her drive to develop what she and her team offer. She is now at the point where she is employing two part-time staff as well as sub-contracting to associate SLTs.

We need to be creative about how we recruit. As independent therapists, we may not be able to offer the variety that new graduates would look for within an NHS post. However, what we can provide is the supportive environment to enable therapists to grow and develop their therapeutic skills.

Her early experience has influenced her thinking to some extent.

I work with the expectation that people will look after their own interests.
    Taking someone into my team means that they have insights into my business model and potentially could take my clients. I try to foster a relationship of honesty and transparency. I ask people to speak to me if they are ready to move on and develop their own practice. I have supported people on my team

> This has happened to more than one of the people who shared their personal stories.

to set up their own business and we have continued to work collaboratively supporting each other.

She has learned to say 'no' to things which contribute nothing to the business or will eat into the precious time she needs to spend on herself and (now grown-up) children – both of whom live and work abroad. Life is on an even keel, settled, fulfilling and hopefully the road ahead is completely flat.

> *I didn't realise how much resilience I would need – and how much resilience I had.*

In the world of film and literature, happy endings are synonymous with hope, the belief that obstacles *can* be overcome and 'good' can triumph.

In Chapter 1, we talked about our own 'happy ending'. Readers will be curious to know whether the personal stories we have shared have happy endings too.

All the contributors to these personal stories have moved on, both literally and figuratively, and their stories are not yet at an end – they are merely onto a new chapter.

References

1. Birmingham_City_Council_10051907_PDF_Final.pdf. Available at: https://www.birmingham.gov.uk/news/article/308/joint_local_area_send_inspection_in_birmingham.
2. Birmingham_City_Council. (2021) *Statement from Cllr Kate Booth*. Birmingham City Council. Available at: https://www.birmingham.gov.uk/news/article/920/statement_from_cllr_kate_booth.
3. Gascoigne, M. (n.d.) The balanced system®, better communication. Available at: https://www.bettercommunication.org.uk/the-balanced-system/.
4. Money, D. (1997) A comparison of three approaches to delivering a speech and language therapy service to people with learning disabilities. *European Journal of Disorders of Communication*, 32(4), pp. 449–466.
5. Waiting for NHS hospital care: The role of the independent sector. (n.d.) The Health Foundation. Available at: https://www.health.org.uk/publications/long-reads/waiting-for-nhs-hospital-care-the-role-of-the-independent-sector.
6. Record rise in people using private healthcare amid NHS frustration. (2023) *The Guardian*. Available at: https://www.theguardian.com/society/2023/may/24/record-rise-in-people-using-private-healthcare-amid-nhs-frustration.
7. Hardman, I. (2023) *Fighting for Life: The Twelve Battles That Made Our NHS, and the Struggle for Its Future*. London: Viking, an imprint of Penguin Books.
8. Gascoigne, M. (2006) *Supporting Children with Speech, Language and Communication Needs within Integrated Children's Services, RCSLT Position Paper*. London: RCSLT.

APPENDICES

Contents

Appendix A: Policy framework

Here is our policy 'skeleton'

It can be useful to open your policy with some *key points*. These help to establish the context and set down broad-brush statements which are pertinent to the whole document. Here are the key points for our *data security and privacy policy*.

Key points

1. All staff are bound by a legal duty of confidence to protect personal information they may come across in the course of their work. This is not just a requirement of their contractual responsibilities but also a requirement within the Common Law Duty of Confidence and the Data Protection Act 1998 (DPA)
2. Company systems and procedures comply with GDPR
3. Confidentiality and data protection (DP) risks are managed in accordance with company risk management policy and procedures
4. Incidents (including near misses) related to confidentiality and data protection are recorded and managed in accordance with the company incident reporting policy and procedure
5. Confidentiality and data protection responsibilities are (a) identified on associate contracts and (b) are part of registered speech and language therapists' professional responsibilities as required by the Healthcare Professions Council [HCPC]
6. All therapists are registered with the Information Commissioner's Office [ICO]
7. Company information security policy and procedures apply to all existing and new systems, including electronic and paper-based.

Please note: this summary list should not be viewed as exhaustive.

Key points are followed by the list of contents.

The Data Security and Privacy Policy is a particularly lengthy and complex document, particularly in the light of the General Data Protection Regulations (GDPR).

Don't be put off by the enormous list of contents! Many of these documents are already in existence and being routinely used. The policy brings everything together.

Contents		*page*
1	Introduction and scope	
2	Other company procedures and guidelines to which this relates	
3	Glossary and definitions	
4	Principles	
5.0	Roles and responsibilities	
5.1	• Directors	
5.2	• Lead persons with responsibility	
5.3	• Team members	
5.4	• All roles	
6.0	Confidentiality and data protection	
6.1	The data protection act principles	
6.2	Fair and lawful processing	
6.2.1	• Fair processing	
a)	• Team members	
b)	• Customers	
c)	• Potential customers	
6.2.2	• Lawful processing a) Team members/sub-processors b) Customers and potential customers	
6.2.3	• Consent and recognizing objections to the processing of information	
a)	• Team members	
b)	• Customers	
c)	• Potential customers	
d)	• Proxy customers	
6.3	• Disclosure and sharing of information	
a)	• Team members/sub-processors	
b)	• Customers	
c)	• Proxy customers	
6.4	Data sharing agreements	
6.4.1	• Proxy customers	
6.5	Updating of information	
a)	• Team members/sub-processors	
b)	• Customers and potential customers	
c)	• Proxy customers	
6.6	Access arrangements	
6.6.1	Access to personal information	
a)	• Team members/sub-processors	
b)	• Customers and potential customers	
c)	• Proxy customers	
6.6.2	Access to proxy customer health records in the event of an emergency	
6.6.3	User access controls	
a)	Electronic records	
b)	Hard copy records	

Appendix B: Data flow map

Data	Source	Purpose	Access	Storage	Retention/disposal
Team members/sub-processors (the team)					
Bank account details	Team members Sub-processor	Payment	Directors	Via online banking account	Secure electronic storage for the duration of contract and then deleted
CV	Team members Sub-processor	Offer of contract	Directors	Team members details folder in cloud storage	Secure electronic storage for the duration of contract and then deleted
References	Previous employer	Offer of contract	Directors	Team members details folder in cloud storage	Secure electronic storage for the duration of contract and then deleted
Professional registration information	Team members Sub-processor	Compliance	Directors	Team members details folder in cloud storage Safeguarding folder in cloud storage Electronically stored via HCPC website.	Secure electronic storage for the duration of contract and then deleted *Available online to be checked if necessary*
Other personal details	Team members Sub-processor	Contact details including, name, phone number, address and email		Team members details folder in cloud storage	Secure electronic storage for the duration of contract and then deleted

This is an example and for every business there will be similarities but also differences. For instance, where the team is employed rather than sub-contracted, additional information will be collected and stored. In the same way, there will be similarities and differences in terms of business-sensitive and client information collected and stored. Perhaps the greatest similarity will be in terms of the clinical information we collect in order to carry out our professional role.

Appendix C: Risk register examples

Example 1	*Probability*		*Severity*	*Score*	*Colour*
	3		**3**	**9**	Amber
Source of risk	Risk assessment				
Summary description of risk	**Under-performing associates**				
Summary of risk management plan	Regular contract review meetings. Directors keeping in regular contact with associates. CPD events and regular random case note audits. Feedback from customers when specific concerns arise. The introduction of the conduct, performance and ethics guidelines.				
Anticipated resource implication (will managing the risk cost anything?)	Who is responsible for implementing the plan?			Expected date of completion	
None	Directors			Ongoing	
At review (management plan has been implemented)	**Probability**		**Severity**	**Score**	**Colour**
	3		3	9	Yellow
Now complete your risk review by asking ...	Is this an acceptable level of risk?				**YES**

Example 2	*Probability*		*Severity*	*Score*	*Colour*
	3		**3**	**9**	Amber
Source of risk	Ongoing monthly assessment				
Summary description of risk	**Cash flow**				
Summary of risk management plan	Delay paying directors' invoices, 'borrow' from saver account, chase later invoices, apply government guidelines re late payments, send invoices out in a timely manner, directors to cap earnings if required				
Anticipated resource implication (will managing the risk cost anything?)	Who is responsible for implementing the plan?			Expected date of completion	
Cost of running an overdraft	Directors			Ongoing	
At review (management plan has been implemented)	**Probability**		**Severity**	**Score**	**Colour**
	2		3	6	Yellow
Now complete your risk review by asking ...	Is this an acceptable level of risk?				**YES**

Appendix D: Risk scoring tool

probability	1	Rare	May occur only in exceptional circumstances
	2	Unlikely	Could occur at some time
	3	Possible	Might occur at some time
	4	Likely	Will probably occur in most circumstances
	5	Almost certain	Is expected to occur in most circumstances

Severity		
1	Insignificant	No injuries, low financial, no reputational loss
2	Minor	Low financial loss, reputational loss contained at a local level
3	Moderate	Some financial loss, reputational loss may not be containable at a local level, the involvement of external agencies such as ICO, HCPC, local agencies
4	Major	Extensive impact/injury, loss of business, potential for major financial loss
5	Catastrophic	Death, huge detrimental effect on business, finance and reputation, business closure

Probability X severity = risk score					
score	Risk category	Colour code	score	Risk category	Colour code
1–3	Low	Green	4–7	Moderate	Yellow
8–14	Significant	Amber	15–25	High	Red

Appendix E: Safeguarding guidelines contents

Safeguarding guidelines contents page Appendix X		
Number	Title	page
1.0	Purpose of guidelines	
2.0	Other policies, procedures and guidelines to which this document relates	
3.0	Basic principles	
4.0	Specific guidance on possible scenarios in school	
5.0	Online safeguarding guidance	
5.1	In circumstances where therapy is being delivered remotely	
6.0	Responsibilities and contact information	
7.0	Common presentations and situations in which child abuse may be suspected	
7.1	Immediate actions	
7.2	What to do with allegations of abuse from a child	
8.0	Confidentiality	
9.0	Responding to requests for safeguarding/child protection information	
10.0	References	
11.0	Appendices	
A	Situations and signs that may be associated with a cause for concern	
B	Children Act proceedings before the family courts	
B1	Private proceedings	
B2	Public proceedings	
B3	What therapists should know	
C	In the event of being asked to write an 'expert witness' report	
C1	Care proceedings	
C2	Private law proceedings	
C3	Immigration tribunals	
C4	Content of the report – brief guidance	
C5	Request for patient records	
D	Soundswell Safeguarding checks – information for schools	
E	Soundswell Safeguarding checks – in-house	
F	Therapists' safeguarding and refresher training	
G	Safeguarding within the context of delivering teletherapy	
H	Referral form	

Appendix F: Impact report

Insert your header/footer with company name, author and date etc.

INTRODUCTION

The following impact report details activity by the speech and language therapist from Soundswell Speech and Language Therapy Solutions at Unnamed Primary and Nursery School during the academic year 2022–2023.

This year, the therapist has delivered a total of **nine contracted days** under the theme of **building capacity** through developing the knowledge and skills of staff. This was to be achieved through:

- Increasing the awareness and use of universal strategies for supporting children with speech, language and communication needs (SLCNs) that can be embedded into teaching and learning
- Increasing staffs' confidence and knowledge in using the Wellcomm Early Years screening tool and ensuring learning from training was embedded into practice
- Increasing parent engagement and awareness of SLCNs through the development of parents' communication coffee mornings
- Continuing to directly assess individual children for whom the class teachers had identified possible speech, language and communication difficulties

Soundswell's provision is based on the three-tier model of service delivery: universal, targeted and specialist levels. This model aims to deliver a prevention, early intervention and therapeutic approaches to service delivery. The aim is to improve communication and emotional well-being, together with functional and academic attainment amongst children and young people. Information on interventions at each level is provided in the table below.

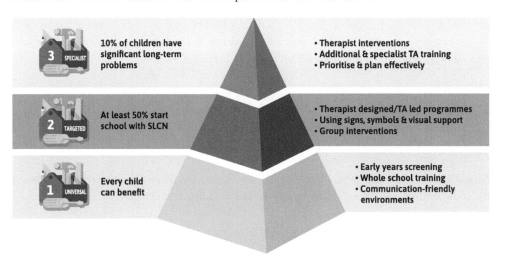

The following activity has been undertaken within school at each tier this academic year:

Universal level *All children*	Targeted level *Additional support*	Specialist level *Those with the most significant need*
• Speech and language therapist (SALT) met regularly with the SENCo to discuss communication requirements within the school and agree priorities for intervention. Priorities were updated as necessary throughout the year. • SALT completed environment audit observations in nursery and reception classes. Reports of findings and recommendations for improvements were provided to each class teacher. • SALT completed two follow-up observations in reception class and visit summary reports were provided. • SALT completed a follow-up observation in nursery class and a visit summary report was provided. • After school SALT drop-in session held with staff from Early Years. Demonstrated how to deliver Wellcomm screening and how to deliver Wellcomm intervention groups. • Direct support provided to set up and deliver Wellcomm screening, group interventions, and recording of progress.	• Attended parents' communication coffee morning and provided information handouts for parents of targeted students.	• Initial assessment carried out with three students. Assessment reports provided with recommendations for universal and targeted interventions. • Formal communication reviews carried out with eight students. Review reports provided with updated recommendations. • After school drop-in session held with class teacher to discuss interventions recommended by NHS SALT for one student. Recommended intervention modelled, and supporting resources provided.

At the beginning of the year, there were nine students on the Soundswell caseload. Four new referrals were received, and seven students were discharged as follows:

• Four students now presenting with age-appropriate speech and language
• Two students transitioning to secondary school in September 2023. Recommendations for ongoing support were provided
• One student transitioned to special school

An initial assessment for one student remains outstanding and this will be carried out as a priority in the autumn term. Six students remain on the Soundswell caseload.

WELLCOMM INTERVENTION

On September 5th, Soundswell delivered a half-day training session to all Early Years staff on using the Wellcomm Toolkit. Wellcomm is a universal screening and intervention tool which enables staff to screen the speech and language skills of all children (from age six months to six years).

The SALT provided direct support to help implement Wellcomm screening in both nursery and reception classes, including carrying out some screens directly. Whilst staff initially found it challenging to include a new intervention, staff across Early Years have worked extremely hard to embed the activities into everyday routines and this is reflected in the progress made by the children. The tables below outline progress made over the year.

Author's note: scores for children in both nursery and reception were provided with accompanying analysis

Reception class had changes of teaching and support staff during this year. Whilst curriculum teaching and learning continued, at times this impacted the delivery of Wellcomm interventions. Except for one student, all children made progress throughout the year.

To help staff identify and track gaps in speech and language skills identified from areas failed during Wellcomm screening, the therapist helped to develop a monitoring grid based on sections of the *Big Book of Ideas*. This easily showed commonality between children, making grouping for interventions easier for the staff team.

Author's note: monitoring grids from screen and rescreen were inserted here

STAFF FEEDBACK

The nursery class teacher provided the following feedback regarding Wellcomm intervention:

> *Initially, we were apprehensive about the Wellcomm program. Our main concern was how we were going to fit in yet another intervention with our needs, classroom management and staffing restrictions.*
>
> *We developed a method of working that meant the screening could be done within the classroom in a quiet corner enabling the required staff ratios to remain in place (there are two staff in nursery).*
>
> *Once the initial screening had been completed, I realised that it would be hugely beneficial to have the required interventions plotted onto a grid so that we could see immediately what each child's areas of needs were. There are huge time constraints on us and so having an efficient method matters. As a result, I was able to add the interventions onto our weekly planning to ensure that they were being covered during the children's independent learning times and throughout the session, sometimes discreetly and at other times more directly.*
>
> *This method has been so easy for us to manage, and as a result it has been a resounding success, with all children making progress, some significantly so. We have also tried to ensure that any next steps including access to resources are manageable and achievable by us. Our*

therapist, Denise, has been very supportive, and any queries have been dealt with swiftly and informatively.

Ms Brown
Early Years Educator

RECOMMENDATIONS/NEXT STEPS:

- The Soundswell therapist will meet with the new head teacher in the autumn term to discuss priorities and plan intervention for the next academic year
- Soundswell's directors will also meet with the new head teacher in the autumn term to ensure senior leaders remain satisfied with the service and to undertake a case note audit
- The Soundswell therapist will continue to complete assessments at a specialist level for students identified by the school and monitor the ongoing WellComm screening and intervention of children in Early Years
- It would be useful to increase parent engagement in using communication strategies within the home environment through the provision of more communication coffee mornings

INDEX

Note: *Italic* refers to figures and **bold** refers to tables.